Cyclamen

A Guide for Gardeners, Horticulturists and Botanists

—— NEW EDITION ——

Christopher Grey-Wilson

B T BATSFORD

First edition published 1997

This new revised and updated edition published 2002

ISBN 0 7134 8760 7

A CIP catalogue record for this book is available from the British Library.

Printed in Spain by Just Colour Graphics S. L.

for the publishers

B T Batsford Ltd.
64 Brewery Road
London N7 9NT
England
www.batsford.com

A member of **Chrysalis** Books plc

ACKNOWLEDGEMENTS

I am deeply grateful to all those who have assisted in one way or another in the production of this new edition, in particular Chris Brickell, Chris Clennett, John Fielding, John Grimshaw, Rod and Jane Leeds, Alan Leslie, Brian Mathew, Peter Moore, Robert Rolfe, and Bob and Rannveig Wallis. In addition, many members of both the Alpine Garden Society and the Cyclamen Society have provided notes and information over the years: to all I am hugely thankful. Finally, many thanks to Alan Radcliffe-Smith for providing the Latin diagnoses included in this book.   C.G-W

PICTURE CREDITS BY PLATE NUMBER

[Photos by the author unless otherwise stated]
AGS Slide Library (Mike Ireland) 26
Bob Charman 68
John Fielding 29, 56, 65, 66, 69, 76, 79, 81, 92, 111, 118, 122, 123, 136, 154, 158, 159, 169, 193, 196,199
Gerald Firak 120
Ronald Frank 52
Doug Joyce 13, 48, 67, 91, 99
Rex Mark 15, 117
Brian Mathew 140
Robert Rolfe 12, 14, 59, 60, 62, 73, 74, 139
Sakata (Japan) 174
Sahin (Holland) 196
Eddie Simpson 25
Bob Wallis 63, 75, 90, 94, 95, 96, 141

Contents

Introduction

It is always nice to produce a new edition of a book. I have spent a great deal of time over the years looking at cyclamen, both from a botanical as well as a horticultural point of view. Since the last edition of this work (published in 1997) a surprising amount of new material has come to light to augment our previous knowledge. New DNA investigations into some species and groups have been initiated and there have been further cladistic analyses. Besides this, more extensive fieldwork has been undertaken, both by me and more especially through a series of expeditions sponsored by the Cyclamen Society. I have tried to assimilate as much of this new information as possible. As a result there has been a number of changes in the overall circumscription of the species and in their relationship to one another.

In recent years cyclamen have become increasingly popular in our gardens with a number of nurseries specializing in their cultivation. The thriving Cyclamen Society bears witness to this increased awareness. Interestingly, the popularity of species cyclamen is a particularly British phenomenon and has been so for more than one hundred years. Although there is a growing interest in Continental Europe, the US and elsewhere for the species, it has been the development of the numerous cultivated forms of *C. persicum* that has predominated. Today in countries like France, Germany, the Netherlands, Italy, Switzerland and Japan *C. persicum* is a very important 'flower crop' produced in many millions as a pot plant.

At the same time as updating the text, I have been able to add quite a few new images of both species and cultivars in an attempt to show the great diversity of flower and form found in the genus. *Cyclamen* as it is now understood consists of 22 species. It might seem surprising to some that this relatively small genus can occupy such a lot of attention, but our knowledge about these charming little plants continues to expand and more and more people are being captivated by them. I am quite sure that we still have much more to discover both about the species in the wild and about the species and the many forms and cultivars in cultivation.

Important changes in nomenclature that affect both gardeners and botanists are:

- the recognition of *C. elegans* as a distinct species (formerly *C. coum* subsp. *elegans*)
- the upgrading of *C. repandum* subsp. *peleponnesiacum* to species – now *C. pelopennesiacum*
- the reinstating of the name *C. alpinum* which replaces *C. trochopteranthum*

This I am quite certain will not be the last word on the species, for the taxonomy of any genus evolves as our knowledge on the subject increases. However, I hope that my approach has been both consistent and reasonably logical. I state this in the full knowledge that no revision can ever fully satisfy every reader.

The captions in this book refer to the pictures on the page in order from top to bottom.

Chapter One

The Magic of Cyclamen

If I walk round my garden in the autumn or in the depths of winter, or again in the spring, there are always cyclamen to be seen in flower. Visitors are always attracted to the cyclamen for they seem to want to flower when most other plants are heading for their winter rest or have not yet woken to the early days of spring. The little flowers, which are borne in profusion, charm and delight the eye and lure the unsuspecting.

The genus *Cyclamen* is not large. With 22 species that flower at different times from midsummer to late spring, there is scarcely a month when there are none in bloom. Apart from one recently discovered in the northern wilds of Somalia, all the species can be readily grown either in the open garden or under glass.

The small, arched flowers with their swept-back petals are elegant and deserve to be studied close up, for they are often attractively marked and deliciously fragrant. Few flowers rival them for sheer charm, and what can be more alluring than a patch of pink *C. coum* in full flower early in the year when their only rivals are the pristine purity of the snowdrops, the first shy crocuses, golden winter aconites or bold hellebores? Perhaps it is the fact that they flower at such a discouraging time of year for the gardener that really excites, bringing the hope of spring and a new gardening year. The autumn-flowering *C. hederifolium* equally delights. When most plants in the garden have finished flowering and look tired and untidy at the end of the season, up pop the fresh pink or white flowers from the bare earth heralding the conclusion of summer and the leaf-fall days of autumn. And late in the spring, just when it seems all the cyclamen have finished, *C. repandum* puts on a rush of deep pink bloom, its scent wafting across the garden to attract the busy bumblebees.

But it is not only the flowers that attract the eye, for cyclamen have highly ornamental leaves that can carpet the ground for many months. The infinite variety of shape and patterning among the different sorts is legendary; from deep, plain, lustrous greens, to greys, pewters and silver, from simple heart-shaped patterning to washes, blotches and speckles, each plant has its own leaf characteristics and, like fingerprints, very few are exactly the same. As if that were not enough, turn over a leaf and it will often be deep purple or carmine and shiny beneath.

The fruits can be a fascination to children and adults alike, for few plants have such a bizarre corkscrew arrangement of the flower stalk to pull the fruits so close to the ground. Examine a plant in full flower and the twisting of the flower stalks can be observed in many

1 *Cyclamen graecum* subsp. *graecum*, with elegant nodding flowers and twisted upturned petals, highlights the allure of cyclamen.

2 The hardy *Cyclamen hederifolium* subsp. *hederifolium* is the commonest and most widely grown species in gardens.

3 *Cyclamen coum* (here subsp. *coum*) is one of the brightest jewels of the winter border and is ideal for naturalising between trees and shrubs and will self-sow once established.

4 Borders can be devoted to cyclamen; mixed colours of *C. hederifolium* at Rod and Jane Leeds' garden in Suffolk bejewel the ground in September.

5 The autumn-flowering *Cyclamen hederifolium* naturalizes perfectly beneath trees, harmonising with ferns and other shade-tolerant plants.

stages as the young fruits begin to develop. At first the petals drop off and then the young fruit is pulled down as the top of the flower stalk begins to arch then loop. In just a few days the stalk has corkscrewed into a series of tight loops pulling the enlarging fruit tight to the ground. In the summer it can be equally enthralling to watch the open fruits display their sugary seeds and to see a succession of ants carry them away to their nests; that is, of course, if the seeds are not required for other purposes, in which case they need to be gathered up quickly before the ants gain all the spoils.

The cultivated forms of the florist's cyclamen, *C. persicum*, are among the most popular pot plants today, grown in large numbers on the Continent, especially in Holland and Germany where they are even used as a cut flower. Indeed, picking small bunches of hardy cyclamen with a few leaves and presenting small posies to friends can delight as much as a sweet bunch of violets, and they last in water equally well.

Cyclamen are certainly addictive. Once one species has been obtained it is difficult to resist collecting all the other species. But then that is only a starting point for there is an infinite variety of leaf shapes and patterns, selected forms and cultivars to gather into the collection. Then comes one of the greatest pleasures, collecting your own seed, sowing it and awaiting the results, for often novelties with different leaf patternings or flower colours will appear.

I can remember cyclamen from childhood. My grandfather had a small patch of *C. purpurascens* in the front garden that always seemed to bear a few flowers from summer through to autumn. In Northern Ireland, where my parents lived in a farmhouse for several years, the grassy banks along the muddy driveway were alive in the spring with snake's-head fritillarias with their lively chequered flowers and drifts of *Cyclamen repandum* spilling down between the trees onto the verge.

However, it was not until I went to Wye College that I had a chance to see cyclamen in the wild. In 1965 I took up a summer vacation job at 'Floraire' just outside Geneva where the famous alpine nursery started by Henry Correvon in the late 19th century still prospered and was run by Henry's grandson Aymon and his wife Heidi. On several occasions Heidi took me up into the mountains to see the wild flowers and I remember particularly clambering through the wooded slopes of the Saleve close to Geneva and seeing the myriad blooms of *C. purpurascens* (then called *C. europaeum*) dotting the leafy slopes. The following summer, with three friends from Wye College, I set off on a long expedition overland to western Iran on the Southern Zagros Botanical Expedition. Green and naïve in the art of plant collecting, we had an immensely enjoyable time and achieved moderate success botanically. On our way home through southern Yugoslavia in early September we passed via Skopje to Kotor on the Adriatic coast, where in a number of places there were scented drifts of *C. hederifolium*, pristine and leafless in the early warm days of autumn. After college I joined the staff at the Royal Botanic Garden, Kew, where I worked for a while for Desmond Meikle whose enthusiasm for plants, especially from the Mediterranean region and western Asia, spurred on my interest. His passion for cyclamen was unsurpassed, aided by a thorough knowledge of the complicated nomenclature of the genus at that time. In 1971 Professor Tom Hewer from Bristol invited me to join him on an expedition (again overland) to Afghanistan. With the backing of Kew and a generous grant from the Royal Horticultural Society we set off on the long road to Kabul in mid-January. The outward journey was punctuated by the bitter weather of the Anatolian Plateau in midwinter, yet along the mild Black Sea coast in early February, spring had already arrived and we were entranced by the catkin-covered hazel groves, yellow with pollen, and the leafy slopes dotted with Lenten roses (*Helleborus orientalis*), pink primroses (*Primula vulgaris* subsp. *sibthorpii*) and scattered snowdrops (*Galanthus rizehensis*) and, most memorable of all, masses of pink and magenta *Cyclamen coum* in their first flush of bloom. They have entranced me ever since.

PLANT ASSOCIATIONS

Different species of cyclamen come into flower at different times of the year so they can be associated with a range of plants in the garden setting. Their bright, jolly little flowers bring inspiration through the seasons. They are small plants, less effective as individuals but truly impressive *en masse*. The range of good companion plants is a large one but it is particularly interesting to note the sorts of plants that they accompany in their native habitats and some of these are listed under the individual species of cyclamen later in the text. Many of the companion plants in the wild make first-rate garden plants in their own right: anemones, buttercups, chionodoxas, colchicums, crocuses, hellebores, certain irises, primroses, scillas, snowdrops, sternbergias, violets and winter aconites to name but a few. Of course, not all these will be found with each cyclamen species in the wild but it gives an idea of the sorts of companion plants that can be grouped in the garden. In addition, cyclamen can work well with shrubs such as daphnes, some of the smaller willows and witch hazels for instance. I once saw a stunning spring display of rich pink *Cyclamen repandum* beneath a group of *Corylopsis sinensis* (= *C. willmottiae*), its filigree of slender branches dripping with pale yellow flowers.

The rich pinks and magenta flowers of some hardy cyclamen can be difficult to place in the garden and the colours can clash with yellows and reds in particular. Placed among cooler colours, especially varying shades of green provided by ferns or the smaller epimediums, or bronzed-leaved ajugas, they can look at ease in attractive harmony.

In fact, only the minority of cyclamen species can be grown in the open garden with ease and I refer to them as the 'hardy cyclamen' for want of a better title: luckily their flowers cover not only the autumn, winter and spring seasons but they offer the gardener a good deal of variety in flower colour and leaf interest. The prime species include *C. coum* and *C. hederifolium*, the two most commonly seen in gardens, as well as the delightful little autumn-flowering *C. cilicium* and the spring-flowering *C. repandum* with its delicately twisted petals.

A CYCLAMEN BORDER

The simplest way to grow cyclamen is to mass them together in a single border of their own; this can be not

6 A bank of *Cyclamen coum* at the Royal Horticultural Society's Garden, Wisley, brightens the winter garden.
7 A drift of *Cyclamen hederifolium* at the base of a hedge makes an interesting feature.

only very effective but relatively easy to maintain. But a word of warning: cyclamen species do not mix particularly well in such a border unless it is very carefully controlled. I thought at one time that it would be nice to mix *C. hederifolium* and *C. coum* in a single border, thus having an autumn display of flowers from the former and a winter show from the latter; however, *C. hederifolium* is far more vigorous and leafy and soon begins to dominate such an association to the detriment of the more refined *C. coum*. On the other hand, *C. coum* and *C. cilicium* mix tolerably well, being of more or less equal vigour.

A border devoted to *C. hederifolium* can be a truly arresting sight in the garden, especially if the various shades of pink are mixed with white-flowered forms. Once established, the plants will sow themselves around freely. Having flowered, the variegated leaves in hues of green, grey, pewter and silver add interest through the winter months and well into spring. Such borders look fine beneath the dappled shade of old trees such as an oak, pear or apple and require little maintenance save for an annual dressing of bone meal and a generous mulch of leaf mould or bark chippings.

Cyclamen hederifolium mixes very well with ferns, the subtle greens of the dissected fronds a gentle foil to the perky blooms in pinks and white. Useful ferns that remain fresh late in the year include the male fern, *Dryopteris filix-mas*, holly fern, *Polystichum lonchitis*, and the soft shield fern, *Polystichum setiferum*, but there are many others from which to choose.

By summer the *C. hederifolium* leaves have died away and the area can be tidied up. There are few plants that really associate well during this low season for the cyclamen, yet clumps of lungworts or epimediums can provide foliage interest. A few years ago I saw a border of *C. hederifolium* interspersed with *Arum italicum* 'Pictum' whose bold, variegated foliage provides a lively contrast to that of the cyclamen in autumn and winter. The leaves of both die away at more or less the same time leaving the bold, stiff-stemmed heads of green arum fruits standing sentry-like through the summer months. Then in the autumn as the cyclamen come into bloom the arum heads are turning scarlet to produce a startling display of form and colour, almost too brazen to some eyes. When it comes down to it the choice of planting and colours is very much a personal one; the fun is in trying out different combinations to see which best suit the cyclamen.

Many so-called autumn crocuses, *Colchicum* species, flower at the same time as *C. hederifolium* and their bold flowers can provide an interesting contrast, although the leaves of some can prove too coarse in the spring when they develop to their full extent; carefully placed, the two can harmonize rather well. Other autumn-flowering bulbs make even better companions. The true crocuses are especially effective and of those most widely

available *C. speciosus* is perhaps the easiest and will, like the cyclamen, tolerate dappled shade. In sunnier sheltered positions few can be better than *C. goulimyi*, white or pink with its elegant goblet-flowers drawn aloft on delicate stems like the finest wine glass. To impress neighbours plant a group of autumn-flowering snowdrops, *Galanthus reginae-olgae*, among the cyclamen and watch them come into flower long before their leaves appear.

Cyclamen coum can be equally effective. Placed in a border close to the house the display of small flowers can be enjoyed in the depths of winter from the warm confines of lounge or kitchen. Borders can be devoted to single colours but are really more effective (as with *C. hederifolium*) when the different colours are allowed to intermingle; thus the whites, pinks, purples and reds enliven one another against a mat of plain and variegated foliage. Because *C. coum* flowers in midwinter and early spring it can be associated with winter shrubs in a border. What can be more striking than the red or yellow stems of dogwoods (for instance *Cornus alba* 'Sibirica' with scarlet winter shoots, or *C. stolonifera* 'Flaviramea' with its bright greenish-yellow winter stems) set upon a sea of *C. coum* in full flower, or the even brighter and more robust stems of the coloured willows, *Salix alba* 'Britzensis' (orange-red stems) or var. *vitellina* (orange-yellow stems). Both cornus and willow can be pruned hard back in the spring to produce a new flush of colourful growths for the following winter. A hazel coppice is another good setting for *C. coum*, reflecting one of its associations in the wild. A tapestry of cyclamen can be interspersed with clumps of yellow or pale pink primroses (*Primula vulgaris* and its subspecies *sibthorpii*), snowdrops and celandines (*Ranunculus ficaria* cultivars) in bronzes, creams and yellows, punctuated by bold clumps of Lenten roses, *Helleborus* x *hybridus*, with their enticing saucer flowers in greens, yellows, pinks, purples, smoky blues or almost black. For a bolder, perhaps more shocking combination, try planting some of the early flowering corydalis such as *C. solida* 'George Baker' or 'Wilhelm Schacht', where the reds and bright pinks will vie with the magentas, pinks and whites of the cyclamen.

Other useful associated shrubs include: *Daphne odora*, *D. mezereum*, *Hamamelis mollis* (especially 'Pallida'), *H. japonica*, *Viburnum* x *bodnantense*, *V. farreri*. Other associated herbs include: *Adonis amurensis*, *Eranthis hyemalis* and *E. cilicica*, *Euphorbia amygdaloides* 'Purpurea', *Hacquetia epipactis*, *Iris lazicus* and *I. reticulata*, *Leucojum vernum*, *Omphalodes verna*, *Pulmonaria* species and cultivars, *Viola odorata*.

In more open borders *Cyclamen coum* mixes delightfully with *Crocus tommasinianus* in its various shades of mauve, pink, lilac and purple, or *Anemone blanda* (blue, white or pink), which burst with colour on sunny days.

An area devoted to the Pewter Group of *Cyclamen coum* can also be very effective with the subtle greys and silvers of the foliage contrasting delightfully with the pinks, purples and reds of the flowers. Less vigorous than some of the green-leaved forms of *C. coum*, they are best isolated lest their more thuggish cousins overwhelm them.

As spring advances the choice of subjects multiplies rapidly so that by the time *C. repandum* unfurls its first carmine-pink blooms there is plenty of colour in the garden. *C. repandum* is not the easiest species to please in the garden, although it is reasonably hardy. In my experience it greatly resents draughty exposed positions

8 Hardy cyclamen mix well with spring bulbs; here *C. coum* Pewter Group harmonizes with *Galanthus* 'Magnet' and *Helleborus foetidus* 'Westerfisk'.
9 *Cyclamen coum* Nymans Group and *Crocus tommasinianus* ('little tommies') enliven the garden in March.

in the garden, preferring quiet banks or glades in dappled shade. It, like the others, will naturalize well in short grass and its rather startling colour is perhaps best displayed against a lush green background. However, it can be subtly associated with some of the less bright lungworts, *Pulmonaria*, and the dainty yet tough epimediums whose filigree of small flowers in whites, yellows, pinks and reds seems to counteract the bolder flowers of the cyclamen. *C. repandum* can look wonderfully impressive beneath deciduous flowering shrubs such as the various kinds of Corylopsis, *Ribes sanguinea* (e.g. 'Brocklebankii'), *Salix hastata* 'Wehrhahnii' or even the common Forsythia.

Other useful associated herbs include: *Anemone nemorosa* and its cultivars, *Cardamine enneaphylla* and *C. heptaphylla*, *Dicentra* species, *Erythronium* species and cultivars, *Fritillaria meleagris* and *F. pyrenaica*, *Hepatica nobilis* and *H. transsilvanica*, *Hyacinthus* (*Muscari*) *azureus*, *Narcissus bulbocodium* and *N. cyclamineus*, *Omphalodes capadoccica*, *Polygonatum* species, *Tiarella cordifolia* and *T. wherryi*, *Trillium* species, *Uvularia perfoliata*, *Vinca* species and cultivars, *Viola labradorica* 'Purpurea' and *V. septentrionalis*.

Among the hardy cyclamen should be included the small *C. intaminatum* with its delicate flowers of white and grey. This little treasure is too small for the open garden where it is easily overlooked and readily swamped, but it is a gem worth every effort for it is not difficult to grow and will reward you by seeding around once it is happily situated. The confinement of a trough or raised bed among alpines and small bulbs suit it admirably and will show this charmer to the best advantage, being one of the first species to burst into flower during the autumn.

Cyclamen purpurascens is perfectly hardy but a 'little devil' to please in many gardens. It rarely produces the bold flowering display of its cousins, yet its pink flowers are so delightfully scented that it is impossible to resist trying it somewhere in the open garden. It is a plant that requires no detractors; a quiet cool, shady corner where it can grow away undisturbed suits it best of all. A setting amongst small ferns, in dappled shade with a copious mulch of pine needles may suit it best, and when you are tired of the bold displays in the rest of the garden in the height of summer seek solace in such a 'corner', for there will

invariably be one or two of the sweet blooms at their perfect best.

If a warm, fairly dry, sunny corner can be found in the garden then it is well worth trying to grow *C. graecum* in the open. This, a plant of sun-baked Mediterranean rocks, relishes all the heat and sun that can be provided. The base of a south-facing wall, especially if the border is raised, is an ideal location and some growers have been remarkably lucky with it in such a situation where it will reward the gardener by a display of flowers in the late summer and early autumn. This is a plant that dislikes disturbance once established and it should not be hemmed in by too many other plants, otherwise its attractive and often delightfully ornamental mounds of leaves cannot be seen at their best. Associated plants include other sun-lovers: try some of the autumn-flowering crocuses, *Crocus goulimyi*, *C. niveus* and *C. medius*, the winter or Algerian iris, *Iris unguicularis*, or *Sternbergia lutea* and *S. sicula* with their sumptuous autumn goblet-flowers of bright gold. Associated shrubs include *Cistus* species, *Euphorbia characias*, *E. c.* subsp. *wulfenii*, *Lavandula stoechas* and *L. lanata*, *Phlomis fruticosus* and *Rosmarinus officinalis*; all sun worshippers.

Some lucky gardeners have had success with *C. mirabile*, noted for the rich pink and red hues of its young foliage (in the best forms), and *C. alpinum*, with its early spring display of whirligig blooms, in the open garden. Both are reasonably hardy though not the easiest to please, but if enough plants are available it is worth experimenting with them in the garden. Otherwise I find they perform best when grown in frames or pots.

Chapter Two

The Cultivation of Cyclamen

Cyclamen are not difficult to grow, it is just that some are more difficult than others. This might seem a rash statement to make but it is quite easy to possess and maintain a large selection of cyclamen in the garden or in airy glasshouses or frames. They will reward careful cultivation with a show of flowers at the appropriate season as well as an attractive display of leaves long after the flowers have faded. Of course, a lot depends on where the plants are being grown. Some species (*C. coum* and *C. hederifolium*, *C. parviflorum*, *C. purpurascens*) are completely hardy, withstanding temperatures as low as –20°C (–4°F). Others (*C. cilicium*, *C. intaminatum*, *C. mirabile*, *C. alpinum*) are less hardy but will tolerate subzero temperatures provided that they do not fall below –14°C (7°F). At the other extreme are those species that will not tolerate temperatures below freezing for any length of time; the popular florist's cyclamen, *C. persicum*, belongs here, as do *C. rohlfsianum* and *C. cyprium*.

These are general notes on cultivation; for more specific details please look under the individual species.

UNDERSTANDING CYCLAMEN CULTIVATION

Cyclamen is a primarily Mediterranean genus and a knowledge of the species' natural habitats in the wild can provide valuable information for the cultivator. The Mediterranean climate is basically one of cool, wet winters and hot, dry summers. There is little or no frost and cold biting winds are rare. Cyclamen are well adapted to the Mediterranean climate, growing and flowering in the cooler, moister winter and spring months and becoming dormant as the dry, hot summer months approach, when they disappear below ground to rest. The last phase in the annual cycle of the cyclamen plant is the ripening of the fruits, which often happens after the leaves have withered away. This event generally takes place in the summer months; it is no coincidence that this is also the time when foraging ants are at their most numerous, for the sugary-coated seeds are almost exclusively distributed by ants (see p.40).

It would be wrong to assume that all cyclamen require a hot, dry summer baking, for relatively few grow in such conditions in the wild, the best-known examples being *C. graecum*, *C. persicum* and *C. rohlfsianum*. Those

who have travelled to the Mediterranean in search of *C. repandum* and its allies (*C. balearicum*, *C. creticum* and *C. peloponnesiacum*) know that they occupy not the sun-baked habitats but the cooler, moister glades of woodland and valley floors and ravines; they have thin leaves that would soon desiccate in more exposed positions, but they still become dormant in the hot, dry summers. In Crete where *C. graecum* and *C. creticum* are sometimes to be found growing in the same valley or on the same ridge their preferred habitat is quite pronounced with the former opting for the more open, sunnier aspects, while the latter seeks the coolness and shade of sheltering rocks or trees.

Many of the other species prefer the shadier, cooler habitats often well away from the Mediterranean shoreline in the hills and mountains where the conditions are less extreme during the summer and where any severe winter weather is often offset by a protective blanket of snow; among these one can include *C. alpinum*, *C. cilicium*, *C. coum*, *C. cyprium*, *C. hederifolium*, *C. intaminatum*, *C. libanoticum* and *C. pseudibericum*.

Three outlying species in particular, *C. colchicum*, *C. parviflorum* and *C. purpurascens*, grow in more temperate climates where the winters are longer and more severe and the summers less hot and dry. *C. purpurascens* is widespread in the woodlands of central Europe, north as far as southern Poland, and breaks the general pattern by being practically evergreen and coming into flower in the middle of summer; the closely related *C. colchicum* is the same but is confined to a small region of the Caucasus close to the eastern shore of the Black Sea. *C. parviflorum* can perhaps be described as the only truly alpine species in the genus, growing in the extreme conditions at altitude in the eastern Pontus Mountains of northern Turkey where the summers are cool and moist and the winters extremely cold with deep snow lying for many months. It is not surprising therefore that this charming little species can often still be found in flower well into summer where snow lingers late on the mountain slopes and meadows.

In more temperate climates cyclamen have to contend not only with rather wetter and often cooler summers but often colder winters, sometimes with severe frosts or even prolonged periods below freezing, which is rarely accompanied by an insulating blanket of

11 *Cyclamen coum* subsp. *coum* is very hardy, withstanding heavy frosts and snow unscathed, even when it is in bloom.

snow. It is necessary to provide some of the species with more equable growing conditions by cultivating them in pots in frames or glasshouses where the extremes of climate can be modified. What is perhaps surprising, considering their origins, is how hardy and resilient certain species are, in particular *C. cilicium*, *C. coum* and *C. hederifolium*. In my East Anglian garden, which rarely receives much snow, the plants are often subjected to severe frosts or even prolonged freezing over a number of days. The plants look awful during such conditions with limp and frozen foliage, yet the moment warmer weather returns they perk up and look as if nothing has affected them whatsoever.

Yet most of the other species will not stand such harsh conditions. In milder gardens many can be grown in the open provided that they are given a sheltered niche which is reasonably dry during the winter months. Indeed, all but *C. africanum*, *C. cyprium*, *C. persicum* and *C. rohlfsianum* can be grown outside in certain British gardens.

Strangely enough, one would perhaps expect *C. purpurascens* to be the easiest and hardiest species to grow in the open garden. It is very hardy but, unfortunately, not particularly easy to cultivate well, rarely making a decent display in our gardens.

Hardiness is not simply a question of temperature. It is a complex subject that involves the interaction of different elements of which temperature is just one facet. Other factors that affect hardiness include soil type, moisture content, aspect, exposure and age of the plant. It is quite possible for plants to survive freezing temperatures in dry, well-drained soils while the same species will succumb at similar temperatures in wet soil conditions. Incidentally, the same can be true of plants grown in pots, especially during periods of prolonged freezing, those in pots succumbing

whilst the same species outdoors survives without difficulty. Low temperatures accompanied by bitter winds can shrivel and desiccate plants whilst those in sheltered sites survive unscathed.

For these reasons, apart from the reliably hardy and tolerant cyclamen species and cultivars, most growers opt to cultivate their plants in pots in an alpine house or frame where conditions can be more easily controlled. The finest collections of cyclamen are grown under such conditions.

HOW HARDY ARE THEY?

Of course, hardiness is a complex matter and it is difficult to set hard and fast rules. However, under average garden conditions in sheltered areas and with a good fibrous, yet well-drained soil, cyclamen can be classed in the following hardiness groups which are dependent on temperature. Having said this, however, I am rather hesitant to place the species into groups because there will always be those who will claim that certain are hardier or more tender than I state, but so much depends on local conditions. For this reason several species will be found in more than one group.

Group One: Frost-hardy Species (will withstand temperatures as low as –20°C (–4°F), even prolonged freezing).

C. cilicium, *C. coum* (subsp. *coum* and *caucasicum*), *C. hederifolium*, *C. parviflorum*, *C. pseudibericum* (in some gardens only), *C. purpurascens*. *C. hederifolium* has been known to have survived prolonged freezing at temperatures as low as –30°C (–22°F).

Group Two: Frost-tolerant Species (not as hardy as Group One but will withstand temperatures as low as –14°C (7°F) but not prolonged freezing below this point).

C. alpinum, *C. colchicum*, *C. elegans* (higher altitude forms), *C. intaminatum*, *C. mirabile*, *C. pseudibericum*, *C. repandum* (not consistently so in all gardens); many would also place *C. cilicium* in this group rather than the first but I have found it to be equally as hardy as *C. coum*.

Group Three: Half-hardy Species (will tolerate some frost as low as –4°C (25°F) for a few hours but not prolonged freezing).

C. balearicum, *C. creticum*, *C. elegans*, *C. graecum*, *C. libanoticum*, *C. peloponnesiacum*.

Group Four: Tender Species (best kept frost-free, although some forms will tolerate slight, short-term frost).

C. africanum, *C. cyprium*, *C. persicum*, *C. rohlfsianum*; *C. somalense* probably also belongs in this group.

In temperate gardens all those in Group One can be grown successfully in the open garden given the right conditions, and in the mildest gardens most of those in Group Two can also be tried with varying degrees of success. In fact a series of mild winters in Britain and other parts of western and north-western Europe in recent years has allowed many cyclamen growers to try a greater range of species in the open, even some from Group Three. At the Royal Botanic Gardens, Kew even *C. persicum* was kept alive outside beneath a sheltered south-facing wall for several years, although the plants never bloomed very freely. Such experiments generally fall foul of the first harsh winter that comes along but the experiment is well worth doing, especially if you have enough plants of the more tender species with which to experiment. It is exciting to be able to coax them into flower under adverse conditions.

For best results however, all the species listed under Groups Two, Three and Four are best grown in pots under glass, or planted out in beds under glass. It is wise to keep all those in Group Four frost-free at all times, although in reality plants will survive a few degrees below freezing overnight, but certainly no more, although even that may damage the foliage to some extent; the plants certainly do best in a frost-free environment. As stated before, the same species will tolerate less frost if the compost is wet than when it is on the dry side, so culture can affect hardiness to some extent.

Frost-tender species do not need to be kept too warm, otherwise they will produce a lot of soft growth and the attractive leaf patterings will be diminished. A minimum temperature of just 2–3°C (36–37°F) is enough. During frosty periods they are best kept on the dryish side but must be watered should the foliage show any sign of wilting.

WHERE TO START

Many people's first encounter with cyclamen is with one of the blowsy forms of *C. persicum*, with cabbagy leaves and over-endowed with blossom, acquired at a florists or garden centre. Carefully nurtured in the confines of the house, they can remain in flower for many weeks but more often than not the leaves begin to yellow and the flower buds fail to open. The plant soon begins to look sick and unhealthy and is quickly discarded. Such experiences put many off growing cyclamen in the future but with a little care even the florist's cyclamen can reward us for many years: I know at least one person who has managed to keep a single plant growing and flowering annually for more than twenty years.

My advice would be not to start with the florist's cyclamen but to go for some of the daintier hardy species and then gradually to develop one's collection by adding some of those that are less easy to cultivate. Undoubtedly the best to start with are the various forms of *C. coum* and *C. hederifolium* which can be grown in most garden soils

provided that they are not waterlogged at any time of the year and, once established, they will reward by self-sowing in adjacent parts of the garden. These are easy dependable species for the average garden. Later, both *C. cilicium* and the hardier forms of *C. repandum* can be added and these four will provide a display of flowers to delight the eye from late August until early May, with *C. hederifolium* coming into bloom first in the late summer and *C. repandum* completing the display in the late spring. Later still, species such as *C. intaminatum*, *C. mirabile*, *C. alpinum* and *C. purpurascens* can be added to the collection.

BUYING PLANTS

Many people are seduced by the packets of tubers sold with brightly coloured wrappings in garden centres and department stores. These tubers are dried and often look as though they have been through a potato scrubber, without a vestige of root or shoot remaining. Unfortunately, many of the larger dried tubers sold have been stripped from the wild (see p.22). Furthermore, they are often misnamed so that the contents are not the same as the plant depicted; for instance plants labelled *C. hederifolium* often have the picture of *C. cilicium* on the packet but they may in fact not be either species, so they are unreliable unless they come from a reputable source. Worse still, these poor dried tubers, although admittedly often very reasonably priced, are generally very difficult to coax into growth, sometimes staying dormant for a year or so before coming into leaf or flower. Many never show any sign of growth and merely, like the proverbial tortoise, shrivel away over a period. To make matters worse, it is often not clear which way up the tubers should be planted. Here the advice is simple: if the tuber has a flat or concave side then plant this uppermost with the rounded side of the tuber at the base. However, this is not always apparent; the growing points which give rise to leaves and flowers are usually located only on the upper surface of the tuber (in old tubers of *C. graecum* and *C. purpurascens*, in particular, growing points may be located on various 'faces' of the tuber due to distortion or uneven development). To coax dried tubers into activity it is often a good idea to place them in shallow boxes of moist peat and wait for signs of renewed growth. Regular inspection will reveal any such activity and, once detected, the tuber(s) can be placed in the garden. This method has one great advantage as it matters little whether or not tubers are placed upside down for they can be righted between the 'sprouting' trays and their planting in the garden. An alternative method advocated by some gardeners is to place the tubers in moist peat in a sealed polythene bag. Unfortunately, whichever method is chosen there will be a high percentage of losses among dried tubers, so expect disappointments. Luckily, only a few species are sold in this manner; they include mainly *C. cilicium*, *C. coum*, *C. hederifolium*, *C. purpurascens* and *C. mirabile* and, very occasionally, *C. alpinum*.

It is far better to seek good plants in growth from a specialist cyclamen nursery or from an alpine nursery or garden centre that sells pot-grown plants in full growth. They will certainly cost a little more, but it is well worth the extra cost for reliability. There is no doubt that cyclamen are far easier to establish from 'plants in the green' than dormant tubers; the same is very true of snowdrops and winter aconites. Apart from the obvious benefits of acquiring such plants there is the opportunity to see plants in leaf and/or flower and to be able to select the most desirable for oneself. If it is impossible to reach the desired nursery most will send plants 'in the green' through the post. Most of the species and their cultivars and some of the hybrids, even the rarer ones, can be purchased in this way, and a quick glance at *The RHS Plant Finder* will help find an appropriate source of plants.

Some nurseries (especially bulb nurseries) sell only dormant tubers, generally between May and November and will say so in their catalogues. Others prefer to sell plants in growth and these are usually available between September and May.

It perhaps goes without saying that if plants are chosen at a nursery or garden centre it is wise to select only the healthiest and more vigorous plants, not those that look in any way diseased or impoverished. Reputable nurseries will sell clean stock but there is always the danger that some pest might be introduced with bought-in plants. Of those likely to affect cyclamen potentially the most serious is the vine weevil (p.31), which especially seems to favour peat-based composts. To overcome potential risk I always remove all the compost from the roots of the plants and place them in fresh 'clean' compost of my own. The initial compost is discarded together with eggs or larvae of vine weevils should they be present. This is a wise precaution, although it can be a bother, especially if a number of plants are bought in; yet vine weevil, if allowed to gain a hold in a collection, can cause a great deal of damage, besides infecting other groups of plants. Incidentally, removing all the compost from a growing cyclamen plant will not cause any harm, provided that plants are potted up or planted out without delay, watered moderately and kept shaded for a week or so if the weather is hot.

GROWING CYCLAMEN IN THE OPEN GARDEN

The hardier cyclamen can be grown outside without any winter protection. They thrive best in a good humus-rich soil (one containing plenty of decomposed organic matter such as compost or leaf mould) but the most vital factor is that it must be well-drained. Naturally, a sheltered site is preferable but *C. coum* and *C. hederifolium* will tolerate fairly exposed positions without ill effects. Indeed, for the average garden, and certainly for the beginner, these two species stand supreme. *C. hederifolium* will in fact survive long periods of freezing without harm and in parts of Europe and North America it has been known to survive conditions where the ground freezes to a depth of 30cm (12in). It is also a species that will put up with temperatures in excess of 30°C (86°F) for short periods.

For sheltered places outdoors *C. cilicium*, *C. purpurascens* and *C. repandum* are well worth trying and will withstand severe cold conditions but generally dislike bitter winter winds. Incidentally, both *C. intaminatum* and *C. parviflorum* are equally as hardy in the open garden but because they are so small it is perhaps wise to confine them to sinks or raised beds where their delicate beauty can be better enjoyed and where they will not be overlooked.

Another requirement of most of the hardy species is that they receive reasonably good light during the bleak days of winter: after all, their leaves are mostly well-developed at that time of the year. At the same time, too much sun in the late spring and early summer can prove harmful (though *C. cilicium*, *C. coum* and *C. hederifolium* remain generally unaffected by strong and continuous sunshine); a sheltered site with dappled shade as provided by deciduous shrubs is ideal. Growing cyclamen amongst shrubs or beneath a hedge or trees has one other advantage, in that the roots of trees and shrubs will mop up excessive moisture, creating just the right conditions for many cyclamen.

Soil Type

Cyclamen are quite adaptable and will in fact grow in a range of soils from light sandy loams to leafy clays or a good average loam. They seem happiest in neutral to alkaline or slightly acid soils; some will tolerate acid soils suitable for rhododendrons and other ericaceous plants but, in my experience, they never look as robust and healthy on unduly acid soils – say below pH5.5. Peat is not necessary for cyclamen, except perhaps for *C. parviflorum*, although it can be a useful additive to improve soil structure and friability. The use of peat will become more restricted as the need for conservation becomes increasingly important and besides, good leaf mould (especially of beech or oak) cannot be bettered. The ideal soil is one that is just above neutral but not unduly alkaline, although some will no doubt argue that many humus-rich soils which suit cyclamen (especially in the wild) may well be acidic.

The drainage of the soil can be improved if necessary by digging in plenty of grit in the top 20cm (8in) or so. If the soil is very heavy and poorly drained then the best answer is to build raised beds to accommodate cyclamen and other plants that demand perfect drainage.

Position

The edge of woodland, sloping leafy banks, stream sides, shrubberies and areas beneath sheltered walls are all ideal places to plant the hardier cyclamen. They can look delightful among the roots of an old tree or in crevices in the rock garden or in open woodland glades, or even naturalized in grassy places. Cyclamen, like many bulbs, look best in drifts and are rarely as effective on their own. A border devoted to a single species such as *C. coum* or *C. hederifolium* can be very appealing and a most arresting sight when the plants are in full flower. Cyclamen also make effective plants outdoors for large troughs, containers of various sorts and window boxes.

Cyclamen do not mind competition from the roots of other plants, especially trees and shrubs, but they may be crowded out by vigorous leafy herbaceous plants. They compete well with some of the small, slender-leaved bulbs and various ferns but some care needs to be taken when associating them with other plants in the garden. Another advantage of planting cyclamen in informal settings *en masse* is that during the summer months they will have died down leaving the area bare. At such times it is easy to remember where they are and it also gives an opportunity to collect the seeds, clean up the site and to top-dress the area with a leafy mulch in preparation for the autumn when most resume growth.

Cyclamen hederifolium will naturalize well in grassy places if the grasses are not too vigorous. Once the leaves have died down in early summer the grass can be mowed (keeping the blades of the mower high) or scythed, but this should be stopped by late August when the first blooms will begin to arise. *C. coum* will also thrive in such places if the grass is thin and low as it often is beneath large trees.

Planting Cyclamen in the Open Garden

When planted in informal groups, cyclamen produce an attractive dense, leafy cover that helps to subdue weed growth. In addition, once the colony is established, it will begin to seed around freely and to expand.

Cyclamen species do not mix very well in the open garden; they are seldom found growing together in the wild! *C. hederifolium* is too vigorous for *C. coum* and will soon overwhelm it. On the other hand *C. coum* and *C. cilicium* mix tolerably well and are of more or less equal vigour, with the additional bonus of flowering at different seasons, thus prolonging the interest of the planting.

There is no perfect planting time, although many advocate late August and September when the weather has begun to cool and when many species are commencing renewed root activity. If the weather permits and the soil is in good condition plants can be placed out at almost any time of the year, although it would be rash to plant the less hardy species outside in the autumn or winter before the onset of harsher weather.

Most cyclamen tubers can be planted at a distance of 8–12cm (3–5in) apart, although *C. hederifolium* is better planted at a distance of 15–20cm (6–8in) as the tubers will become very large in time. A planting depth of 4–6cm (1.5–2.5in) is ideal for the hardier species but 15cm (6in) depth or more for the less hardy ones; in the wild *C. hederifolium* and *C. repandum* have been recorded growing at a depth of more than 30cm (12in)!

Most species will transplant successfully in full growth but care should be taken not to damage the roots or tubers unduly.

Cyclamen hederifolium, and to a lesser extent *C. coum*, are often prolific seeders and colonies can become overcrowded in just a few years. In the case of the former the tubers become so large that they can push one another out of the soil. When this stage is reached it is probably best to lift all the plants, replenish the bed and start all over again. Excess plants can be placed elsewhere in the garden or given away to friends; they make super Christmas presents or gifts at any time.

The less hardy cyclamen such as *C. graecum* and *C. creticum* will grow outside in favourable sheltered gardens. Deep planting will ensure extra protection for the tubers from frosty weather. Planting tubers beneath steps or at the base of a warm sunny wall will encourage success. Some growers advocate placing the tubers in a deep hole with a little compost above followed by a slate or brick then more compost. This has the double benefit of adding extra insulation from frost as well as keeping excess moisture away from the tubers. During the winter extra protection can be afforded by placing fern fronds, straw, or other insulation over the plants, taking care not to damage the leaves. However, beware of slugs and snails that delight in hiding in such places. Plastic or indeed any insulator that holds moisture and creates a humid atmosphere is wholly unsuitable and is likely to encourage fungus infections.

Mulches

Cyclamen certainly benefit from mulches in the open garden. Mulches help conserve moisture and suppress weeds, whilst at the same time they can greatly enhance the border. Various types of mulch can be applied. Best of all is a good oak or beech leaf mould, but in fact any good friable leaf mould will suffice (you should seek the permission of the landowner before removing leaf mould from woodland). Pine needles can be equally effective and are said to be excellent for *C. purpurascens* and *C. repandum*, but I have had little personal experience in using them.

If leaf mould is unavailable then bark chippings are a good and readily available alternative. I find the coarser types better as the pieces do not get blown around in gales so easily. I remember once applying a large bed with fine bark chippings which I thought would be ideal. A week later a fierce autumn storm struck removing the entire mulch to a distant corner of the garden, where it piled up against a fence, sand dune-like.

Other mulch materials include stone chippings, coir and coconut husks. None of these are as good in my opinion; furthermore they do not look so attractive.

Mulches are best applied during the dormant season so that when the new leaves and flowers appear they push their way through the mulch to the light. Mulches can be applied every year or every two years. A top-dressing of bonemeal can be applied at the same time, if required.

Feeding Cyclamen in the Garden

Cyclamen are not gross feeders, indeed most actively dislike excess feeding. Many fine colonies survive healthily for many years in gardens without ever being fed. A dressing of bonemeal lightly pricked into the surface around the plants will do no harm. Other feeds may lead to over-lush and uncharacteristic leaf growth that may well be more prone to fungus infection. An annual top-dressing of leaf mould or well-rotted compost applied in the late summer will certainly do no harm and will enhance the look of the bed.

Raised Beds, Troughs and Containers

Cyclamen grow well in raised beds, especially where the garden soil is too heavy for them. The beds need not be raised high, even 9–12cm (4–5in) will have the desired effect. The compost placed in the bed can be controlled so that it is exactly right for the plants. A good gritty, free-draining mixture is essential. A suitable compost can be made from equal parts of good fibrous loam (or John Innes Potting Compost No. 2 or its equivalent), grit or coarse 'angular' sand and a good flaky leaf mould (in preference to peat) which is best sieved to remove unduly large pieces. If the loam is on the heavy side then the grit or sand can be doubled to increase the drainage. To this can be added bonemeal or a similar organic slow-release fertilizer but it is not essential. The compost should be mixed thoroughly and placed in the raised bed and firmed in. Water well to ascertain that the compost drains freely and then allow the bed to settle for a few days before planting proceeds. If necessary more compost may need to be added to the bed to 'top it up'.

A similar compost is suitable for troughs and other containers. To prevent undue weed growth a gritty top-dressing can be added as a final touch once planting has been completed.

A well-planted raised bed devoted to a single species or with different areas for different species of cyclamen can be a very effective feature in the garden: for instance, when planted with patches of different colour forms of *C. coum* or simply a mixture of the ordinary pink and white forms of *C. hederifolium*.

GROWING CYCLAMEN UNDER GLASS

Unless one is fortunate enough to live in a mild, practically frost-free, area only a few of the delightful species of cyclamen can be grown in the open garden. The remainder will need to be grown under glass. None requires heat to grow but they do require frosts to be excluded; the occasional light frost will not affect most (except perhaps *C. africanum*, *C. persicum*, *C. rohlfsianum* whose foliage may be damaged even though the plants may survive the occasional overnight low of –4°C (25°F), but most will not survive long periods of freezing (see p.12), especially if the containers are frozen right through for days on end. Even species hardy in the open garden such as *C. coum* and *C. cilicium* will not put up with such treatment, whilst perfectly able to survive the same freezing period planted in the soil outdoors.

12 *Cyclamen hederifolium* (here forma *albiflorum*) can make a very fine and floriferous plant for pot cultivation; cultivated by Mike Brown.
13 An award-winning pot of *Cyclamen coum* Pewter Group, an excellent species for showing in March and April.

14 The small *Cyclamen intaminatum* makes an ideal pot plant where the beauty of its little blooms can be all the more readily appreciated.

15 The rather rare *Cyclamen graecum* subsp. *candicum*, with its darkly marked leaves and handsome flowers, is best grown in pots, rarely succeeding well in the open garden.

16 The appealing foliage of *Cyclamen hederifolium* 'Silver Cloud' is just as attractive as the pink flowers, the foliage lasting from autumn to early summer in the garden.

17 The pewtered foliage of *Cyclamen graecum* subsp. *graecum* 'Glyfada', an unusual selection.

Like many plants grown under glass, cyclamen require plenty of moisture when in full growth, shade from excessive sunshine and, most important of all, a buoyant atmosphere with plenty of air movement and an even temperature regime which is on the cool side; most heartily dislike high temperatures when they are in full growth, despite their mainly Mediterranean origins. Adequate ventilation is therefore required at all times, the vents only being closed down when severe cold weather threatens in the depths of winter. For large collections the installation of electrical fans to aid air movement is an optional extra, but during exceptionally hot summers they are a positive advantage in moderating temperatures within the glasshouse. Many growers advocate the use of cold frames rather than glasshouses for housing the less hardy cyclamen and others prefer to use the more shaded areas beneath glasshouse benching, which is ideal for cyclamen and other plants such as ferns, if it is not too gloomy; it is an especially useful area for sheltering pots and trays of young cyclamen plants, particularly in those glasshouses that are glazed to ground level. *C. balearicum*, *C. creticum*, *C. cyprium*, *C. libanoticum* and *C. repandum* are particularly suitable for growing beneath the staging and, in my experience, thrive there better than on top; *C. repandum*, *C. balearicum* and *C. creticum* and their various forms make up a closely allied group which have thinner leaves than other cyclamen species and they quickly flag in bright sunshine so naturally prefer more shaded conditions, especially when they are grown in pots. The only care that needs to be taken is to be careful that water does not drip excessively on the plants from above.

Of course, it is nearly always advised that glasshouses be placed in a sunny and open position in the garden; however, those contemplating a house for cyclamen alone might wish to consider a position where the glasshouse is in shadow for a part of the day, especially the midday hours.

Shading can be applied at any time from March onwards, especially if the weather turns warm and bright and most cyclamen will take immediate benefit by not wilting during the day and keeping their leaves

18 The beautifully marked foliage of *Cyclamen graecum* subsp. *candicum*, each plant, like fingerprints, having subtly different markings and tones.
19 The striking foliage of *Cyclamen mirabile* 'Tilebarn Nicholas' is flushed with raspberry pink when young.

for longer, which in turn helps to build up tubers for the following season.

Even in slightly frosty weather the vents of the glasshouse can be left partly open, for the frost will rarely penetrate inside unless temperatures fall well below zero. At the same time, plants are best kept fairly dry during cold periods. If water needs to be applied this is best done during the morning so that by nightfall excessive moisture has drained away, leaving the plants dry but the compost moist.

When temperatures fall below −3°C (27°F) it is advisable to protect plants further. An electric fan or paraffin heater will keep out the worst of the frost, but if conditions get very cold extra insulation may need to be considered. The cheapest form is simply to lay sheets of newspaper over the plants, especially those closest to the glass. Today thermal fleece is ideal, effective and light

enough not to damage the plants by its weight; this is especially important if temperatures fall below −5°C (23°F) for more than 24 hours. An alternative is to use small-bubble polythene sheeting which is widely sold for greenhouse insulation. As it is heavier than fleece and may damage the plants under its weight, the sheets can be kept just clear of the plants by supporting them on short bamboo canes pushed into the plunge. This has the added advantage of keeping up the humidity and preventing desiccation but it must be removed the moment temperatures rise. Even a modest frost may harm, even kill, plants of *C. africanum* and *C. persicum*, and especially *C. rohlfsianum* (although this latter species is hardier than generally supposed) and these plants are best removed from the glasshouse and placed in a safe frost-free environment until the inclement weather has passed.

Except in mild areas the following species are generally grown under glass: *C. alpinum*, *C. africanum*, *C. balearicum*, *C. creticum*, *C. cyprium*, *C. elegans*, *C. graecum*, *C. libanoticum*, *C. mirabile*, *C. peloponnesiacum*, *C. persicum*, *C. pseudibericum* and *C. rohlfsianum*. However, in addition, growers often grow especially fine forms of the hardier species under glass, especially if they like to show plants, so it is usual to see *C. cilicium*, *C. coum*, *C. hederifolium*, *C. intaminatum*, *C. parviflorum*, *C. purpurascens* and *C. repandum* also under glass.

Of all these only *C. graecum* and *C. rohlfsianum* like abundant sunshine, while the remainder prefer at least some shade. Strong sunlight can be just as damaging to growing plants of some species as can frost to others and developing foliage can be easily damaged by scorching. For most some shade is therefore necessary; however, a balance has to be struck as many of the finest leaf forms only develop their full potential (leaf patterning and colour) given adequate light and become duller and larger in too-dense shade. If it can be arranged for plants to be shielded from the excesses of the midday sun then all should be well.

Shading can be simple and cheap such as the various grades of shade-netting available today or better still, wooden slats fixed on frames and placed on the roof of the glasshouse. More expensive forms are also available such as automatic vents and shading systems as well as alloy slat-shading. The cheapest, yet very effective, method is a suitable whitewash such as Coolglass painted on the glass on the sunny sides of the house, although it is less attractive generally and is a nuisance to apply in the spring and to remove at the end of the season. All these systems aim at reducing the fluctuations in temperature throughout the day and keeping the houses cooler overall.

Many growers use clay pots and plunge their plants in special raised beds. These need to be stout and the staging must be strong enough to support both the weight of the plunge material as well as the full pots, especially when they are wet. There is nothing worse than having the staging collapse and ruining plants in full growth and muddling the labels. Pots need to be plunged to a depth of about 8–10cm (3–4in). The plunge material used varies from vermiculite to coarse, angular sand to Hortag; all are equally effective, although Hortag dries out rather more quickly. Plunging has the benefit of helping to even out wild fluctuations in water content of the compost and temperature, both harmful to the growing cyclamen plant.

In the average glasshouse or alpine house there will be a mixture of different plants. Cyclamen will fit well into such a house but the grower will need to seek the right positions for the various plants and this may differ from season to season according to the demands of the various plants being grown. For instance cyclamen mix extremely well with pots of dwarf bulbs as many require similar treatment.

Plants can also be planted out in permanent beds in the glasshouse; in full sun *C. graecum* will thrive in these conditions, remembering that plants need to be kept just moist during the summer months once they have died down. Other species can be tried in cooler, partly shaded beds. Alternatively, plants can be placed out in specially prepared beds in cold frames. A frame brim-full of different forms of *C. coum* or *C. repandum* can be a very attractive feature and the plants respond by luxuriating in these conditions and seeding around prolifically while they can even be used as a cut flower. Frames need to be kept ventilated at all times except during very frosty weather when they can be closed down temporarily. For the less hardy types some form of insulation needs to be placed over the frames during severe cold spells; rush matting or bubble polythene is ideal and care should be taken to ensure that it is well anchored, especially if it is windy. Any insulation should be removed the instant the weather relents and the frames given a proper airing by opening up the vents. In the spring the frame lids can be removed and rain allowed in but once the plants have died down in early summer the lids can be replaced to prevent excess water getting inside but left open enough to allow plenty of ventilation. In the autumn the lids can be again removed to allow the plants to get a good soaking, then, as the weather cools down at the onset of winter, place the lids on once again. This routine seems a bit fussy but one can soon get used to it and the rewards are seen in the healthy growth of the plants and abundant bloom.

Potting Cyclamen

Potting cyclamen is often regarded as a chore but it does give a good opportunity to overhaul one's collection, to examine the tubers to see whether they are growing well and, more importantly, that they are healthy and without any obvious signs of pests or disease. Plants bought 'in the green' from a nursery by post will need to be potted up the moment they arrive, carefully removing any damaged leaves or buds. However, the best time to pot on cyclamen in a collection is when they are dormant, just before they start back into active root growth. Not only do plants seem to respond best to this treatment but it also avoids possible damage to emerging leaves or flower buds if the operation is carried out later in the year. The ideal potting time for most species is when growth begins. The earliest to start into growth such as *C. hederifolium* can be potted on in mid-August but for those that start into growth very late (viz. *C. balearicum*, *C. creticum*, *C. peloponnesiacum* and *C. repandum*) September and early October will do just as well, although even these species may be putting on active root growth in the summer when there is no sign of growth above ground; some growers prefer to pot on these latter species shortly after they die down in the late spring as they tend to have delicate and rather brittle leaf-stalks that can be easily damaged. In essence, species can be potted on from mid-August onwards in flowering order until the job is finished. *C. colchicum* and *C. purpurascens* are slightly more problematical as, under optimum conditions, they never seem to be out of growth and rarely seem to go dormant. They can be potted on carefully during the late spring and early summer before the first flowers begin to appear. Another exception is *C. rohlfsianum* which, in my experience at least, is best repotted in the late summer shortly before it is first watered at the end of its long rest period; plants treated in this way appear to flower more regularly and profusely. When potting on young or established plants it is important not to damage the roots or tubers in any way and complete the operation as quickly as possible to avoid desiccation.

In fact most cyclamen seem to flower more profusely if somewhat under-potted, so it is best to avoid giving them too large a pot. Having said this though, certain species (*C. hederifolium* and *C. repandum* in particular) look odd and crammed if placed in pots that are too confining; their natural mode of growth is for both leaves and flowers to grow outwards away from the tuber, emerging round the inner edge of the pot, so they require large pots in order to develop properly and unhindered.

Most growers opt to grow single plants in pots but there is no reason why several should not be placed in a single large pot or pan and some of the smaller species such as *C. coum*, *C. intaminatum* or *C. parviflorum* can be very effective when, say, five or six tubers are placed in a single container. For exhibition purposes or growing perfect specimens, especially of the finest leaf and flower cultivars, plants are best grown one per pot.

The depth at which tubers are planted in pots is another point on which few growers agree. Some advocate deep planting for all species whilst others prefer to plant the tuber on or close to the surface. However I, like the majority of growers, prefer a more intermediate approach, planting the tubers of the majority of species and cultivars with the top of the tuber just clear of the surface of the compost and topping this with 10–15mm (0.4–0.6in) of stone chippings, grit or even coarse sand. This has several benefits apart from keeping the top of the tubers relatively dry, for the topping also helps protect the vulnerable growing points on the tuber surface, while at the same time keeping the tubers cooler. There are naturally exceptions to this regime. In my experience *C. persicum* thrives best with the upper part of the tuber exposed and not buried in either grit or compost and *C. graecum* seems to do well with its tuber on the surface (as they often are in the wild) or shallowly buried beneath a layer of chippings or grit. However, *C. colchicum*, *C. purpurascens*, *C. balearicum*, *C. creticum*, *C. peloponnesiacum* and *C. repandum* seem to positively dislike this surface treatment, instead flourishing best when deeper buried in the compost; in fact they can be planted about halfway down in the pot with an ample layer of compost above. However they are planted, a surface dressing of stone chippings or grit not only looks attractive but also helps to suppress weeds and retain moisture which is especially important when plants are in active growth.

Compost should be firmed in around the plants as potting proceeds but over-firming is best avoided as this may compact the compost too much and even damage the sides of the tubers. Firming can be accomplished by knocking the pots several times on the potting bench to settle plants and compost.

Remember to transfer labels to new pots as potting on proceeds, rewriting any that have become faded. Plastic labels become brittle after two or three years and readily fracture, although there are long-lasting and more durable plastic labels available on the market today.

Containers

Whether clay or plastic pots are used is a matter of preference. Many growers consider that clay pots are aesthetically more pleasing and they have the advantage that they are porous and cooler than plastic, but though they dry out more quickly and are certainly today a good deal more expensive, some growers would never be persuaded to turn to plastic. For large collections most, however, opt for the standard range of plastic pots available. Both standard and half pots can be used with equal success, as many cyclamen are fairly shallow-rooted. *C. graecum* is an exception and has deep delving, fleshy, thong-like roots that require deeper than average pots and these can be acquired if sought. Species that need deeper potting such as *C. colchicum*, *C. peloponnesiacum*, *C. repandum* and *C. purpurascens* also greatly benefit from the deeper types of pots and rarely grow well when planted in shallow pans or trays.

Whatever containers are used it is essential to ensure that they are clean. Old containers will need to be scrubbed clean and dried before use; this minimises possible diseases from contaminated pots and old compost.

Young two-year-old plants of most species will thrive in 7cm (3in) pots and can be gradually moved up to 10, 12.5 and 15cm (4, 5 and 6in) pots over a number of years. However, much depends on the amount of space available. Some growers discard plants when they get too large, whilst others sport prize specimens of *C. africanum*, *C. hederifolium* or *C. rohlfsianum* in pots as large as 30cm (12in). However, there is no advantage in overpotting. As a general guideline it is normal to allow a 1–2cm (0.5–0.8in) gap between the tuber and the pot, perhaps a little more for very large ones.

How often to repot

Some growers repot most of their cyclamen every year or every two years, discarding all the old compost and replacing it with fresh. This has one great advantage in that it is easy to inspect tubers and make sure they are sound and healthy. However annual repotting is not actually necessary in my experience and I have several old plants that continue to thrive each year despite not having been repotted for at least five years. In fact some species seem to fare better when not repotted too often; *C. libanoticum* especially.

Plants that are not repotted should not, however, be neglected. In the early summer the pots are cleaned up, the old foliage and fruit remains carefully removed (a gentle tug will generally suffice to pull off the brittle remains) and the surface grit and compost removed down to almost the base of the tuber, but leaving the roots undisturbed. The pots are then made up with fresh compost with a little bonemeal added for good measure and the surface completed with the usual layer of chippings or grit.

Composts

No two gardeners can ever agree on the perfect compost for any plant and this is true for cyclamen. We have already examined the conditions that suit most cyclamen, and compost should reflect these basic requirements; moisture, free-drainage and a pH that is preferably about neutral. In reality a wide range of different composts can be used with great success, based either on manufactured compost available at garden centres and stores or on the gardener's own unique recipe using home-made composts, leaf mould and sterilised loam. The preparation of composts is a vital factor in the successful cultivation of cyclamen in pots and it is best to spend some time in preparing composts, rather than to dash headlong into potting.

An average compost based on soil would consist of: one part (by volume) sterilised loam (John Innes Potting Compost No. 1 or 2 will suffice, provided that the loam is neither too silty nor too claggy), one part fibrous sphagnum peat or sieved leaf mould, and two parts fine grit or coarse (angular) sand. To this can be added a small quantity of bonemeal or John Innes base fertiliser or other potting fertiliser at a lower rate per volume than recommended by the manufacturer but only if sterilised loam is used instead of a John Innes compost. As an example half an average teacup of bonemeal or base fertiliser can be added to about 10 litres of the compost, which should then be thoroughly mixed. This will feed a plant for two to three years.

An alternative compost can be based on a soil-less mixture by using: one part soil-less compost (peat-based ones are widely available as well as other fibre-based composts), one part Perlite and one part fine grit or coarse sand.

Yet another which is equally effective is: one part sterilised garden soil (preferably of the loamy kind and sterilised to eliminate weeds and pests), one part sifted leaf mould, one part of coarse sand and one part of limestone grit.

The choice of compost depends to some extent on what is available locally and what you have experience of using. Some growers, for instance, dislike any compost except their own home-brew and repot all new plants that they acquire, carefully removing any vestige of the previous compost. This has the added benefit of getting rid of any imported pests.

Generally it is best to buy in sterilised compost and to add the various quantities of leaf mould or grit; however, small quantities of loam can be sterilised in the home using an ordinary oven or even a microwave oven, if the cook does not object too violently. Small soil-sterilising units are also available at many garden centres.

However the compost is prepared and whatever the proportions of the various ingredients, the final product should feel light and friable and in no way claggy. A good test of free drainage is to fill a pot with the compost and firm it down moderately well and water it thoroughly. If the water drains away immediately the drainage is fine, but if water sits on the surface for more than a minute the compost is not free-draining and the cyclamen will suffer as a result. In such cases add more grit to the compost; so much depends on the nature of the loam base, for even John Innes compost can differ markedly in character from one part of the country to another.

Some nurseries grow-on young plants straight into a John Innes-type potting compost. For those wishing to make up their own the proportions are as follows: 7 parts sterilised loam to 3 parts sifted leaf mould or fibrous peat to two parts grit or coarse sand. To this can be added John Innes base fertiliser or bonemeal at the manufacturer's recommended rate. Buckets or large flower pots are useful measures.

Mentioning peat-based composts is problematic today because of the very real needs of conservation. However, no really effective substitute is on the market at present and few of us have adequate supplies of fine leaf mould to cater for all our potting requirements. I have tried to use one of the coir composts as an alternative but with only partial success and some disasters, especially with cyclamen. But if everyone took to coir, supply certainly would nowhere near meet demand for it.

To assist perfect drainage it is generally a good idea to place a centimetre or so of grit at the bottom of pots, especially plastic ones, but this is no substitute for a well-balanced and free-draining compost in the first instance. For clay pots and pans the drainage holes can be covered with broken crocks or disks of perforated zinc and then a layer of grit. The zinc disks have the advantage of preventing worms creeping through the holes into the pots, especially if they are stood on earth in a cold frame or on the floor of the glasshouse.

Watering

Cyclamen require ample water when they are in full growth and this reflects the conditions they receive in the wild. At the same time, they should not be over-watered and certainly should never be allowed to stand in water for any length of time. If composts are correctly prepared and well-drained then it is in fact quite difficult to over-water cyclamen. Over-watering will undoubtedly cause the roots to die with resultant harm to the plant and can also lead to other problems. In particularl during dull, mild weather during the late autumn and winter a humid atmosphere can cause the build-up of moulds, especially botrytis, which may mark the foliage and rot the young flower buds or developing fruits. The answer is to try to water as little as possible during muggy, dull weather and during fine weather to water in the mornings so that by evening the plants, especially the foliage, are relatively dry once again. In any event plants should be given a good soaking once or twice a week remembering the old motto that a little often is less effective than a lot seldom as far as cyclamen are concerned.

Watering the plants overhead refreshes the foliage but can leave marks on both leaves and flowers, especially if the water is unduly alkaline. For this reason some growers prefer to water their plants from below, either through some form of capillary matting or by carefully soaking the plunge material. Those who grow prize specimens for showing also often prefer to treat their finest plants individually, watering them by lifting the pots and steeping them in a basin of water (almost up to the rim) for an hour or two, then returning them to the bench.

Signs of under-watering are generally immediately apparent as the foliage and flowers begin to wilt. A quick application of water will generally remedy the problem, but prolonged or repeated wilting will damage the plant causing yellowing of the leaves and malformation of the flowers, with the young flower buds often aborting.

When to commence or reduce watering

A carefully planned watering regime is essential for the successful cultivation of cyclamen in pots. Once plants are in active growth then watering, as has been discussed, is relatively straightforward but when to apply or when to withhold water can prove daunting to the newcomer to cyclamen cultivation. The main essential to remember is that the watering regime should try as far as possible to mimic the natural regime of the wild plant, bringing the plants into growth and flower at more or less the same season as they would in the wild (leaving aside *C. persicum* that can be brought into flower under commercial pot plant production techniques at almost any season, see p.175).

Few cyclamen benefit from a complete summer baking without any water, although *C. africanum*, *C. rohlfsianum* and *C. persicum* will certainly tolerate such treatment and *C. cyprium* and *C. libanoticum* are certainly not harmed by it. At the other extreme *C. purpurascens* and *C. colchicum* will quickly decline given such harsh treatment and they are best kept watered throughout the year, easing off the water somewhat only in the late spring and early summer, but increasing it once flower buds and new leaves begin to emerge in the summer and early autumn. The majority of other species thrive best when they are given a summer rest with very reduced watering. In fact they will succeed perfectly well if the plunge is kept just moist around the plants throughout the summer months, without the need to apply any water directly to the pots; *C. graecum*, which was once thought to require a long summer baking, flowers more freely if the tubers are kept just moist through the summer months.

It is important to remember that cyclamen roots are perennial and that if they die back due to a lack of moisture during the dormant season then this will undoubtedly harm the plant and will be manifested in poor growth and flowering the following season.

Cyclamen repandum and its allies, *C. balearicum* and *C. creticum*, are best kept cool and just moist, but during long hot and dry periods in the summer it may be necessary occasionally to moisten the pots overhead and to give them extra shading, but under average conditions this really is unnecessary.

After their summer rest the time eventually comes to start plants back into growth. The best time to do this is in the late summer or early autumn (say the first two weeks in September) by giving the pots a thorough soaking. This treatment certainly stirs species like *C. africanum*, *C. rohlfsianum* and *C. graecum* into

growth. Many of the others (especially *C. alpinum*, *C. cilicium*, *C. coum*, *C. hederifolium*, *C. intaminatum* and *C. mirabile*) anticipate the moister season by coming into growth as the days cool and the daylight decreases and the application of water merely spurs them on, although leaves and flowers may not appear above ground for some weeks or months. *C. balearicum*, *C. creticum*, *C. peloponnesiacum* and *C. repandum* are the last species to appear above the surface and rarely do so before February or March.

Initial watering should not be overdone and after their thorough soaking plants are best left alone until signs of renewed growth can be detected. This is especially so for those species that have been kept completely dry during the summer, as too much water (i.e. repeated waterings) can lead to the early emergence of the leaves which can spoil the display of flowers by almost hiding them; this is especially true of *C. africanum*, *C. rohlfsianum* and sometimes *C. graecum*. At the same time, over-watering at this stage may cause the tubers to rot. However, once water has been applied, plants should not be allowed to bake dry again (especially if the weather is hot and sunny) as developing flowerbuds or leaves may abort; the amount of water applied should be small, but is somewhat dependent on the weather and the particular season. A delicate compromise has to be achieved between under- and over-watering but regular checks on the plants should indicate how they are reacting and once they are in full growth again their watering requirements become simpler.

In the spring as the leaves of autumn- and winter-flowering species begin to yellow, this is the signal to reduce watering; the plants are beginning to go dormant and no longer need so much water. Watering can gradually be curtailed over a four- or five-week period. Even in the absence of regular watering the immature fruits will continue to develop, sustained by the tuber below. Where quicker drying is required, as with *C. africanum*, *C. graecum* or *C. rohlfsianum*, the pots can be placed on their sides, but this is not usually necessary; it was common practice in Victorian times, especially for bulbous plants, when, to make room for the summer display, pots were stacked on their sides below the staging or on shelves in the eaves of the house.

Long-dormant tubers

Occasionally, despite having apparently been given all the correct treatment, a tuber (or several) fails to come into growth at the expected time of year and may sometimes miss an entire year, eventually sprouting as if nothing was wrong. The reason for such an enforced dormancy is unclear. It may be that the plants were checked just before coming into growth; maybe by a sudden rise in temperature or failure to take up moisture at the right moment. Such plants can be quite difficult to deal with, for if they are over-watered in this condition they may easily rot. I have found that this is particularly true of *C. graecum* and, to a lesser extent *C. repandum*. The best advice is to keep the compost barely moist and watch the tubers carefully for signs of renewed growth. Once this is detected, watering can be gradually increased. If nothing happens by late spring plants are best rested as normal with the hope that they will sprout again the following season. I had one tuber of *C. graecum* that stayed dormant for three years before eventually bursting into growth; it showed no apparent decrease in vigour despite its long 'sleep'.

Another way to deal with this problem is to place the tubers into sealed polythene bags with moist (not wet) moss peat and to check regularly for signs of growth. The moment this is detected then the tubers can be potted up and treated in the usual way.

Feeding

Cyclamen have always been said not to be gross feeders: in fact there is a good deal of evidence, from the commercial production of *C. persicum*, that excess feeding weakens plants by restricting root development, whilst at the same time promoting lush and overlarge foliage which is soft and prone to fungal infections. Feeding therefore must be undertaken with caution. Having said this, another school of thought advocates more regular and heavier feeds for pot-grown cyclamen and certainly some amazingly large and floriferous specimens are being produced by this method today by one or two growers; especially plants for exhibition of *C. coum*, *C. graecum* and *C. hederifolium*. Certainly, some would argue that these plants (see plates 12–13) are 'out of character' and you would never see such plants in the wild. However, cultivation itself makes many species grow differently from their wild counterparts and the selective pressures in cultivation are quite different to those in the wild. In fact some 'species' begin to look rather different after several generations in cultivation.

The application of slow-release organic fertilizers such as bonemeal to the compost is ideal, allowing the plant to take up nutrients slowly. Foliar feeding is generally unnecessary and may well mark the leaves, spoiling the plant's attractiveness. However, the application of weak liquid feeds at intervals through the growing season (once, say, when plants come into flower and then at fortnightly intervals until the leaves start to yellow) can prove beneficial, especially for plants that are not repotted on a regular basis. I generally use a standard flower or pot plant liquid feed which is low in nitrogen and high in potash at half the manufacturer's recommended dilution rate; in fact standard tomato feed is ideal!

GROWING FROM SEED

Many cyclamen can also be grown from seed, an interesting and absorbing pastime in itself. Seed can be obtained from seed companies, though in a rather limited range (excluding florists' forms of *C. persicum*). It is better to join one or other of the societies that have an annual seed distribution scheme. In Britain both the Alpine Garden Society and the Scottish Rock Garden Club have extensive seed lists including cyclamen. However, if the passion for growing and learning more about cyclamen is fast becoming an obsession and a lasting interest, then the Cyclamen Society is the ultimate goal with plenty to offer members, including a seed distribution scheme. Cyclamen Society seed is generally distributed in July and August when it is fresh; germination will usually be rapid and good. This may not be the case with other seed distributions.

The great advantage of growing from seed is that you can quickly build up a good stock of plants, although it may take three or four years for the majority to reach flowering size. Seed raising is fun and it is exciting to watch young plants come into flower for the first time with the possibility of novelties (perhaps with interesting colours, leaf patterning or flower size or shape) appearing in the collection. Inevitably as the collection grows one is able to collect one's own seed and to pass the excess on to fellow enthusiasts. As with most hobbies, the more you put into it the more reward you get out and what started as a simple interest becomes one of lasting pleasure.

Seed is by far the best way of propagating cyclamen, indeed it is often the only method available, in the absence of a successful micropropagation technique for the genus. Seed is generally set in abundance on the hardy outdoor species and cultivars of *C. cilicium*, *C. coum* and *C. hederifolium*. Pot-grown cyclamen will also often set plenty of fruit especially if the frame or glasshouse has a buoyant atmosphere with plenty of air movement.

Cyclamen are basically outbreeders and to ensure a decent set of fruit two or more plants of the same species or cultivar need to be grown in close proximity. Many plants will set seed without much assistance; however, they set best in a breezy atmosphere. Those who show cyclamen often remark that the plants set seed extremely well when transported in full flower in the back of a car where, no doubt, the bumpy and warm journey greatly aids nature in her work. To help pollination (and subsequent fertilisation) of especially fine cultivars or the rarer species pollen can be passed from the flowers of one plant to another by means of a small camel-hair brush, or indeed the plant can be selfed by passing pollen between the flowers on the same plant. Successful fertilisation is obvious within days of pollination when the pedicels begin to coil and thicken to some degree (curving but not coiling in the case of *C. persicum*). Unsuccessful fertilisation is indicated by limp pedicels that soon begin to shrivel away.

Except in the *C. repandum* group, where hybridization between species may happen all too readily, chance hybridization between adjacent species is unlikely to occur. Seed cannot, however, be guaranteed to be similar genetically to the parent plant or plants, even if plants are selfed and some variation can normally be expected. For instance some white-flowered forms of *C. hederifolium* (forma *album*) produce only white-flowered progeny while others produce a proportion of pink as well as white. Some cultivars produce variable progeny; many of the offspring will differ and may be very interesting and attractive but they will not necessarily mirror their parent(s).

When the plump, rounded fruit capsules are ripe they soften and pale to some extent, the coiled stalks relax somewhat (except those of *C. persicum* which are uncoiled) and the capsules split rather irregularly, almost like miniature earth stars, to reveal the seeds. This moment has to be anticipated as in the garden ants will certainly quickly discover the sugar-coated seeds and cart them away and all will soon be lost. This is less of a problem under glass. If the ripening of the fruit can be anticipated they can be picked a day or two in advance and placed in saucers or similar containers to complete ripening. With a little experience the ripeness of the capsules can be judged by gently squeezing them (not too hard) between the fingers and the softening prior to full ripening can be clearly felt as the flesh beneath the outer skin softens. I read once that the ripe capsule feels like the 'bobbles on bubble plastic sheeting' or even 'like pressing a floury potato cooked in its skin'. Both give a good indication of the feel of the ripe capsule just before it splits open.

The seeds are rather sticky and need to be teased from the open capsules. Before maturity they are white but as they mature (and before the capsule bursts) they turn a pale honey or hazel colour which is the ideal moment to gather them up and to sow them. Once the fruits have burst open widely the seeds quickly turn to dark brown and dry.

Strangely enough, the fruits of most species ripen more or less at the same time, generally in midsummer (from late June and through July), independent of when the species happens to flower. This means that the fruits of species such as *C. hederifolium* and *C. africanum* that flower in late summer and early autumn mature at the same time as the late winter- and spring-flowering species, so for these maturation is a far longer process.

There is no doubt that cyclamen seed germinates better and more reliably the fresher it is. The ideal technique is to sow the seed the moment it is ripe, straight from the parent plant if possible. Fresh-sown seed certainly gives a quicker germination but not necessarily a higher percentage of germination. Often, however, seed will be received dried and in packets from seedsmen or other growers. If the seed is known to be reasonably new then it can be sown as normal, but older seed is best soaked in tepid water for twelve to twenty-four hours before sowing; this plumps it up and certainly has a marked effect on germination. Some growers advocate a shorter soak in warm water with a dash of detergent followed by a two-hour rinse in fresh warm water, but this procedure does not give any better results to my knowledge. It used to be thought that cyclamen seed was only viable for a short while but this is now known to be incorrect and seed up to five years old will germinate reasonably successfully, particularly if it is given a pre-soaking before it is sown. In general terms though, the drier and older the seed is, the slower and more unreliable the germination. Old seed is hard to soak as it tends to float and not sink. A little amount of washing-up liquid, or a similar solution that helps to reduce the surface tension, will generally work, with the aid of a judicious stir.

Sowing Cyclamen

Fresh seed can be washed before sowing to remove the sticky sugary coating; this makes the process easier but it is not essential. It may be helpful to roll unwashed seed gently in silver sand and this separates the sticky seeds and makes them easier to handle when it comes to sowing.

Seed varies in size from species to species. *C. repandum* tends to have small seeds while *C. graecum* has large seeds, yet whatever the size it is generally quite easy to handle, and space-sowing using the fingers is relatively easy.

It is quite easy to get seed of the commoner species (*C. coum* and *C. hederifolium* for instance) but more difficult to acquire seed of the rarer species and forms. Joining societies such as The Cyclamen Society or The Alpine Garden Society allows access to their seed distribution scheme and to an interesting range of cyclamen. Alternatively, one can get to know individual growers who are often willing to pass on spare seed or seedlings to fellow enthusiasts.

For small amounts of seed of rare species or cultivars where seed is very limited a different procedure can be adopted to ensure the highest possible germination percentage. Fresh or pre-soaked seed can be placed on damp tissues (a layer of absorbent kitchen towel is ideal; some prefer capillary matting) in large petrie dishes, plastic boxes or shallow jars; whichever is used it should have a lid on it and the container placed in a cool dark place such as a cupboard. A careful watch can be made by checking the containers at regular intervals. As the seed begins to germinate a tiny tuber is developed before the seed-leaf (cotyledon) can be seen emerging from within the seed coat (John Parkinson, in 1629, was the first to report the formation of the tuber before the cotyledon emerges). At this time the germinating seeds can be removed and potted on. This operation needs to be done at the first sign of germination, otherwise the emerging cotyledon or roots may be easily damaged in the transfer from container to pot and it will at that stage be more difficult to establish them in the compost.

Seed composts should be both moisture-retentive and free-draining, but it should have a low fertilizer content. A useful compost consists of one part of a standard seed compost (peat or loam-based), two parts fine grit or coarse sand and one part of fibrous peat or finely sieved leaf mould or equal parts loam, peat and grit will do if the resulting compost is well-drained. Other media such as vermiculite or a mixture of Perlite and peat-based composts are used by some growers to great effect.

Space-sowing 2–3cm (0.8–1.2in) apart is ideal but not practical for large quantities of seed. Plastic pots (12.5cm/5in) can be used for small quantities of seed but many growers prefer plastic or strong wooden trays which for preference should be at least 10cm (4in) deep. The compost should be thoroughly watered prior to sowing and once sown the seeds can be covered by a fine layer of grit or oyster chips; this helps keep the environment around the seeds nicely moist and, at the same time, prevents the growth of undesirable mosses, or worse, liverworts. The ideal temperature for germination is 15–16°C (59–61°F); higher or lower will retard germination, or prevent it altogether. Pots and trays can be encased in plastic or have a sheet of glass placed overhead to prevent the compost drying out, but the moment germination occurs this should be removed. For this reason they are best placed in a shady and rather cool place to await germination; widely fluctuating temperatures will hinder quick and even germination, even of freshly sown seeds.

Thin sowing is essential as in most cases the young plants will remain in their original container for at least a year and crowding at an early stage will inhibit and retard their growth. Small containers also dry out more readily and this again can severely retard development. One way of ensuring steady progress is to sow seeds in cellular (modular) trays that are usually made of plastic or polystyrene; many commercial growers now favour this system which undoubtedly aids the potting-on of young plants and reduces root disturbance. In general, young plants are left in the cells until the roots begin to emerge through the basal holes at which time they are easily moved on. Another method is to use one of the modern range of peat pellets. These swell up in water to form small filled pots, generally with fertilizer incorporated, and are ideal for sowing individual seeds. Young plants can be readily potted on when large enough without disturbing the roots.

The ideal to aim for is to keep young plants growing as evenly and for as long as possible. This can be achieved by keeping plants moist at all times and keeping them cool and well ventilated. It helps to some extent to give growing seedlings a weak liquid feed at fortnightly intervals but the temptation to produce lush leafy plants too quickly is best avoided otherwise problems of wilting and fungal infections may result, especially if conditions become hot and humid during the summer. A low-nitrogen, high-potash feed is therefore to be recommended. Under optimal conditions seedlings will grow right through the first year and into the second season before becoming dormant and this will certainly bring young plants into bloom more quickly. However, if conditions become hot and dry, seedlings will go into early dormancy (denoted by yellowing and dying of the leaves) and they should then be given a rest period in the usual manner.

As the seeds germinate a small root emerges and, shortly after, a tiny tuber swells immediately below the seed. Only after this does the cotyledon appear above the surface of the compost. Premature dying down of young seedlings may lead to the death of the plants as the tiny tubers may not be enough to sustain the plant through a long hot or dry period; it is therefore wise to try and keep the seedlings growing for as long as possible.

Germination time varies from a few weeks to months. Interestingly, the seed of the different species tends to germinate at the time of year when the parent species come into flower, so one can expect species like *C. hederifolium* and *C. cilicium* to germinate quickest, while *C. pseudibericum* and *C. repandum* are far slower. I have found that some (*C. repandum* and its allies in particular) usually wait to the following spring before germinating, however fresh the seed was when sown. On the other hand I have known *C. hederifolium* and *C. graecum* to germinate in 20 days, although this is exceptional in my experience.

In general *C. cilicium*, *C. coum*, *C. graecum*, *C. hederifolium*, *C. intaminatum*, *C. mirabile*, *C. libanoticum* and *C. rohlfsianum* can be expected to germinate in 20–45 days; *C. alpinum*, *C. balearicum*, *C. creticum*, *C. cyprium*, *C. pseudibericum*, *C. peloponnesiacum* and *C. repandum* in 35–55 days. *C. purpurascens* is often very slow and can take more than 100 days to germinate, while the allied *C. colchicum* has been reported to take a full year. At the other extreme is *C. persicum* which can germinate in as little as 10 days under optimal conditions but rarely takes more than 35. I must stress though that germination success and speed depends on a whole combination of factors not least of which are the age of the seed and how it has been stored and treated before sowing, the method of sowing, the compost and the amount of available light (or darkness) and moisture. Only under scientifically controlled conditions, like those employed by the commercial growers of cyclamen in countries such as Holland, can germination be strictly calculated and guaranteed, for the imbalance or absence of just a single factor can vastly delay germination, or sometimes prevent it altogether. The advice is not to give up even if nothing germinates for months and containers should be kept for a minimum of three years before they are abandoned.

The University of Reading has done detailed investigations on cyclamen germination and they have come up with some very interesting results. The 'Reading Method' developed shows that seed germination (at least for *C. graecum* and *C. hederifolium*) depends on the complete absence of light for a period of 15–26 days, a temperature of about 15ºC (59ºF) but certainly no higher than 20ºC (68ºF) and an even moisture regime allowing the compost not to become too wet or too dry. Fresh seed is ideal for this method, but old seed will do well if it is given the pre-sowing soak first. Keeping the temperature uniform is probably the most difficult factor for many gardeners without having elaborate temperature controlled facilities. Placing pots in cool places, away from direct sunlight is essential otherwise temperatures in and around the pots are likely to soar well above 20ºC (68ºF).

The 'Reading Method' undoubtedly is well worth trying and certainly speeds up germination, giving seeds the optimal conditions in which to do so; however, it has to be said that it is not an essential requirement for successful germination. For years I have simply sowed all my cyclamen seed the moment it is available (fresh or otherwise) and placed the pots or trays in a cool, shaded frame to await results. I have rarely had a failure, although some batches have clearly not germinated quite as well as they might under more even and controlled conditions.

Darkness certainly seems to speed up germination of widely grown species such as *C. coum*, *C. graecum*, *C. hederifolium* and *C. repandum*. Some growers find that sowing seed in the winter (say in December) rather than in the late summer or early autumn is preferable and germination better. The reason for this may well be that temperatures are lower during the winter while in late summer and early autumn they may well soar too high and inhibit germination.

If the 'Reading Method' is adhered to it is essential to check the containers at regular intervals for any sign of germination, for if left, the young seedlings will quickly etiolate and make poor weedy, soft little plants more prone to fungal attacks. Another problem with this method is that germination can be sporadic and uneven, as containers must be brought into the light the moment the first seeds begin to germinate.

Unusually for dicotyledonous plants, cyclamen produce only a single cotyledon (seed leaf) above ground and this is rarely similar to the true leaves. Apart from *C. persicum* , pricking out is generally not advisable and most growers keep their seedlings in their original containers for the first 18 months, moving on the young plants once they have become dormant in their second year. The reason for thin sowing thus becomes readily apparent, for thick sowing would inhibit the growth of the young plants. Young seedlings should be kept growing if possible right through their first year by keeping them in a cool, semi-shaded place (in shaded frames or beneath the staging in an airy glasshouse is ideal) and by regular watering.

Young cyclamen plants take some while to develop their full leaf characteristics and seedlings of especially fine-leaved forms whose parents had striking leaf patterning or colouring may take a year or two to develop their full potential; some patience is required.

Labelling

As each pot or tray is sown it is wise to label it immediately to prevent possible confusion. Various labels are readily available in plastic, wood or metal. They should be large enough to include the name of the plant, its source and the date of sowing for future reference. Many growers also keep a log book as a duplicate record and to note other details such as germination date, percentage germination and when plants were potted on.

Once sown, containers of the hardy types can be placed in a shaded position in an airy cold frame. Frequent checks need to be made to ensure that the containers do not dry out and also to keep a watch for germination. Once this has begun the containers can be moved into a lighter, though not too sunny position.

Half-hardy and tender types can be placed under the staging in the glasshouse or conservatory to await germination. Young plants should be protected from frost during the winter months by keeping the house just above freezing; conditions which are too warm are best avoided as this invites soft, disease-prone growth.

When to Prick Out

The ideal time for most species and cultivars is in the summer of the second or third year, separating out the young tubers just before they come into active growth; if they are left too long then the leaves and leaf-stalks will become meshed together and difficult to tease apart without causing some damage. Even if plants have produced young leaves no harm will come to them if they are moved on, in fact even mature cyclamen move well 'in the green', that is when in full growth. As always, however, there are exceptions: *C. repandum* and its allies, *C. balearicum*, *C. creticum* and *C. peloponnesiacum*, are rather more delicate and the young leaves and leaf-stalks (petioles) can prove to be rather brittle. To move them on in young growth will cause some damage and it is therefore advisable to move them on earlier in the year; shortly after they have died down is ideal. The small tubers can be grown on in individual pots (7cm/3in pots are ideal) or, if large numbers are involved, a large deep tray may prove more satisfactory and less time-consuming, placing the small tubers 5cm (2in) apart for convenience. Trays have the added advantage of drying out more slowly and evenly, keeping the young plants in a more even environment. Gentle overhead sprays of water, especially during warm weather, will help the plants to establish quickly but care should be taken not to overdo this to help minimize possible fungal attacks and rotting of the young tubers.

How long do young plants take to flower from seed?

This depends to some extent on how they have been treated from germination but some species are slower than others. *C. alpinum*, *C. coum*, *C. hederifolium**, *C. cilicium*, *C. intaminatum*, *C. mirabile*, and *C. parviflorum* will often put out a few flowers in their second season; I have even known the former flower in the first year from seed but that was an exception and I have only once achieved it. The first good flowering for most will be in the third and fourth year. On the whole I have found that the high polyploid species such as *C. graecum*, *C. purpurascens* and *C. rohlfsianum* are the slowest to flower from seed. The exception here is the popular florist's *C. persicum*: wild forms generally flower in their second or third year from seed; some of the large-flowered cultivars can be flowered in seven to nine months without great difficulty but this is only likely to be achieved under ideal growing conditions where light, temperature and moisture are carefully controlled.

For many of the other species greater patience is required. *C. alpinum*, *C. africanum*, *C. balearicum*, *C. creticum*, *C. cyprium*, *C. libanoticum*, *C. mirabile*, *C. purpurascens*, *C. pseudibericum*, *C. peloponnesiacum* and *C. repandum* can usually be flowered in their third season but they may take four if conditions, especially during their first season, have not been optimal. *C. rohlfsianum* is probably the slowest species to reach flowering size; four years is quick and I usually find they do not reach flowering size until they are five years old; this also applies to some forms of *C. graecum*. However, the event is well worth the wait, for once plants reach a flowering regime they can be relied upon to flower regularly for many seasons thereafter.

COLLECTING YOUR OWN SEED

Seed should be collected the moment it is ripe carefully recording details of each gathering to avoid confusion. Seed for growing on can be sown immediately but the rest will need to be stored for dispatch to seed exchanges or for sending to other growers. Although under-ripe seed is ideal for immediate sowing (when it is at that pale brown stage) seed for packeting and storage must be fully ripe, when it becomes dark brown. Fruits normally ripen over a period during July and early August, with species like *C. hederifolium* and *C. coum* ripening ahead of *C. cilicium* and *C. repandum*. However, plants in sunny dry sites are likely to ripen their fruits ahead of the same species in a cooler shadier position, whether in the open garden or under cover. *C. colchicum* is very slow maturing its fruits and the next crop of flowers can arise and have partly gone to fruit before last year's fruit crop has ripened; July and August.

Seeds can be stored in a cool, dry place until they are required. Some advocate putting them in sealed containers in a refrigerator and this will certainly ensure more uniform storage.

Commercially, seed of cyclamen is washed to remove the sugary coating and then dusted with a fungicide to prevent infection (especially from fusarium) but for non-commercial samples this is unnecessary.

One word of caution. Beware of mice and voles which can devastate a collection of cyclamen seed. I once left two packets of a scarce cultivar in the potting shed over a weekend only to find the envelopes shredded and the seed gone when I remembered them. Ants can also be attracted to ripe seeds and may cart many away before they are noticed.

PROPAGATION BY DIVISION

This is not a method generally undertaken for it takes some nerve to dig up a particularly fine specimen of a cyclamen and to cut it in half or into quarters, but the method can work. I visited a garden many years ago where there was a charming driveway lined with hundreds of well-flowered plants of *C. hederifolium* in white and pink. I asked the old gardener there how he got such a show and he said that he had started with just a few tubers (he called them 'corms') many years previously and that every few years he dug up the bed, replenished the soil with fresh compost and cut the existing tubers up with a sharp knife and replanted them immediately. This operation was carried out after the plants had died down in midsummer. I enquired if he treated the cut surfaces and he told me that he did nothing to help the healing process. This would seem to be complete folly to the cyclamen enthusiast and I am sure it would be doomed to disaster if I were to try it. However, it is worth considering as a way of increasing stock of especially fine-flowered or fine-leaved forms, especially of some of the rarer cultivars which perhaps do not come very true from seed.

Mature tubers which have several distinct growing points on the upper surface should be selected. The tuber should be cut from the top downwards using a very sharp

temperature. Any acaricide will also kill the predator so one or the other must be employed.

Incidentally, the predator may have some difficulty in passing from one plant to another, especially if the plants are well spaced. The answer to this is to link plants with strands of cotton thread which act as bridges for the predator to cross; it looks odd but it is very effective.

The broad or cyclamen mite, *Polyphagotarsonemus latus* may infest the buds and young leaves of cyclamen plants, especially those grown under glass where their feeding causes growth distortion and stunting. The affected areas often show up as harder tissue covered in small brown scales. The mites are very small being barely 0.25mm long. Hygiene is essential to control this pest, together with the removal and destruction of infected leaves and buds. No control is available to the gardener: Dicofol spray or Aldicarb granules are used by commercial growers.

Mice and Voles

Small rodents can occasionally prove bothersome. Plants in leaf or flower are rarely attacked and neither are the tubers which are probably toxic but these small creatures are sometimes greatly attracted by the ripening fruits, the sugary-coated seeds being apparently irresistible. Even worse, they will sometimes demolish complete fruit crops during the winter, long before the seeds are ripe. However, patches of cyclamen can remain unmolested for years then suddenly, one year all the fruits will be taken in just a few days. Traps (preferably of the humane type; the caught mice can then be released at a safe distance from the garden) or baits can be laid to counteract such problems.

Nematodes

Several different nematodes or eelworms are known to infect cyclamen, especially commercial *C. persicum* where capillary matting is used and the minute 'worms' can easily move from pot to pot. The stem and bulb eelworm, *Ditylenchus dipsaci*, root-knot eelworm, *Meloidogyne hapla*, *M. incognita* and *Pratylenchus pratensis* are all known to be a problem. They mainly attack the underground parts of the plant, especially the roots, but may also infect the leaf and flower stalks causing distortion and eventual death. All infected plants and compost are best destroyed. Commercially the problem is controlled by the application of Nemacur (Fenamiphos) but good hygiene and the use of scrupulously sterilized composts are the long-term solution as the eelworms often reside in old compost and plant remains. Plants should also be purchased from a reputable nursery. Unfortunately, there is no effective control that can be used by gardeners. Commercial growers use chemicals such as Aldicarb, Metam-Sodium and 1,3-dichloropropene as well as hot water treatment of 'bulbs', a complicated procedure requiring considerable skill.

Sciarid Flies

These are known under various common names including mushroom flies and fungus gnats and, like the vine weevil, have proliferated since the widespread use of soil-less composts was introduced (see also under Vine Weevil). The flies are small and black, mostly 2–3mm (0.08–0.12in) long, and they often run over the surface of the compost rather than fly. The larval stages of the fly damage the roots and stems of both seedlings and established plants, particularly under glass. Severe infestations will result in wilting and eventual death of plants. Gamma HCH, Imidacloprid and Malathion* are effective chemical controls. Sciarid flies are short-lived and rapid breeders so an infestation can quickly build up. Good hygiene is a sensible control measure but is unlikely on its own to cure the problem.

Scale Insects

Various scale insects attack a wide variety of plants in the garden. However, only the oleander scale, *Aspidotus nerii*, is likely to attack cyclamen, especially pot grown *C. persicum*. They form characteristic yellowish-brown scales, up to 5mm (0.2in) long, pressed hard to the stems and leaves, under which the mature female insect lurks; immature stages, juveniles, are mobile and difficult to spot. Damage is caused to the plant by the feeding habits of the scales and the copious sticky honeydew exuded by them onto the plant. The honeydew in turn facilitates the growth of unsightly sooty moulds. Systemic insecticides will control scale insects but some may also harm the plants; Malathion*, Permethrin and Pirimiphos-methyl are all effective controls. For minor infestations the scales can be wiped off leaves and stems using a soft cloth dampened with soapy water, or even a small brush similarly dipped.

Slugs and Snails

These can attack and destroy seedlings and young plants and in wet seasons outdoors they may also go for the flowers and buds. Various controls are available on the market and gardeners must choose according to their cultural regime and whether or not they want to introduce potentially hazardous chemicals into the garden environment. The manufacturers' instructions are paramount when using any control in the garden. My garden is blessed by a large population of both frogs and toads which can be very effective at limiting the numbers of slugs in the garden and do not cost any money to keep.

Springtails

Although several species are beneficial in the garden, others are harmful, particularly under glass. Springtails are minute wingless creatures (not insects). They are so named from the fork-like 'tail' at the end of the body, which is released forcibly against the ground to propel the creature through the air. The harmful springtails (species of *Hypogastrura*, *Onychiurus* and *Orchesella*) attack stalks and young leaves of seedlings causing lesions and the collapse and death of the young plants, generally the result of secondary fungal infection through the wounds made by the springtails. They dislike alkaline and well-drained composts and can be controlled by the use of soil pesticides such as Chlorophos.

Squirrels

Fortunately, I do not have squirrels in my garden, or only rarely so, but those who do can lose their entire crop of ripening cyclamen fruits within a few days. Squirrels (usually the grey variety), like mice and voles, are unpredictable in their attacks but they can be a dreadful nuisance and they seem to be able to eat a prodigious number of fruits in just a few hours. Apart from ruthless extermination of the perpetrators the most effective deterrent is using wire netting to protect the plants as the fruits begin to mature but beware, the slightest gap in the netting will be quickly discovered by them.

Thrips

Thrips may attack a wide variety of plants including cyclamen. Thrips are tiny, 1–1.5mm (0.04–0.06in) long, sap-sucking insects which puncture leaves and flowers, marking and distorting petals and leaf-blades, sometimes severely so. Several species are involved including the western flower thrips, *Frankliniella occidentalis*, the glasshouse thrips, *Heliothrips haemorrhoidalis*, *Scirtothrips longipennis* and the onion thrips, *Thrips tabaci*, all of which have similar effects on the cyclamen plant, but they are rarely a major problem for the gardener. I have noticed thrip damage especially to the early flowers of *C. purpurascens*, which is not surprising as there are far more thrips around during the summer than in the autumn and winter. Thrips can be controlled by many systemic insecticides including Ambush, Endosulfin, Folimat, Gamma HCH, Tamaron, Thiodan and Cymbush. For the gardener Malathion* and Hexyl (which is a dual-purpose systemic insecticide and fungicide) are good and effective, although the thrips tend to live in cracks and crevices which are often difficult to get at. Biological controls include a predatory mite, *Amblyseius cucumeris*.

Vine weevils

Undoubtedly the most serious pest of cyclamen is the vine weevil, *Otiorhyncrus sulcatus*, which will attack a wide range of plants in the garden including many

20 A dreaded vine weevil on the leaf of *Cyclamen hederifolium*.

bulbous and succulent species. The adult weevil is about 8–10mm (0.3–0.4in) long overall and a dull greyish-black colour with a rough and parallel-lined abdomen. The grubs (larvae) are whitish and characteristically C-shaped, about two-thirds the size of the adults. The adult weevils roam about over the plants chewing leaves and flowers indiscriminately, notching petals and leaf margins, sometimes eating well in from the margin. They are often introduced into gardens through purchased plants (especially pot or house plants); they can, for instance, quite often be seen on windowsills in the house where they have escaped from a pot plant, especially from plants like begonias and of course cyclamen. The grub spends all its time underground causing untold harm to the plants' rootstock. Cyclamen tubers are particularly appealing to their insatiable appetites and the grubs generally eat into the tuber from the base, often hollowing it out completely. By this stage the plant is in terminal decline and will show severe symptoms of wilting, yellowing of the foliage and overall stunting.

There is little doubt that the widespread use of peat-based composts has favoured the vine weevil for they allow it to move easily through the compost and from pot to pot. The use of soil-based composts can help to deter attacks to some extent as can the use of a deep layer of sharp grit on the top of each pot.

A careful watch needs to be kept over cyclamen collections to look for signs of attack from these weevils. The adults can be collected up by hand and destroyed (they are particularly active in the evening and night). Most of the chemicals that control the vine weevil are too dangerous and have been banned, especially Aldrin and Dieldrin. Gamma HCH (hexachlorocyclohexane) or BHC (benzene hexachloride) powders (both based on hexachloracyclohexane) can be used as a soil additive which will kill the grubs, as can Diazinon, Permethrin and

Pirimiphos-methyl if they can be acquired. Chlorophos can be partially successful used in a similar manner but beware, these chemicals used at greater than the recommended rate will often cause distortion of the flowers and buds, even the young leaves in some instances. Suscon Green is probably the most effective chemical at present available commercially but it is not generally available to amateur gardeners. Provado (Carbufuran and Imidacloprid commercially) is excellent at controlling vine weevil, especially when applied to pots of cyclamen or on raised beds or in troughs, but less effective for large areas in the garden, besides being expensive. All these chemicals are fairly dangerous and must be used with great care wearing protective clothing, especially gloves when mixing them into the compost. Good husbandry, especially clearing away leaf accumulations and regular clearance of any corners where the adults are likely to hide up during the day, will help to control this pest. Any infested compost should be destroyed, as should badly affected plants, unless they are a fine or rare form which one would hate to lose. In this instance, plants can be cleaned up thoroughly, treated with the appropriate chemical and replanted. Even severely affected plants can sometimes make a full recovery. As the adult beetles are mainly active at night then regular night patrols is another way of reducing the problem: simply descend on your plants with torch in hand and scan for the beetles, picking off and destroying all that are found.

To add to the misery of vine weevils there is a related species, *Otiorhyncus rugostriatus*, which is somewhat smaller, that can also attack cyclamen in a similar manner.

Wasps

These are rarely a problem but wasps can be attracted to the ripe fruits seeking out the sugary covering of the seeds. On several occasions I have watched fascinated as a whole succession of wasps descended on one of my beds of *C. hederifolium*, prising out a seed each (with some difficulty) and then flying away with them, presumably taking them back to their nests. Where large numbers of fruits are involved wasps are unlikely to make a great impact on the seed harvest but precious plants which produce little in the way of seed may need to be guarded from their advances.

DISEASES

Bacterial Rot

A bacterium, *Erwinia caratovorum*, may occasionally afflict cyclamen tubers, especially if they have been kept too hot and moist during the dormant season.

Mature plants tend to die off in patches with the leaves yellowing and dying. Inspection of the tubers will reveal dark brown areas which are soft and wet to touch, oozing an unpleasant-smelling whitish or yellowish pus. This is most serious when it affects the top of the tuber where the growing points are located. Badly affected tubers are best destroyed; however, if only small areas of the sides or base of the tuber are affected then the 'sores' can be carved off until clean and healthy tissue is reached. The wounds can be dressed by sterilising them with methylated spirits or a liberal dusting with flowers of sulphur (yellow sulphur), the tuber replanted and kept moderately dry until it begins to sprout, whereafter it can be treated as normal. I have also been successful in cauterising wounds by burning the surface with a lit candle (a cigarette lighter would probably do just as well!) Some advocate leaving the tuber exposed for a week or so to ensure that the wound really has dried out, while at the same time keeping the vulnerable root system moist by wrapping the roots in damp moss peat or similar moisture-retentive materials.

Botrytis

The commonest fungus to attack cyclamen, especially those grown under glass, is botrytis, *Botryiotinia fuckeliana* (= *Botrytis cinerea*). It is particularly common in dull, humid, cool weather in autumn and winter when many cyclamen are in active growth. The fungal spores attack the softer tissues of the plant (young leaves and petals are particularly vulnerable, especially flowers that are beginning to fade). The infected parts become spotted or blotched and begin to brown and the fungal spores arise as grey 'hairs' over these areas. Left unchecked the fungus will spread across the leaves or petals and down the stalks, infecting healthy leaves and flowers and buds as it advances. Eventually the tuber is infected and may well be lost. Infected parts should be cleared away immediately and destroyed, pulling away the entire leaf or flower with their accompanying stalks. In the spring botrytis may attack the developing fruits and can spoil a potential seed harvest.

Good hygiene will help prevent botrytis and under glass ample ventilation is essential at all times. Not watering plants during close, muggy weather will also help; if watering is essential it is best carried out early in the day so that the plants are relatively dry by nightfall. Systemic sprays of a suitable fungicide will control botrytis but may mark the foliage and petals. I have found flowers of sulphur effective on developing fruits and the yellow deposit scarcely matters if it helps save the seed crop, especially of the rarer species and cultivars. I have rarely known botrytis to be a problem in the open garden.

Chemical controls include Benomyl, Captan, Carbendazim, Quitozene, Thiram and Zineb.

Fusarium

Fusarium, *Fusarium oxysporum*, is a particular problem in the commercial production of *C. persicum*, although it can attack other species, especially when they are grown under glass. Fusarium fungus spores infect the root system causing gradual death of the roots and tuber. The above-ground signs of the disease are in the yellowing of the entire plant followed by a complete collapse and browning, the foliage generally ending up dry and crisp, by which time the plant is beyond help. All affected plants must be destroyed otherwise the problem will undoubtedly spread. Once identified, plants (especially healthy ones) should be treated with an appropriate systemic fungicide such as Benlate (Benomyl), Carbendazim, Mancozeb, Octave, Prochloraz (Octave), Thiabendazole or Thiram.

Powdery Mildew

Oidium cyclaminis may occasionally attack cyclamen and is readily recognized by its characteristic whitish-grey growth over infected parts of the plant, particularly leaves and dying flowers, often with a prolific production of fungal spores. Infection can quickly spread to the entire plant causing rapid death unless treated soon enough. The disease is particularly common during warm dry weather. Various fungicides are available for the control of powdery mildews but their use should be rotated as the fungus often becomes resistant if the same fungicide is used repeatedly. Benomyl, Bupirimate, Cardendazim, sulphur and Triforine are all effective when used in rotation.

Other Fungal Diseases

Other fungi include *Thielaviopsis basicola* (= *Chalara elegans*) which causes black root rot in plants under glass and appears to be worst when plants are under stress for one reason or another. *Gleosporium cyclaminis* and *Nectria radicicola* may infect leaves, flowers and stalks of cyclamen in various ways but they are rarely a problem for the gardener and are chiefly diseases that may appear in large-scale commercial production of *C. persicum* cultivars, where the higher temperatures of production and the close confinement of many thousands of plants under one roof may accentuate the problem.

Virus Diseases

Various viruses may infect cyclamen although the best-known is cucumber mosaic virus which is transmitted from plant to plant by aphids. Infected plants have distorted foliage and streaking of the flowers. Good hygiene, destruction of infected plants and eradication of aphids will help to reduce the problem. It is also wise not to touch clean plants after handling infected ones. A number of common garden plants act as reserves for the cucumber mosaic virus; they include buddleias, daphnes, magnolias and vincas, among others.

Viruses are not always easy to detect. Fortunately cyclamen do not seem as prone to virus attacks as some other plants, or perhaps viruses have a less devastating effect on them. Any plant that shows any indication of virus infection (such as mottling or streaking of foliage or flowers, a loss of vigour, distortion of the flower buds) should be destroyed. There is no cure.

Others

Moss and liverworts can become a problem. especially in pots and trays of seedlings, less so to adult plants. Under certain conditions, especially when the surface of the compost has become compacted and the atmosphere is too humid, mosses and liverworts will quickly establish themselves and will form a dense cover that may choke the seedlings, besides being unsightly. Good open composts, surface dressings of sharp grit and regular weeding will help to control this problem. The use of moss killer will control both mosses and liverworts and, in my experience, applied carefully will not damage the cyclamen plants.

NOTE. All the control products listed must be checked carefully before use and the accompanying instructions followed vigilantly, reading carefully the relevant product statutory conditions relating to their use. All pesticides should always be used in accordance with the product recommendations.

---

* *Product now off label.*

Chapter Four

The Cyclamen Plant

Cyclamen are long-lived tuberous perennials which undergo an annual cycle of growth and rest, usually with the plant dying down to ground level for part of the year. Plants put on most of their growth in the wild during the cooler time of the year, primarily the autumn and winter. This cooler period also coincides with the wettest months. Most parts of the cyclamen plant are glandular, but particularly the petioles and pedicels, the leaf undersurface, and to some extent the upper surface (particularly in young leaves) and the calyx. The corolla is glandular in some species, eglandular in others, or in some plants within a particular taxon only.

TUBER

The tuber is generally large and fleshy with a smooth or corky, often fissured, surface. The shape is often regular and subglobose to depressed, with or without a

depression or concavity on the upper surface. However, in some instances (especially *C. purpurascens* and *C. rohlfsianum*) the tuber may become very irregular in time and consist of several swollen sections joined together by narrower 'necks' of tissue. The size of mature tubers varies enormously from species to species; in *C. parviflorum* they rarely exceed 2cm (0.8in), while in *C. hederifolium* tubers 24cm (10in) are not uncommon and those in excess of 30cm (12in) have been recorded. Young tubers generally have a single growing point on the upper surface, but as they age the growing point divides and these may eventually end up well separated on the upper surface; the growing points (those producing leaves and flowers) are confined to the upper surface of the tubers.

Some (but not all) tubers develop slender woody necks (often called floral trunks) with the growing points at the tip; these may be short or long and those 5–8cm (2–3in) long are not uncommon in the wild; *C. graecum* has been recorded with a floral trunk as long as 30cm (12in); they may also sometimes develop in cultivated plants. The purpose of floral trunks is unclear, though it is often associated with plants that grow in rather rocky soils, especially in woodland or on screes, where plants are deeply buried by successive layers of rocky debris, soil and leaf litter. What is indisputable is the fact that the floral trunks bring the growing points of the plant close to the soil surface. They do not normally produce roots but they have on occasion been noted to do so, even to swell at the base and become tuber-like, and these may in the long term act as daughter plants and become detached from the parent plant, though this is far from certain: vegetative reproduction is in fact virtually excluded in cyclamen. It may, of course, happen by chance as in the case described above or, as in *C. purpurascens* and *C. rohlfsianum*, when the growing points become widely spaced and the tubers become increasingly irregular, especially when they become squeezed

21 The tuber of *Cyclamen africanum* has a depression in the top and roots from all over the shoulders and sides.
22 The rounded tuber of *Cyclamen graecum* (here subsp. *graecum*) has characteristic thick anchorage roots produced only from the centre of the base.

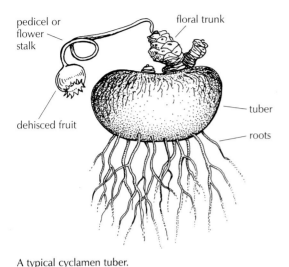

pedicel or flower stalk

floral trunk

dehisced fruit

tuber

roots

A typical cyclamen tuber.

between rocks. They may eventually part into several separate tubers. This, however, is not a factor of any importance in the evolutionary history of the cyclamen; if vegetative reproduction was important then it would be a considerable boon to the cyclamen grower.

The roots are borne on characteristic areas of the tuber depending on the species. They may be confined to the lower surface, or to a single area on the lower surface, or they may be confined to the sides or shoulders, or they may in fact be scattered more or less over most of the surface of the tuber; they are rare on the upper surface, except in *C. africanum* and *C. hederifolium*. Roots are mostly thin and fibrous but they may also be thick and fleshy as they are in *C. graecum*.

In some species the roots may bear small nodules, although the function of these is not yet understood. They are most noticeable in *C. coum*, *C. cyprium*, *C. mirabile* and *C. persicum*.

There has been disagreement in the past by various authors as to whether the storage organ of the cyclamen is a tuber, bulb, corm or rhizome, some being unsure and not committing themselves. Botanically speaking, bulbs are storage organs composed from the swollen bases of leaves and these can be clearly seen if one cuts a typical bulb such as an onion or hyacinth in half; clearly cyclamen do not belong here. A corm is a swollen stem base and is replaced annually by another being built on top of the existing one, which eventually shrivels away. Both *Crocus* and *Gladiolus* are typical cormous plants; again cyclamen clearly does not belong here! Rhizomes are swollen underground stems and like stems they have a regular arrangement of nodes capable of producing shoots at intervals; this is typical of plants like the rhizomatous irises and quite different to the situation found in cyclamen. Tubers, on the other hand, are fleshy

organs without the above characteristics; they mostly develop from roots as in the case of the dahlia, with a crown above which supports the growing point or points. This is exactly the situation found in cyclamen. In cyclamen, in fact, the tuber is technically developed from the hypocotyl, that region of the seedling plant between the roots and stems. The development of the tiny tuber in young cyclamen seedlings is fascinating to watch, although the details are soon obscured as the plants grow.

The cyclamen tuber is a long-term storage organ, its prime purpose being that of a food and water store to help the plant through the dry summer season as well as the cold winter one. Plants may live for many years, both in the wild and in cultivation, and the tubers appear to have few natural enemies in the wild, perhaps apart from man, that is.

At first glance the tubers of cyclamen all look rather alike but with experience many can be told apart, even in the absence of leaves and flowers. This factor has proved of benefit in the past in identifying importations of cyclamen tubers from the wild. In the 1980s at the Royal Botanic Gardens, Kew, we were able to show convincing proof to Her Majesty's Customs and Excise officers that tubers being imported illegally into the country under one name were in fact those of a far rarer species. Many thousands of tubers from Turkey were involved and were said to be *C. hederifolium*, which is of course very common in cultivation. However, from the details of the tubers that we examined we were certain that they belonged to the far rarer, and at that time, rather little-known, *C. mirabile*. To prove this, a large sample of the tubers was planted in a frame and the following autumn they all spouted and flowered, establishing conclusively that they were indeed *C. mirabile*.

Cyclamen can in fact be grouped together according to their mature tuber characteristics:

- **Tubers velvety, rooting from the centre below** – *C. balearicum*, *C. creticum*, *C. peloponnesiacum*, *C. repandum* (spring-flowering); *C. alpinum*, *C. cilicium*, *C. coum*, *C. cyprium* (in part), *C. elegans*, *C. intaminatum*, *C. parviflorum* (autumn- or winter-flowering).
- **Tubers corky, rooting from the lower surface (not the centre)** – *C. libanoticum*, *C. mirabile*, *C. persicum*, *C. pseudibericum*.
- **Tubers corky, rooting from one side of the base** – *C. cyprium* (in part).
- **Tubers corky, rooting from the shoulders and sides** – *C. africanum*, *C. hederifolium*.
- **Tubers corky, often knobbly or uneven** – *C. purpurascens*, *C. rohlfsianum*; possibly *C. colchicum*.
- **Tubers corky, rooting from below with both thick fleshy and fibrous roots** – *C. graecum*, *C. persicum*.

LEAVES

All cyclamen leaves are basal, borne directly from the tuber or from the tips of floral trunks. As they emerge the leaf-blade is folded inwards (this protects the leaf-blade as it pushes through the soil to the surface) with the two halves of the leaf lying side by side. The two halves of the blade eventually expand and push apart as the leaf increases in size, the blade eventually becoming more or less flat. It is the expanding leaf-stalk (petiole) that pushes the leaf-blade above the soil surface and only at that point does the blade expand, eventually being cupped or flattened. The mature leaves are generally rather thick and fleshy, sometimes with a leathery feel.

The petiole may rise vertically or may be ascending, as in *C. africanum* and *C. persicum*. However, in the majority of species the petioles are partly decumbent, spreading out horizontally for some distance from the tuber before turning, elbow-like, into an ascending upper part. The elbow is very typical of species like *C. hederifolium* and *C. repandum* and can be clearly seen when plants are grown in pots, for all the leaves emerge around the perimeter of the container as though wishing to escape. The petioles and the main veins on the leaf undersurface are usually covered in small reddish or purplish glands; these may sometimes extend over much of the leaf surface as well, especially when they are young.

The leaf shape varies considerably from species to species; from rounded- or kidney-shaped to heart-shaped or hastate (spear-head shaped) and it may, in addition, be symmetrically lobed. In *C. hederifolium* and *C. repandum* the most characteristic leaf shape is reminiscent of those of ivy (Hedera helix), but in the former species, at least, many different leaf forms can be observed. In *C. rohlfsianum* the leaves are broad and symmetrically and evenly lobed, quite unlike those of any other species.

In most species the leaf margin is toothed, but it may be shallowly scalloped or untoothed altogether; in both *C. colchicum* and *C. graecum* the marginal teeth are noticeably thickened and cartilaginous and feel like a row of tiny beads to the fingers.

Leaf patterning and colouring is one of the most distinctive features of many cyclamen, singling them out from most other members of the Primulaceae, which tend to have plain and often rather uninteresting leaves. The patterning frequently takes the general shape of the leaf (often as a heart-shaped or hastate mark) in a different shade of green or in a contrasting colour such as cream, white, silver or pewter. Leaf patterning is rather like fingerprints in that no two individual plants ever seem to have precisely the same design or degree of colour and this is what has made them of such interest to gardeners. Often the leaf patterning becomes more fragmented consisting of

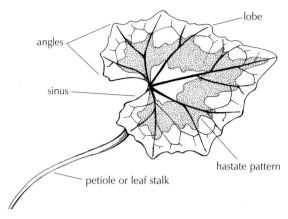

Cyclamen leaf showing main features.

a series of blotches which still conform to the basic heart-shaped or hastate pattern, but sometimes this is taken to extremes and the fragmented pattern spills all over the leaf surface in a series of small blotches, dots or dashes. This is perhaps seen at its best in some of the forms of the widespread and variable *C. repandum*, but it is also marked in forms of *C. balearicum*, *C. creticum* and *C. cyprium*. Occasionally the young leaves are blushed with pink or red and this has been particularly noted in *C. mirabile*, though not all forms of the species show this coloration. The silvering effect often seen on the upper surface of cyclamen leaves is a result of the lifting of the epidermal cells allowing in air between the skin and the tissue immediately below. Silvering is a highly desirable character of some cultivated forms.

In contrast, the lower leaf surface is far less variable. Often rather shiny, it may be plain green, or green flushed with pink or purple, but in the majority of species it is richly suffused with beetroot-red or purple-carmine.

Whereas leaf shape can be, and often is, an important diagnostic character, it is difficult to regard leaf patterning as such; it is variable and complex, often within a species, sometimes even within a single population in the wild. It is true to say that one can get a very misleading impression of this patterning from cultivated plants as many growers have carefully selected out the more beautiful and distinct forms, often at the expense of those that might well be considered more the norm in the wild; but that is true of the history of so many cultivated plants.

PEDICELS

Like the petioles, the pedicels or flower-stalks can arise vertically or they may be distinctly elbowed with the lower half spreading out horizontally (generally beneath the soil surface) and the upper half ascending, this latter type having the characteristic of pushing the flowers

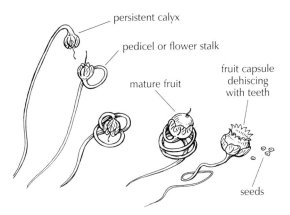

Pedicels coiling in *Cyclamen hederifolium*. The pedicels coil from the top downwards.

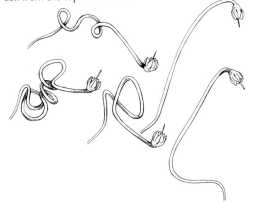

Pedicels coiling in *Cyclamen graecum*. The pedicel coils from the middle in both directions, or from near the base.

23 The pedicels of *Cyclamen persicum* curve and thicken as the fruits develop but, unusually for cyclamen, they do not coil.

farther apart. Pedicels are often rather thick and fleshy and are glandular, particularly in the upper part where they curve over to meet the calyx.

The most curious feature of the pedicels is seen when the young fruits begin to develop, for most undergo a series of contortions, turning round in a series of spirals or coils. This has the effect of pulling the fruits close to the surface of the ground. In fact, when many fruits are produced on a single plant they form a mass below the leaves, crammed together just above the tuber. In a bizarre quirk of evolution not all species coil in the same way: in the majority, coiling starts from the top of the pedicels downwards, but in *C. rohlfsianum* it starts from the bottom upwards, while to be different *C. graecum* has not quite made up its mind, often coiling from the centre of the pedicel in opposing directions at the same time. In some instances the developing capsule can be pulled down into the soil surface, especially when it is soft and friable, at a young stage, thus obscuring them from view. This has been observed in the wild in *C. coum*, *C. peloponnesiacum* and *C. purpurascens*. Of course, some

of the autumn-flowering species will be partly covered by the leaf fall.

To add to the variety, two species, *C. persicum* and the recently discovered *C. somalense*, do not have coiled pedicels at all: instead the pedicels arch over and become stiff and thickened as the fruit develops; this achieves the same objective by pulling the fruit in close to the ground surface, where they are no doubt fairly safe from most large browsing animals.

FLOWERS

The flowers of the cyclamen with their characteristic reflexed petals are unmistakable and no other flower is likely to be confused with them. The flowers are always solitary and are in fact borne in the axils of the basal leaves, with one or several being borne at each axil. The flower buds push through the ground on crosiered stalks with the tip of the bud pointing directly downwards and they never change from this position until the stalks begin to twist or bend in the fruiting stage. The flowers appear at different seasons according to the particular species or subspecies but they can be conveniently grouped as follows (not allowing for aberrant 'out of season' flowers):

- **Summer-flowering (June–August)** – *C. colchicum*, *C. hederifolium*, *C. intaminatum* and *C. purpurascens*.
- **Autumn-flowering (September–November)** – *C. africanum*, *C. cilicium*, *C. colchicum*, *C. elegans*, *C. cyprium*, *C. graecum*, *C. hederifolium*, *C. intaminatum*, *C. mirabile*, *C. persicum* var. *autumnalis*, *C. purpurascens*, *C. rohlfsianum* and *C. somalense*.

- **Winter-flowering (December–February)** – *C. alpinum, C. coum* subsp. *caucasicum* and subsp. *coum, C. cyprium, C. elegans, C. hederifolium* subsp. confusum, *C. libanoticum, C. persicum.*
- **Spring-flowering (March–May)** – *C. alpinum, C. balearicum, C. creticum, C. libanoticum, C. parviflorum, C. peloponnesiacum, C. persicum, C. pseudibericum* and *C. repandum.*

Most of the species, but not all, have fragrant flowers though some species such as *C. graecum* and *C. hederifolium* have both scented and unscented forms (both in the wild and in cultivation). Fragrance is always difficult to describe and various authors have tried to qualify the various types of scent from species to species. The majority have a sweet and pleasant, sometimes rather invasive scent that is reminiscent of primroses (*C. coum*) or lily-of-the-valley (*C. parviflorum*), or even sweet violets (*C. repandum*). *C. persicum* has a very heady scent which is somehow a sweet mixture of all the foregoing. *C. alpinum* has a scent that I can only liken to coconut, although scent is a very subjective character. *C. libanoticum* has a scent that is pleasant to some yet unpleasant to the majority; it is both sweet and peppery at the same time and often described as peppery-acetylene. In the related *C. pseudibericum* the sweet scent prevails, yet to me there is still a faint peppery undertone. Overall the scent is one of the most appealing aspects of cyclamen, an added bonus to be cherished.

The scent is in fact produced by specialized cells in the wall of the corolla-tube so that when the corolla falls so it is lost.

The flowers are basically 5-parted as follows:

CALYX
The cyclamen calyx, the outer whorl of floral parts, consists of 5 simple, small and rather undistinguished sepals. These are all equal in size and shape and are generally elliptical or lanceolate with a pointed apex,

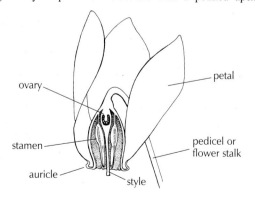

uniting together at the base close to where the calyx merges into the pedicel. The sepals are always glandular, sometimes densely so. In some species they have an entire margin, while in others they may be undulate or somewhat toothed but rarely markedly so. In addition, some species have a single vein to each sepal while others have 3–5, and this is consistent within a particular species.

The sepals are pressed closely to the wall of the corolla tube and are generally about the same length as the tube itself. When the corolla falls the sepals remain to clasp the sides of the developing fruit capsule.

COROLLA
The most obvious part of the flower is the corolla which is often brightly coloured, especially in shades of pink, purple and red, though some species have white flowers. In normal flowers there are 5 petals which are fused together towards the base into a short subglobose tube which houses the stamens and ovary. In bud, the corolla is straight and down-pointing with the petals wrapped round one another in a spiralled fashion (contorted), but as they unfurl they bend backwards and twist at the same time. In the majority of species the corolla-lobes are reflexed backwards through 180 degrees so that they point directly upwards. However, in *C. trochopteranthum* and *C. parviflorum* var. *subalpinum* they are bent through only 90 degrees to face sidewards. Whatever the lobes do, it leaves the open mouth of the corolla pointing downwards and carefully protected from rain should it fall when they are in bloom.

The corolla lobes vary in shape from narrow elliptical to broadly elliptical or almost rounded. They may be plain or with a distinctive mark or blotch towards the base. The lobe margins may be untoothed, or toothed in a few instances; toothing is most marked in the petals of *C. mirabile.*

In general the corolla is far less glandular than the calyx but in most of the species with 3–5-veined sepals the corolla is glandular on the inner or the outer surface. Glandular corollas are found in *C. cilicium, C. cyprium, C. intaminatum, C. libanoticum, C. mirabile, C. pseudibericum* and in some (a minority) specimens of *C. coum.* In addition, some species bear a few glands only along the petal margins, especially towards the apex, and this is most marked in *C. africanum, C. colchicum, C. hederifolium* and *C. purpurascens,* besides those already listed.

Another feature of the corolla which is important in both the classification of the genus as well as the identification of the individual species, is the presence or absence of auricles. Auricles are small ear-like projections which are located at the base of each corolla-lobe (one on

Anatomy of a Cyclamen flower.

each side) where the lobe actually reflexes. In species with obvious auricles the mouth is generally wide and markedly pentagonal in outline (when viewed from beneath), the mouth generally being 7–10mm (0.3–0.4in) across, occasionally wider. In contrast, species without auricles tend to have a narrow mouth which is less obviously pentagonal and more circular in outline and rarely more than 5–6mm (0.2–0.23in) across. Species with well-defined auricles are *C. africanum*, *C. cyprium*, *C. graecum*, *C. hederifolium* and *C. rohlfsianum*. In addition, both *C. colchicum*, *C. libanoticum* and *C. purpurascens* often have rather poorly defined auricles, although the latter may have obvious auricles in some specimens.

As the corolla fades (generally after pollination) it is shed as a single unit with the stamens attached.

STAMENS

There are 5 stamens which are attached by short filaments to the base of the corolla tube. The anthers are more or less spear-head shaped and form a close (not united) ring around the style. The lower half of the stamens contains the sacs that hold copious amounts of pollen while the upper half consists of a pair of tapered processes divided from one another by a narrow slit on each side. As the stamens point downwards, when the pollen is ripe it is shed through the slits onto visiting pollinators. At this stage, in fact, the slightest knock to the blooms will cause the pollen to shower downwards.

The anthers are often adorned with small wart-like protuberances, but in *C. parviflorum* they are quite smooth. In addition, a few species have aristate anthers, that is, adorned with a short, needle-like appendage (an extension of the connective) which is often somewhat deflexed. This applies only to *C. cilicium*, *C. coum*, *C. elegans*, *C. intaminatum*, *C. mirabile*, *C. parviflorum* and *C. alpinum*. The purpose of these tiny appendages is unknown.

In all the species except *C. rohlfsianum* the stamens are included within the corolla-tube. *C. rohlfsianum* is unique in having the cone of anthers projecting beyond the rim of the corolla by 2–3mm (0.08–0.12in).

POLLEN

Chris Clennett has written about cyclamen pollen in studies he undertook for an M.Sc. degree at the University of Reading, and the gist of this was included in the *Journal of the Cyclamen Society* in June 1999. I do not wish to repeat all of this here; however, the results are presented here briefly.

Cyclamen pollen is colporate, that is grains with outer openings or colpi (slits in cyclamen) which coincide with openings (ora) in the inner wall. The typical pollen grain is 3-colporate (with three openings) in cyclamen. However, *C. alpinum*, *C. cilicium*, *C. coum*,

C. elegans, *C. intaminatum*, *C. mirabile* and *C. parviflorum* (sometimes 3-colporate) possess 4-colporate grains, while both *C. coum* and *C. elegans* sometimes also have 5-colporate ones.

Interestingly, in many flowering plants an increase in chromosome number is often accompanied by a corresponding increase in the numer of colpi on the pollen grains, but this is not the case in cyclamen, where those species with the lowest chromosome numbers have the higher number of colpi.

In addition to the numbers of colpi, differences can be observed in the texture, size and aperture openings of pollen from different species, but this requires further investigation.

OVARY AND STYLE

The ovary is more or less globose with a single straight style projecting from the top (in fact pointing downwards as the flowers are nodding). The ovary consists of 5 fused carpels without partitions separating them. The ovules (unfertilized seeds) are crowded around a knob-like placenta (free-central placentation) which is attached only at the base of the ovary.

The solitary style bears a rather truncated and simple stigma and extends through and beyond the cone of anthers. In most species the style projects for 1–3mm (0.04–0.12in) beyond the rim of the corolla. Plants do not exhibit any form of heterostyly (anthers and styles of different lengths from plant to plant within the same species) as in some members of the family, most notably in primula and dionysia.

FRUITS AND SEEDS

The fruit is globose in all species, with the persistent calyx attached and closely adhering in the basal half. The fruit, which is held very close to the ground, is quite hard until maturity and is often described as being 'woody' but this is misleading; the capsule is actually firmly fleshy. When ripe the fruit capsule splits fairly regularly at the apex into as many as ten small triangular teeth which turn backwards to reveal the crammed seeds within.

The fruit is slow to develop and in all species (regardless of when they flower) the capsules are not ripe until the summer with the first species generally starting to ripen in July, rarely sooner. In my garden I find that *C. coum* and *C. hederifolium* are generally the first to ripen in July and *C. colchicum*, *C. pseudibericum* and *C. mirabile* the last in early August, although some pot-grown specimens of *C. persicum* may be even later. In general terms the fruits of autumn-flowering species take a lot longer to mature than spring-flowering ones.

The developing seeds are imbedded in a white pulp which becomes progressively more soft as the fruits ripen.

24 The ripe fruit capsules of *Cyclamen hederifolium* nestle on the ground on tightly coiled pedicels.
25 A pair of ants carry away a sugary-coated cyclamen seed; wasps will do the same.

Initially the seeds are white but just before the fruits ripen they turn honey-coloured and then quickly become dark brown. The number of seeds varies somewhat from capsule to capsule and from species to species. In *C. mirabile* there may be as few as 5–8 seeds, while in *C. hederifolium* there may be as many as 40, sometimes more. The seeds are plump and fleshy when the capsules burst open and they are covered in a sweet and sticky mucilage that is attractive to ants, wasps and some other insects, which act as dispersal agents. The seeds that are carried off by ants generally end up in ants' nests, both in the wild and in cultivation. The ants are not interested in the seed itself but in its appetising sugary coat, so once this has been consumed the seeds are left alone. For this reason they often germinate in the cracks between rocks or paving where they have been deposited, or abandoned, by the ants.

After two or three days in dry conditions the seeds become less sticky and as they darken in colour they shrink to some extent, becoming rather angular in the process. After a further period of a fortnight or so the stickiness has gone altogether.

POLLINATION

Cyclamen are basically geared to outbreeding, that is crossing from one plant to another within the same species. However, that is not to say that some inbreeding does not occur. Self-fertilization is precluded primarily by protandry, that is the anthers ripen before the stigma. In fact the anthers often ripen shortly before the flowers open. At first the pollen is rather sticky and the grains adhere closely to one another but it gradually becomes less sticky and more dust-like and is far more easily removed at this stage. The stigma ripens later and is only receptive at this stage, becoming sticky so that the pollen grains adhere quite readily to its surface. The pollen can be cream in colour, although it is most often yellow and in some forms of *C. rohlfsianum*, at least, it can be a rich golden colour. The fact that the pollen is readily dislodged can be demonstrated by tapping the nose of a mature flower gently with a finger; pollen will shower down onto the finger, although this happens more readily in warm buoyant weather than during cold and damp periods.

Cyclamen are visited by a number of insects including bees (of various sorts), hoverflies, bee flies, butterflies (occasionally) and pollen beetles and no doubt other insects as well. The chief pollinators though are undoubtedly bees. One would imagine that bees are attracted to the flowers by colour and scent in most instances and seek out the nectar. However, there are no obvious nectaries in the cyclamen flower and in many species no nectar can be seen at all. In fact in the many flowers I have examined nectar is only obvious in those of *C. parviflorum*, whose flowers sport five blobs of nectar inside, near to the base of the corolla. The presence of nectaries and nectar requires further close investigation and it may be that certain concealed cells in the wall of the corolla are capable of secreting nectar. The alternative explanation is that the bees are attracted to the flowers for pollen rather than for nectar and, from the observations I have managed to make in the garden and in the wild, this certainly seems to be the case.

A visiting bee will receive pollen on its head and proboscis as it probes the flower. Some of this pollen will then adhere to the receptive stigma of the next flowers that it visits. In nature this is likely to be flowers of the same species as it is rare for two different species to flower at the same time in the same region.

Visiting bees (primarily species of bumble bee) latch onto the mouth (rim) of the corolla with their front pair of feet then swing their heads up into the flower. Corolla auricles (on species such as *C. hederifolium* and *C. graecum*) provide ideal footholds for bees and they invariably make use of them when visiting the flowers. The bee then uses its middle pair of legs to pull down the pollen through the anther slits, transferring the pollen to the pollen sacs on its rear legs at the same time. Bees may visit ten or more flowers before they have collected enough pollen to return to their nests.

The late maturing of the stigma and the fact that it is located on a projecting style away from the anther cone is also indicative of flowers that cross-pollinate. However, self-pollination is possible should cross-pollination fail for one reason or another: it can be effected simply by the pollen falling downwards onto the receptive surface of the stigma. This can only really happen in windy conditions as the surface of the stigma points away from the falling pollen. All gardeners who grow cyclamen for showing know that plants often set copious fruits when they have been moved in a car to the show. The reason for this is undoubtedly that the buffeting they receive in transport dislodges the pollen and causes self-pollination.

According to Hildebrand (Berlin-Dahlem Bot. Gard. 15: 292–8, 1897) the species of cyclamen are at first entomophilous (insect-pollinated), then later anemophilous (wind-pollinated), and this is certainly borne out by the way they behave in cultivation at least: cross-pollination via insects is only possible in the first instance because the stigma simply is not receptive, but as the stigma becomes receptive any buffeting by wind or any other agent is likely to dislodge pollen onto the now receptive stigma to allow self-pollination to occur. Hildebrand also indicates that the pollen is at first sticky (and this would aid cross-pollination and transfer by insect pollinators) and later less sticky and more dust-like, the grains separating and not adhering to one another (this presumably happens after the stigma is receptive, the pollen simply dislodging and falling onto the sticky receptive stigma, thus effecting self-pollination, provided that cross-pollination has not already happened). The latter system is certainly not wind-pollination; a system that wafts large amounts of pollen through the air, often over considerable distances as in species of oak, hazel, and poplar. Wind-pollinated species nearly always have the male and female parts separated out into different flowers that are borne on the same or on different plants.

Initially the system caters for cross-pollination (outbreeding) but if this fails to happen for one reason or another then self-pollination acts as a secondary backup, as it does in many other species of plant. This, of course, at least ensures that the species sets some seed.

Whether or not any incompatibility mechanism operates in cyclamen as it does in various other members of the Primulaceae (Primula and Dionysia in particular) it is not known. In the horticultural trade, repeated selfing of *Cyclamen persicum* quickly leads to a weakening of the stock which can then only be rejuvenated by outcrossing; this is very typical of many species that are natural outbreeders. Outbreeding ensures a constant mixing of the genes and greater variability (and hence adaptability) within the species. Self-incompatibility, when it does occur, also precludes self-fertilisation. Sometimes it is found that a partial self-incompatibility mechanism operates allowing some plants in a population to self-fertilize but not all. Such an idea is borne out by observing cyclamen species in cultivation, where some plants can be readily induced to set seed on their own while others cannot.

However, it is easy to conjecture. The fact is that precious little is really understood about the pollination and fertilization biology of cyclamen and much remains to be investigated.

As a final note on the subject of self-pollination it is quite possible that if pollination has not occurred then it may happen as the spent corolla (with attached stamens) is shed, for the anthers have to brush past the receptive stigma. By this time most of the pollen will already have been dispersed but self-pollination by the action of the falling corolla should not be ruled out as another possibility.

Far more needs to be known about the pollination biology of cyclamen. Pollinators for the different species need to be carefully recorded and tabulated. For instance, it would be interesting to know if both the auricled species and those without auricles are pollinated by the same insects. Auricles clearly provide 'toe-holds' for visiting insects such as bees of various species, but how do insects hang on to the non-auricled species which tend to have a far narrower mouth?

Chapter Five

The Genus Cyclamen

The genus *Cyclamen* holds a rather isolated position within the family Primulales (see p.44) and is generally afforded its own tribe in the Primulaceae, the Cyclamineae. However, the genus is without obvious close relatives and bears several unusual characters that are abnormal among the other genera in the family. The most important of these are the possession of a single visible cotyledon instead of the usual two characteristic of dicotyledonous plants, the tuberous rootstock, the hard rounded, yet fleshy, fruit capsules.

NOMENCLATURE

No account of the genus can successfully avoid the N-word. Nomenclature, the system of names, is important to both scientists and gardeners if the plants are to be given their correct identity. This applies equally well for wild species as it does for cultivated species, hybrids and cultivars. Consistency and accuracy are all-important. Changes in names come about as a result of detailed research and for good reason, and not just at the whim of the author. This account of Cyclamen updates my monograph of 1997. Readers will not find many name changes, although some adjustments have been made because more data on the species in the wild and in cultivation has come to light in the intervening years. The following changes are worth pointing out at this stage:

- *Cyclamen coum* now contains two subspecies rather than the previous three: subsp. *coum* and subsp. *caucasicum*.
- *Cyclamen coum* subsp. *elegans* is raised to species level (*C. elegans*); in fact it was first designated a species as long ago as 1860.
- The name *C. graecum* subsp. *mindleri* is shown to be wrongly applied: subsp. *mindleri* is a synonym of subsp. *graecum*. *Cyclamen graecum* is thus divided as previously into three subspecies: subsp. *graecum* from Greece (including Crete), subsp. *candicum* from Crete and the subsp. *anatolicum* from Turkey, Rhodes and Cyprus.
- *Cyclamen hederifolium* is divided into two subspecies (formerly varieties), subsp. *hederifolium* and subsp. *confusum*.
- The varieties of *Cyclamen parviflorum* are upgraded to subspecies, viz. subsp. *parviflorum* and subsp. *subalpinum*.

- *Cyclamen repandum* subsp. *peloponnesiacum* is upgraded to species following Kit Tan (2001), *C. peloponnesiacum*, and now includes three subspecies: subsp. *peloponnesiacum*, subsp. *vividum* and subsp. *rhodense*.
- *Cyclamen trochopteranthum* is replaced by an earlier name, *C. alpinum*, previously thought to be a *nomen confusum*, an assertion now shown to be unjustified.

The rank of forma, which literally means 'a form', is used to denote single character differences, such as flower colour. Although the rank of forma can be equally well applied to cultivated as well as wild plants, in this work I have restricted the use of the name solely to plants found in the wild. This is done partly out of stubbornness and partly because I think it is more logical and proper to restrict the use of a botanical rank to wild plants. In cultivated plants the cultivar name performs more or less the same function. In addition, less confusion is caused by restricting the use of forma in this way. In the wild all odd colour forms (especially albinos) that have been recorded to date are found as individuals, often isolated individuals, in otherwise normal-coloured forms. The same is nearly always true of plants with unusual leaf patternings or leaf colorations.

Unfortunately, some old names, long abandoned by botanists and the majority of gardeners and horticulturists, still persist in the horticultural and gardening literature to this day, especially in nurserymen's catalogues.

Cyclamen europaeum should correctly be *C. purpurascens*; *C. neapolitanum* should correctly be *C. hederifolium*; *C. fatrense* is simply *C. purpurascens*; *C. ibericum* and *C. abchasicum* (or. *C. coum* var. *ibericum* or var. *abchasicum*) are both correctly *C. coum* subsp. *caucasicum*; *C. latifolium* is correctly *C. persicum*, and *C. orbiculatum* and *C. vernum* are correctly *C. coum* subsp. *coum*. If nurserymen wish to distinguish plants under these outdated names in their catalogues perhaps the best answer is to put them into quotation marks, thus "*C. fatrense*" (or *C. purpurascens* Fatra form) or "*C. ibericum*", thus indicating their non-validity as acceptable names. Certainly the first two, *C. europaeum* and *C. neapolitanum*, should not be used under any circumstances.

In my monograph 'The Genus Cyclamen' of 1988 I concentrated primarily on the botanical and taxonomic details and to some extent on cultivation, with little on the various kinds and cultivars of cyclamen found in gardens and in the horticultural trade in general. In the present work (and the 1997 edition) I have tried to concentrate more on the horticultural merits of cyclamen, while at the same time adhering to the taxonomic principles outlined in the former work. This has been achieved partly by placing much of the necessary but technical botanical jargon in appendices at the end of the book for those who need to refer to them, whilst at the same time reducing technical botanical terms in the main text to a minimum. This does not mean that the reader will not find detailed descriptions of the species in the main text for they are as important to the gardener and horticulturist as they are to the botanist and they help in the overall study and understanding of the species as well as in their identification. In the former work there were 19 species recognized, while in the present one there are 22. This has been achieved by reinstating the Caucasian *C. colchicum* and *C. elegans* as species in their own right, and the splitting of *C. repandum* into two allied species *C. repandum* and *C. peleponnesiacum.*

However, once I started a more thorough research of cultivated cyclamen I soon entered a muddled world full of inconsistencies and ambiguities. Whereas I certainly do not pretend that I have solved all the problems by any means, I hope that I have at least achieved some sort of order. My prime concern has been to standardize the use of cultivar names and to abandon those that are no longer applicable for one reason or another; either because the cultivar has been lost or not traced, or because the name has been applied to the wrong plant. In recent years there has been a tendency to describe colour variants found in the wild; for example the white-flowered forms of both *C. cilicium* and *C. graecum* have been formerly described as forma *album*. Ordinarily the botanist would scarcely give credit to such entities which are merely colour variants which can be readily encompassed within the overall description of the species without further qualification. Formal recognition merely serves to clutter the taxonomic literature with ever more names. However, from the horticulturist's point of view the situation looks very different, for there is a need to distinguish variants (especially colour variants) in gardens and, of course, the more variants there are with distinguishing names in catalogues and lists, the easier it is for the gardener to select and identify specific plants, and the greater the potential profit for the grower. There is nothing wrong with this. It can be accomplished in one of two ways: either by formally recognising variants found in the wild as botanical entities (subspecies, varieties or formas) or by applying cultivar names to those that have come into cultivation.

In the case of cyclamen it is unfortunate that both systems have been applied willy-nilly. For instance white-flowered forms of *C. hederifolium* and *C. purpurascens* which both occur in the wild have been consistently called 'Album', a cultivar name, whereas, as we have seen, similar variants in *C. cilicium* and *C. graecum* have had the botanical recognition of forma. The same also applies to the pink form of *C. pseudibericum* which was discovered in the wild but which has been consistently called 'Roseum'; Latinized cultivar names are generally unattractive and not permitted under the current rules of horticultural, nomenclature, that is those created after the year 1973. In this work it is my intention to even out such ambiguities and to recognize formally all such variants found in the wild as far as I am able to do so. The aim of all this is standardization in the usage of names. At the same time, the use of cultivar and group names has had to be analysed carefully and where appropriate new names have been proposed; in some instances cultivar names are more appropriately group names (see p.145).

As a result the current scheme for the genus, ignoring all groups and cultivars, looks as follows:

C. africanum
C. alpinum
        forma *alpinum*
        forma *leucanthum*
C. balearicum
C. cilicium
        forma *cilicium*
        forma *album*
C. colchicum
C. coum
   subsp. *coum*
        forma *coum*
        forma *albissimum*
        forma *pallidum*
   subsp. *caucasicum*
C. creticum
        forma *creticum*
        forma *pallide-roseum*
C. cyprium
C. elegans
C. graecum
   subsp. *graecum*
        forma *album*
   subsp. *candicum*
   subsp. *anatolicum*
C. hederifolium
   subsp. *hederifolium*
        forma *hederifolium*
        forma *albiflorum*
   subsp. *confusum*
C. intaminatum
C. libanoticum

C. mirabile
>> forma *mirabile*
>> forma *niveum*

C. parviflorum
> subsp. *parviflorum*
> subsp. *subalpinum*

C. peloponnesiacum
> subsp. *peloponnesiacum*
>> forma *albiflorum*
>> forma *peloponnesiacum*
> subsp. *vividum*
> subsp. *rhodense*

C. persicum
>> var. *persicum*
>>> forma *persicum*
>>> forma *albidum*
>>> forma *roseum*
>>> forma *rubrum*
>> var. *autumnalis*

C. pseudibericum
>> forma *pseudibericum*
>> forma *roseum*

C. purpurascens
>> forma *purpurascens*
>> forma *album*
>> forma *carmineolineatum*

C. repandum
>> var. *repandum*
>>> forma *repandum*
>>> forma *album*
>> var. *barborense*

C. rohlfsianum

C. somalense

AFFINITIES

The species of *Cyclamen* are unlikely to be confused with any other plants in the plant kingdom and they present a reasonably uniform feature as far as their gross morphology is concerned. In other words, all those prime characteristics that distinguish *Cyclamen* from other plants are to be found in all the species in the genus and indeed they separate the genus from others within the same family. The prime distinguishing characteristics are:

- The possession of a single visible cotyledon.
- The possession of an underground tuber.
- Reflexed petals; only *Dodecatheon*, in the Primulaceae, and a few *Primula* species share this characteristic, but this feature shows an example of parallel evolution rather than indicating any special and close affinity.
- The presence of a tough, leathery (often described as woody, which is misleading), yet fleshy, fruit capsule.
- Basic chromosome number of $x = 5$ or 6; in other members of the Primulaceae the base numbers are x

$= 8, 9, 10, 11, 12, 13$. However, Professor Greilhuber of the University of Vienna (see *Journal of the Cyclamen Society* 13,2: 57–62, 1989) while reviewing the *C. repandum* complex (subgenus *Psilanthum*) argues that the basic chromosome number is in fact $x = 10$ and not 5, which would put it in line with other genera in the Primulaceae. He states that "There is altogether no valid argument for a basic tetraploid condition in the genus".

Cyclamen belongs to the Order Primulales which contains just two families, the Primulaceae and Myrsinaceae.

The Primulales is distinguished by the following characteristics:
- Trees and shrubs, or herbs (mostly perennial), with opposite or alternate to simple basal leaves which do not have stipules; often gland-dotted or beset with glandular hairs.
- Flowers are regular (actinomorphic) and (4–)5(–6)-parted (generally with 5 sepals, 5 petals and 5 stamens) with the stamens attached to the tube (often near the base) of the corolla and opposite the petals.
- Pollen is 3-colporate; the order possesses four pollen types of which that found in *Cyclamen* is the commonest.
- Superior or semi-inferior ovary is one-celled with a single style and stigma, with the ovules attached to a central placenta that is only attached at the base (free-central placentation).
- Fruit is a fleshy berry (especially in the Myrsinaceae) or a seed capsule that is dry in most instances and contains numerous seeds which possess a linear embryo and oily endosperm.

Recent studies (Kallens *et al* in the *American Journal of Botany*, 2000) using DNA sequencing and other techniques have shown that *Cyclamen*, along with *Coris*, have a closer affinity with members of the Myrsinaceae than with Primulaceae. There is ample evidence given in the paper to support such a view. They conclude with two options: first to place the two genera in the Myrsinaceae or, second, to create a small separate, yet closely allied family, for them.

A feature of the genus *Cyclamen* is its distribution with the majority of species confined to the Mediterranean Basin. Linked to this is another unusual, yet not unique, feature within the family and that is summer dormancy or aestivation as it is technically called. Summer dormancy affects all the species to a greater or lesser extent with species such as *C. graecum*, *C. persicum* and *C. rohlfsianum* having a pronounced summer rest, while *C. parviflorum* and *C. purpurascens* have a far less pronounced dormancy, in fact scarcely a dormancy at all. The summer rest in the wild coincides with the hot, dry months of the typical

Mediterranean summer when conditions become far too extreme. This affects many plants including trees, shrubs and perennials but is perhaps most marked in annual plants that complete their life cycle before the heat of summer gains strength and in the extraordinary range of plants from different families with underground bulbs, tubers or rhizomes. These storage organs allow plants to reside happily below ground during periods of the year when growth is out of the question.

Within the Primulales (particularly the Primulaceae) summer dormancy is not confined solely to *Cyclamen*, although the genus is the only one in which all species are thus affected. In the large genus *Primula* several species exhibit summer dormancy; most notable is *P. fedtschenkoana* which has a spidery thong of fleshy roots which act just like a bulb. This species comes from northern Afghanistan and the neighbouring regions of Central Asia, which have a very pronounced dry summer, and plants flower soon after the snow melts and die away to ground level as the hot months arrive. Several species of *Dodecatheon*, a North American genus, have become adapted to semi-desert conditions and also die down to below ground level during the summer months. Even their distant cousins in the genus *Dionysia* (a genus confined to hot dry regions centred on Iran and Afghanistan), whose species are mostly cushion-forming plants, exhibit a marked 'dormancy' during the hot summer months, achieving most of their growth in the spring and autumn when conditions are cooler and more favourable for growth.

It is clear that the genus *Cyclamen* holds an isolated position within the Primulales, being without any obvious close affinities, a fact which is reinforced by the unique cytological characteristics of the genus which distinguish it from all other members of the Primulaceae at least.

THE SUBGENERIC CLASSIFICATION OF CYCLAMEN

In my monograph of 1988 I stated that 'A wholly convincing infrageneric classification has yet to be devised. The fragmented nature of the genus, containing as it does so many diverse elements, would suggest that it will never be possible to produce such a classification'. In the intervening years I have altered my position on this matter and now, with a few modifications, accept the basic divisions proposed by Schwarz. Having said this it seems to me that the only sensible way to do this is to recognize five subgenera and various series. These are based on gross morphological as well as genetical data. The fact that three large cladistic studies have been undertaken in recent years (Anderberg 1994, Anderberg *et al* 2000 and Clennett 2001) has added much valuable information.

In the first of these, Arne Anderberg (*Kew Bulletin* 49,3:455–467, 1994) makes a case for subgeneric

division based on a cladistic parsimony analysis using morphological and cytological data. From the results of this analysis, Anderberg was able to draw up a subgeneric reclassification of the genus as well as discussing the evolution of different characters within the genus. He was also able to postulate that *C. graecum* was of possible hybrid origin between *C. hederifolium* and *C. persicum*.

Although Anderberg's study throws up some interesting information, especially on the relationship of the various groups within the genus, I am not entirely happy with it, despite the fact that it has much to recommend it. The main reason for this is in the selection and scoring of characters. Although Anderberg selects some 29 characters, certain rather useful ones are omitted altogether. For instance although the presence of a V-shaped blotch on the petals is scored, other petal markings are completely ignored. The elbow in the petioles and pedicels of some species is also ignored as are the thick anchorage roots in *C. graecum*. Mis-scoring is a more fundamental problem that has undoubtedly affected the analysis. There are quite a few examples: for instance, *C. purpurascens* is scored for having even tubers generally 3–5cm (1.2–2in) diameter (both these are wrong for the tuber is nearly always considerably larger in mature specimens and pronouncedly misshapen); *C. coum* is scored for its eglandular corolla (in some forms it can be densely glandular); *C. purpurascens* is said to have 'entire leaf margins, whereas they are more normally finely toothed'; *C. graecum* can have leaves with a decidedly lobed margin (subsp. *anatolicum*), whereas it is scored for being unlobed; the corolla lobes in *C. coum* (especially in subsp. *elegans*) can be longer than wide, whereas they are scored as 'about as long as wide'. The presence or absence of auricles on the corolla is also scored rather haphazardly with *C. purpurascens* being scored as an auriculate species and *C. libanoticum* and *C. hederifolium* being scored as exauriculate.

Clearly Anderberg's work has produced some interesting data but it needs to be interpreted with care in the light of the above remarks. However, this has been overtaken by his second analysis (published in *Plant Systematics and Evolution* 220: 147–160 (2000)) which is a much more thorough study, although it strangely omits various key species without explanation (e.g. *C. alpinum* (*C. trochopteranthum*), *C. cilicum*, *C. elegans*, *C. parviflorum* and *C. repandum*). The Clennett study (shortly to be published by the Linnean Society) is the most thorough and comprehensive. All the cladistic studies basically support Otto Scwarz's 1964 classification of the genus and I go along with this with one or two modifications.

All the authors agree on the subgenus Psilanthum. I also agree with Schwarz on the composition of subgenus *Gyrophoebe*. Anderberg, whilst recognising the same subgenus, removes *C. cyprium* and places it within his third subgenus, *Cyclamen*, together with all the remaining species. Here all the authors differ: Anderberg merges Schwarz's two subgenera *Cyclamen* and *Eucosme* in his first analysis but separates them in the second. I recognize subgenus *Cyclamen* and another subgenus, *Persicum*, which contains just two species *C. persicum* and the recently discovered *C. somalense*.

This new subdivision of *Cyclamen* takes into account gross morphological features as well as cytology, bringing together species with similar chromosome numbers. The position of *C. graecum* and *C. rohlfsianum* is questionable and is likely to be so in any interpretation. Their unique features and distinct chromosome numbers clearly isolate them within the genus. The answer may be to place each in its own subgenus, but this would be to fragment the genus still further and would serve little purpose; they are placed instead in their own series within subgenus *Cyclamen*.

It seems rather unsatisfactory to me to isolate *C. cyprium* from *C. libanoticum* and *C. pseudibericum*. They share many features in common, yet each has one distinctive character not shared by the others. For instance *C. cyprium* is the only one in this group with very distinct auricles, *C. pseudibericum* is the only one without angled leaf-margins and *C. libanoticum* is the only one with a very wide mouth to the corolla as well as untoothed leaf-margins. They have much in common, including their easterly distribution and chromosome number. The fact that *C. libanoticum* has hybridized quite easily in cultivation with both *C. cyprium* and *C. pseudibericum* (but none of these with any other species) cannot be without significance. Despite this, it seems better to ally *C. pseudibericum* to *C. coum* and *C. elegans* although, unlike them, it does not have aristate anthers. In many ways *C. pseudibericum* is halfway between the *C. coum* group and *C. libanoticum* and this may reflect an ancient hybrid origin, although such a hypothesis is thus far unproven.

Anderberg's hypothesis on the origin of *C. graecum* is an interesting one. It is certainly known that species can arise through hybridization between two species or their progenitors. The chances of a fertile cross resulting from *C. hederifolium* (2n=34) and *C. persicum* (2n=48) seems unlikely but not impossible. The artificial hybrid between *C. hederifolium* and *C. graecum* (*C.* x *whiteae*) is sterile! However, it can be argued that hybrid origin accompanied by a doubling of chromosomes, with the addition of two extra chromosomes (2 x 17 + 24 + 2) would give 2n=84. The fact that *C. graecum* can also have additional chromosomes (85, 86 & 87 have been recorded) perhaps adds weight to this view.

Cladistic analyses reveal relationships using a wide spectrum of data obtained from straight morphology, with the additional information derived from cytological, palynological, anatomical and DNA studies. The main problem with cladistic studies is that they are bound to bring together species of closest affinity, even when the species may actually be widely separated evolutionarily. *Cyclamen* represent a highly fragmented genus with many of the species isolated and often very restricted. This no doubt reflects climate changes in the Mediterranean region over the past ten thousand years. Most were probably more widespread in former times but have been restricted during the evolutionary process. This is borne out by pollen and chromosome details of the different taxa. Species of possible hybrid origin, such as *C. graecum* and *C. pseudibericum*, conveniently fill the gaps between very different groups of species and blur subgeneric and series boundaries.

An important factor often overlooked is the pollination evolution of the genus, a subject woefully understudied. Indeed very little work has been done to record which insect species visit the flowers of the different species of *Cyclamen*. It is generally said that bees are the prime pollinators and this may well be so. But there are countless species of bee, especially bumblebees which come in many different sizes and are often host-specific in the wild. However, other insects such as hoverflies, beeflies and even butterflies may play their part. *Cyclamen* basically have two flower types as far as pollinating insect are concerned:

1. Species with a narrow corolla mouth and no auricles, e.g. *C. cilicium*, *C. coum*, *C. persicum* and *C. repandum*.

2. Species with a wide corolla mouth and auricles, e.g. *C. cyprium*, *C. graecum*, *C. hederifolium* and *C. rohlfsianum*.

In addition, flower size is very variable (e.g. *C. persicum* compared with *C. cilicium*), while most species have very distinctive markings which act like homing beacons to visiting insects able to detect the ultra-violet end of the spectrum. Flowering time must also play a critical part; different insects may be abroad at different times of the year and geographical location is likely to be significant.

At the end of the day any reasonable classification has to make sense of a combination of disciplines of which DNA studies (often based on a pathetically small sampling), palynology and cladistics are only a part. Traditional taxonomy, now given a rather minor role in modern plant classification is, in my opinion, still immensely important in our understanding of genera like *Cyclamen*. On the other hand, cladistic analyses are very much in vogue. Studies that throw together disparate elements which appear to have no overall morphological unity can never gain much favour and in the end, despite everything else, a certain amount of common sense must prevail.

I have tried to take all these factors into account when coming up with the following classification.

SUBDIVISIONS OF CYCLAMEN

1. Corolla exauriculate, with a narrow mouth, glandular usually:
    2. Pedicels not coiling in fruit; sepals 1-veined:
        Subgenus *Persicum*
    2. Pedicels coiling in fruit:
        3. Sepals 1-veined; anthers not aristate; corolla eglandular: **Subgenus *Psilanthum***
        3. Sepals 3–5-veined; corolla usually glandular: **Subgenus *Gyrophoebe***
            4. Corolla lobes entire; anthers not aristate (spring-flowering species): Series Two (Series *Pseudibericum*)
            4. Corolla lobes toothed; anthers aristate:
                5. Petal lobes wide, less than twice as long as broad (winter- and spring-flowering species): Series One (Series *Coum*)
                5. Petal lobes narrow, more than twice s long as broad (autumn-flowering species): Series Three (Series *Cilicium*)
1. Corolla auriculate (obscurely so in *C. libanoticum*), with a wide mouth:
    6. Sepals 3–5-veined; corolla glandular:
        Subgenus *Corticata*
    6. Sepals 1-veined; corolla eglandular:
        Subgenus *Cyclamen*
        7. Pedicels coiling from the top downwards:
            8. Corolla strongly auricled, with well-defined basal marking; leaf lamina generally lobed or angled: Series One (Series *Cyclamen*)
            8. Corolla weakly auricled (auricles sometimes scarcely apparent), without basal markings; leaf lamina not lobed or angled: Series Two (Series *Purpurascens*)
        7. Pedicels coiling from the middle in both directions, or from the base upwards:
            9. Stamens not protruding (exserted); leaf-lamina longer than wide, unlobed or slightly lobed: Series Three (Series *Graecum*)
            9. Stamens not protruding (inserted); leaf-lamina wider than long, deeply and evenly lobed: Series Four (Series *Rohlfsianum*)

Subgenus *Psilanthum* Schwarz [2n=20, 22]

Tubers relatively small, smooth and velvety, rooting from the centre below; leaves thin and without cartilaginous teeth; pedicels coiling in fruit; calyx-lobes 1-veined; corolla exauriculate, plain or with a deeper zone of colour around the mouth, egandular; corolla-lobes not toothed; anthers not aristate. Spring-flowering. *C. balearicum, C. creticum, C. peloponnesiacum, C. repandum.*

Subgenus *Gyrophoebe* Schwarz [2n=30; pollen (3–)4(–5)-colporate]

Tubers generally rather small, velvety to corky, rooting from the lower surface; leaves without cartilaginous teeth; pedicels coiling in fruit; sepals 3–5-veined; corolla exauriculate usually, generally with a dark blotch at the base of each petal, generally glandular; anthers usually aristate:

- Series One (Series *Pubipedia* Schwarz): tubers velvety, rooting from the middle of the base; leaves not angled, rarely slightly lobed; corolla glandular or eglandular; corolla-lobes generally toothed, often weakly so, generally about as long as wide; anthers aristate. Winter and early spring-flowering. (the equivalent of Series *Pubipedia* Schwarz with the omission of *C. cilicium* and the addition of *C. elegans*). *C. alpinum, C. coum, C. elegans, C. parviflorum.*
- Series Two (Series *Pseudibericum* Grey-Wilson): tubers corky, rooting from the lower surface; corolla exauriculate, with a narrow mouth; anthers not aristate. Spring-flowering. *C. pseudibericum.*
- Series Three (Series *Cilicium* Grey-Wilson): tubers velvety or corky, usually rooting from the middle of the base; leaves not lobed; corolla glandular; corolla-lobes toothed, often weakly so, considerably longer than wide; anthers aristate. Autumn-flowering. *C. cilicium, C. intaminatum, C. mirabile.*

Subgenus *Corticata* (Schwarz) Grey-Wilson (Cyclamen subgenus *Gyrophoebe* Schwarz series *Corticata* Schwarz) [2n=30; pollen 3-colporate]

Tubers corky, rooting over the base, sometimes on one side; leaves weakly angled or coarsely toothed; corolla glandular, weakly to strongly auriculate, with a wide mouth; corolla-lobes untoothed; sepals 3–5-veined; anthers not aristate. Autumn- to early spring-flowering. (This equals Series *Corticata* Schwarz except for the absence of *C. mirabile* and *C. pseudibericum*.) *C. cyprium, C. libanoticum.*

Subgenus *Persicum* Grey-Wilson [2n=48, 72; pollen 3-colporate]

Tubers generally rather large and corky, rooting from the lower surface; leaves with somewhat cartilaginous teeth; pedicels curving but not coiling in fruit; calyx 1-veined; corolla exauriculate, plain or with a deeper zone of colour around the mouth, eglandular; corolla-lobes untoothed; anthers not aristate. Winter- and spring-flowering. A new subgenus derived by removing *C. persicum* from subgenus *Eucosme* and adding *C. somalense*. *C. persicum*, *C. somalense*.

Subgenus *Cyclamen* (including subgenus *Eucosme* Schwarz)

Tubers generally rather large and corky, sometimes uneven; leaves often with cartilaginous teeth; pedicels coiling in fruit; calyx-lobes 1-veined; corolla auriculate, occasionally weakly so, marked with a deeper zone or lines around the mouth, eglandular (except for petal margins); corolla-lobes untoothed; anthers not aristate:

- Series One (Series *Cyclamen*) [2n=34, 68; pollen 3-colporate]: tubers regular rooting mainly over the sides and the top, the roots always fibrous; leaves lobed or angled, or unlobed; pedicels coiling from the top downwards. Autumn-flowering. *C. africanum*, *C. hederifolium*.
- Series Two (Series *Purpurascens* Grey-Wilson) [2n=34]: tubers becoming irregular, often knobbly, rooting unevenly over sides and base; leaves not angled or lobed; pedicels coiling from the top downwards. Summer- and autumn-flowering. *C. colchicum*, *C. purpurascens*.
- Series Three (Series *Graecum* Grey-Wilson) [2n=84, rarely 85–87]: tubers rooting only from the base, with thick anchorage roots; leaves unlobed or only slightly so; stamens not protruding; pedicels coiling from the base or from the middle in both directions. Autumn-flowering. *C. graecum*.
- Series Four (Series *Rohlfsianum* Grey-Wilson) [2n=96; pollen 3-colporate]: tubers rooting mainly from the lower sides, the roots all fibrous; leaves prominently and evenly lobed; stamens protruding; pedicels coiling from the base. Autumn-flowering. *C. rohlfsianum*.

Note: For new subgeneric taxa see Appendix I, p.210.

CYTOLOGY OF CYCLAMEN

It is not my intention to get bogged down in the complexities of cytology in this work. It has been very well covered in the past by various authors including de Haan and Doorenbos (1951), Legro (1959), Lepper and Schwarz (1964), Ward (1975) and Greilhuber (1989). I would also refer readers who wish to pursue this aspect to read the relevant chapter in 'The Genus Cyclamen' (Grey-Wilson, 1988).

Cyclamen exhibit a range of chromosome numbers and the cytological evidence can be more or less directly related to the gross morphology of the plants so that groups of closely similar species share the same chromosome numbers. The bare facts are as follows:

C. balearicum 2n=20
C. creticum 2n=20 or 22
C. peloponnesiacum 2n=20
C. repandum 2n=20
C. alpinum 2n=30
C. cilicium 2n=30
C. coum 2n=30
C. cyprium 2n=30
C. elegans 2n=?30
C. intaminatum 2n=30
C. libanoticum 2n=30
C. mirabile 2n=30
C. parviflorum 2n=30
C. pseudibericum 2n =30
C. africanum 2n=34 or 68
C. hederifolium 2n=34 or 68
C. purpurascens 2n=34
C. persicum 2n=48
    (to 72, 96 and 136 in some cultivars)
C. graecum 2n=84 (85, 86, 87 also recorded in
    a few individuals)
C. rohlfsianum 2n=96

The chromosome numbers of *C. colchicum* and *C. somalense* are unknown at the present time.

The species with 2n=20 chromosome are morphologically and ecologically a very similar and close-knit group. Within the 2n=30 block, several groups based on gross morphological characteristics can be selected.

Species with 2n=34 or 68 chromosomes also form a reasonably close group in both morphological and cytological respects; this is borne out by the morphology of the somatic chromosomes (De Haan and Doorenbos, 1951).

The remaining species are isolated in chromosome number and in gross morphology they each have several unique characters not shared by others in the genus. *C. persicum* has pedicels that do not coil in fruit, *C. graecum* has thick thong-like roots and pedicels that generally coil from the middle in opposing directions and *C. rohlfsianum* has a protruding cone of anthers and broad, symmetrically lobed leaves, as well as pedicels that coil from the base upwards. None of these latter species have clear and unambiguous affinities with other members of the genus.

De Haan and Doorenbos have pointed out that one can assume that the most primitive species from a cytological point of view would appear to be *C. repandum* (2n=20) and that it probably most closely resembles a 'primitive species' and that the different chromosome numbers have developed from this.

In any event *Cyclamen* species, as found in the wild today, exhibit a range of chromosome numbers in the following progression 20, 22, 30, 34, 48, 68, 84 (85–87) and 96. From this it is easy to deduce that a regular series of numbers does not occur. Clearly those based on 20 and

30 are multiples of 10 whereas those with 48, 84 and 96 are multiples of 12, leaving those with 34 or 68 chromosomes based on a multiple of 17.

Amongst the higher chromosome species in particular, their ambiguous characters and fragmented distribution presents a complex picture that is difficult to analyse. It certainly indicates evolutionary fragmentation of the genus over a relatively long period. This has no doubt been brought about by the increasing aridity of the Mediterranean basin in recent geological time as well as the effects of the last ice ages, causing isolation of the species, perhaps with the disappearance of intermediate types in the process. This has left us with the rather disjunct picture that we observe today.

DISTRIBUTION AND ECOLOGY

The genus *Cyclamen* is distributed around the Mediterranean basin, with species present in every country except for Spain, Morocco and Egypt and present on most of the larger Mediterranean islands. In the southern and eastern Mediterranean the species are restricted to relatively small areas but in mainland Europe two species (*C. hederifolium* and *C. purpurascens*) have a far wider distribution that encompasses eastern France, Switzerland and southern Germany north as far as southern Poland and east as far as Romania, with the more southerly *C. hederifolium* reaching south to Sicily and much of the Balkan Peninsula. In Turkey cyclamen species are found in most parts of the country with the exception of the high austere regions of the Anatolian Plateau. The eastward extension of the genus includes the southern Crimea, the Caucasus Mountains and the western Elburz Mountains of northern Iran. Until fairly recently this was the known distribution of the genus but in 1986 a new species was discovered in a remote region of northern Somalia many hundreds of kilometres south of any previously known locality; it has since been named *C. somalense*.

What is perhaps most surprising about the distribution of *Cyclamen* is that none have been found growing in Spain. One could well imagine that they at one time occupied the mountainous regions in the east of the country, for much of the terrain there would suit them admirably.

They are, after all, to be found not many miles away in the Balearic Islands of Majorca and Menorca (*C. balearicum*) and in southern France. Perhaps they never reached Spain in the first instance, although they are also to be found just to the south in north Africa.

Despite this, it is undoubtedly true to say that the genus was more widespread as a whole in former times than it is today. The history of the Mediterranean region since the last Ice Age has been one of increasing aridity with a pronounced shift in the Sahara northwards to the very coast of northern Africa, an effect that is influencing many Mediterranean islands today, especially Sicily and Crete. The effect has been to confine genera such as *Cyclamen* to rather isolated pockets around the region. In effect this probably not only aided speciation but also resulted in the fact that different species rarely grow together in the wild or, if they do, they are isolated by flowering time or habitat, or both. Perhaps this is most noticeable in the extreme eastern Mediterranean region today where there are few suitable habitats for cyclamen and where three species, *C. cyprium*, *C. pseudibericum* and *C. libanoticum*, are well isolated from one another (the first confined to Cyprus, the second to a small region of south-eastern Turkey and the third to the Lebanon, also in a limited area).

Interestingly, where the climate is more equable away from the Mediterranean coast, the species often have a far wider distribution, sometimes with southern outliers, as is the case with the widespread *C. repandum* complex and *C. coum*.

Judging by the wide distribution of the genus one might expect the species to occupy various types of habitat and this is certainly the case. To the gardener this may not seem of much concern but a little understanding of wild habitats and prevailing climatic conditions can often be a great help to the cultivator, as is a knowledge of associated species in the wild. Whereas *C. graecum*, *C. persicum* and *C. rohlfsianum* are primarily plants of open sites, growing in sun-baked rocks which can become very hot during the summer months, *C. cilicium*, *C. intaminatum* and *C. mirabile* are species that nestle under the dappled shade in more humusy soils that keep the tubers relatively cooler during the hot summer months. (See under the individual species for details of habitats.)

Chapter Six

The Species

IDENTIFICATION

With one or two exceptions *Cyclamen* species present little problem for the gardener in the way of identification. Once the characters of the individual species are learned then it is not difficult to wander round plants in the garden and to apply accurate names to them. Cyclamen greatly aid the process of naming by flowering at different seasons, some in the autumn, some in the winter and others in the spring, only occasionally flowering 'out of season'. So at any one season only certain species will be in flower and the others can be disregarded as far as naming is concerned, until they in turn come into flower.

Of course, it is easier to name the species when they are in flower but, at the same time, most of them can also be readily identified in leaf, long after the flowers have faded.

Natural hybrids between species in the wild are, to my knowledge, unknown; most species grow in isolation from one another and the chance of hybridisation is extremely unlikely even if species were compatible and capable of producing hybrid offspring. The fact that they have varying flowering seasons also precludes hybridization in the wild. In cultivation spontaneous hybrids between species are not common although one can cite authenticated examples such as *C. creticum* x *C. repandum*, *C. balearicum* x *C. creticum* and *C. libanoticum* x *C. pseudibericum* that intermarry freely when grown in close proximity.

Even taking into consideration the wide variations found in some cyclamen, particularly as regards leaf characteristics, the species are not difficult to identify. The difficulties come mainly within the species when it comes to accurately naming subspecies and varieties and, from the gardener's point of view, the cultivars.

So what are the characters that are most useful when it comes to practical identification? I have assumed here that the plants are in growth with either flowers or leaves, or indeed both at the same time. Although tuber characteristics can be useful it is not necessary to dig up any species for naming purposes.

Leaves

The actual shape of the leaves can be important. They may be rounded, oval, kidney- or heart-shaped with a toothed or untoothed margin. The leaf blade may be plain or it may be variously angled or lobed. Leaf patterning may be useful in some instances, yet in most species it is so remarkably variable that it may prove more of a distraction than a help in positive identification; however, on the other hand, leaf patterning may be a key factor in the accurate naming of some cultivars. The presence or absence of leaves at flowering time is of little use, especially in cultivation, as this tends to vary a lot from season to season and pot-grown plants will vary according to when water is first applied to the dormant tubers. Leaf characteristics are in many ways just as important as those of the flower and it is unfortunate that they have taken a rather subordinate role in cyclamen classification. For instance clear differences observable in the leaf shape of *C. cilicium* and *C. intaminatum* and between *C. balearicum*, *C. creticum*, *C. repandum* have been under-stressed in the past, yet they are vital in species recognition. In fact it was the leaf characteristics that finally convinced me that *C. cilicium* and *C. intaminatum* were distinct species. It is all too easy to be tricked into supposing plants belong to the same species purely on the superficially similar characters of the flower (especially the corolla) when these are looked at in isolation. Within both *C. graecum*, *C. peloponnesiacum* and *C. repandum* the characteristics of leaf size and shape have played a key role in determining subdivisions within the species.

Flowers

Having stressed the importance of leaf characteristics it would be wrong to underplay those of the flower for they are the most useful aid to accurate identification. Someone once said to me when we were wandering round the garden 'I don't know how you can name those cyclamen; they all seem to have little pink or white flowers'. This is true up to a point, especially from a distance, but the joy of cyclamen is in observing the flowers at close quarters; look at them critically close to and a whole range of differences are immediately apparent, differences that make accurate identification possible as well as an exciting occupation. The corolla (petals) may be plain or with variously shaped markings or zones around the mouth. The mouth of the corolla may or may not have auricles (small ear-like structures at the base of the petals, one on each side, and at the point where the petals reflex backwards). The petal margins may be plain or finely toothed. The stamens and styles may be included within the mouth of the corolla or they may protrude. Some species such as *C. pseudibericum* and *C. libanoticum* have the petals covered in small glistening glands (best observed under a ×10 hand lens), while others are without glands or with just a few glands confined to the petal margins. The flower stalks (pedicels) often coil in fruit and may do so from the top downwards, or from the base upwards or, to be different, they may even start coiling in the middle; alternatively they may not coil at all but simply bend over.

Although not a botanical characteristic, flowering time can be a very useful guide to the species. Used in conjunction with the other identification features, accurate naming can be assured.

Each species has its own particular combination of leaf and flower characteristics which make it not only unique but, more importantly, identifiable. Such unique characteristics include:

- Protruding stamens – *C. rohlfsianum*
- Thick roots – *C. graecum, C. persicum*
- Roots basal but acentric – *C. cyprium* (sometimes), *C. libanoticum* (somewhat)
- Plain corollas – *C. balearicum, C. creticum, C. peloponnesiacum* (in part), *C. persicum* (in part), *C. purpurascens, C. repandum*
- Petals with pencil-line veining, generally in grey – *C. balearicum, C. intaminatum*
- Spreading corolla-lobes – *C. alpinum, C. parviflorum* var. *subalpinum*
- Anthers aristate – *C. alpinum, C. cilicium, C. coum, C. elegans, C. intaminatum, C. mirabile, C. parviflorum*
- Non-coiling pedicels – *C. persicum, C. somalense*
- Pedicels coiling from the base or middle – *C. graecum, C. rohlfsianum*
- Leaf-lamina broad with even triangular lobes – *C. rohlfsianum*

Beware of abnormalities: plants with malformed leaves or flowers do arise in cultivation (more rarely in the wild), particularly those with more than the usual number of five petals. Such abnormalities may mislead and confuse but they should be viewed as freaks and, fortunately, in most such cases the characteristics are not passed on to the offspring.

HERBARIUM SPECIMENS

Dried specimens are an indispensable asset to the botanist or indeed anyone wishing to study a particular group of plants. Large herbaria such as those at the Royal Botanic Gardens, Kew, Edinburgh Botanic Garden and the British Museum (Natural History) have numerous sheets of cyclamen (arranged by species), some dating back more than two hundred years. Providing the sheets of dried plants are stored in a dry, insect-free environment and are handled with care, they will last indefinitely and are a permanent record. Herbarium specimens allow us to study the differences between species as well as variation within species. In addition, each sheet will generally bear attached field notes indicating the collector of the specimen, a date and locality. Well-collected and recorded herbarium specimens will also include valuable data on the plant's colour, frequency, habitat, associated species and any other details that the collector thought important at the time. Herbarium specimens allow one to build up a quick database of useful information but they are not a substitute for good observations made in the field or from studying live cultivated specimens. The information gleaned from herbarium specimens is an important adjunct.

Interpreting herbarium specimens is easier once we have become familiar with the species in 'the field', for observing dried, flattened and often brown specimens can be very off-putting to the beginner. One word of warning: fleshy plants such as cyclamen often undergo some shrinkage when they are dried so plant parts need to be measured with some caution – this applies particularly to the petals.

BOTANICAL KEY TO THE WILD SPECIES OF CYCLAMEN

1. Stamens exserted from the mouth of the corolla; leaf-lamina with even, broad, triangular lobes:
    C. rohlfsianum
    or Stamens included within the corolla tube; leaf-lamina not as above — **2**

2. Corolla auriculate towards the base where the corolla lobes reflix; flowering in the summer, autumn and early winter — **3**
    or Corolla not auriculate; flowering mostly in the late winter, spring and summer — **8**

3. Fruiting pedicels coiling in two directions from near the centre, or from near the base upwards; tuber with thick anchorage roots: **C. graecum**
    or Fruiting pedicels coiling from the top downwards; tubers without thick anchorage roots — **4**

4. Leaves orbicular or reniform, neither lobed nor angled along the margin; corolla plain, unmarked — **5**
    or Leaves usually cordate, lobed and/or angled along the margin; corolla with basal markings to each lobe (if pure white then the leaf characters apply) — **6**

5. Leaf-lamina very thick and fleshy with a distinct but finely toothed, rather beaded, margin and diverging basal lobes; corolla 11–15mm long (0.4–0.6in):
C. colchicum
or Leaf-lamina thin and generally with an indistinctly toothed, not beaded, margin and converging or overlapping basal lobes; corolla 17–25mm (0.6–1in) long: **C. purpurascens**

6. Corolla with an M-shaped blotch towards the base of each lobe; calyx-lobes narrow-triangular, acuminate; tubers rooting from one side of, or middle of, the base: **C. cyprium**
or Corolla with a V-shaped blotch at the base of each lobe (not present in albinos); calyx-lobes broad-triangular, with an abrupt cuspidate apex; tubers rooting primarily from the top and sides   **– 7**

7. Petioles and pedicels straight, arising straight above the tuber; corolla-lobes 18–35mm (0.7–1.4in) long; tubers generally concave above: **C.africanum**
or Petioles and pedicels with a distinct elbow in the lower half, arising to the side of the tuber; corolla-lobes 14–22mm (0.5–0.8in) long; tubers flat or somewhat convex above: **C. hederifolium**

8. Pedicels thickening and curving downwards in fruit but not coiling   **– 9**
or Pedicels coiling from the top downwards as the fruits develop   **– 10**

9. Corolla-lobes 10–15mm (0.4–0.6in) long; margin of leaf-lamina somewhat angled in the lower half:
C. somalense
or Corolla-lobes 20–37mm (0.78–1.4in) long; margin of leaf-lamina not angled: **C. persicum**

10. Calyx-lobes 1-veined; corolla plain, unmarked or with a coloured zone around the nose; anthers never aristate   **– 11**
or Calyx-lobes 3–5-veined; corolla with a dark blotch or mark at the base of each lobe or, if unmarked, then corolla glandular in part, and anthers aristate   **– 16**

11. Leaf-lamina thin, cordate, generally lobed and/or angled; tubers smooth and velvety   **–12**
or Leaf-lamina thicker and more fleshy, unlobed and unangled; tubers corky   **– 15**

12. Corolla pink to deep magenta overall, or white or pale pink with a deeper pink zone around the nose; leaf-lamina with a deep bright green base colour – **13**
or Corolla plain, white or very pale pink; leaf-lamina generally with a grey-green base colour – **14**

13. Leaf lamina longer than wide, with a well-defined hastate pattern; corolla-lobes 16–21mm (0.6–0.78in) long: **C. repandum**
or Leaf-lamina as long as wide or wider than long, with or without a hastate pattern but, in addition, nearly always with sparse to dense flecking or blotching; corolla-lobes 20–32mm (0.78–1.2in) long: **C. peloponnesiacum**

14. Leaf-lamina with an acute apex, the margin flat; corolla-lobes 15–26mm (0.6–1in) long:
C. creticum
or Leaf-lamina with an obtuse apex, the margin somewhat revolute usually; corolla-lobes 9–16mm (0.4–0.6in) long: **C. balearicum**

15. Leaf-lamina very thick and fleshy with a distinct but finely toothed, rather beaded, margin and diverging basal lobes; corolla 11–15mm (0.4–0.6in) long:
C. colchicum
or Leaf-lamina thin and generally with an indistinctly toothed, not beaded, margin and converging or overlapping basal lobes; corolla 17–25mm (0.6–1in) long: **C. purpurascens**

16. Flowers appearing in the late summer and autumn; anthers always aristate   **– 17**
or Flowers appearing in the winter or spring; anthers aristate or not   **– 19**

17. Corolla-lobes distinctly toothed towards the apex; leaf-lamina often flushed with pink or red above when young: **C. mirabile**
or Corolla-lobes indistinctly toothed to entire; leaf-lamina rarely flushed with pink or red above   **–18**

18. Leaf-lamina longer than wide, usually toothed; corolla-lobes with a distinctive dark blotch towards the base, 14–19mm (0.6–0.77in) long (if pure white then leaf characters apply):   **C. cilicium**
or Leaf-lamina as wide as long or wider, often entire; corolla-lobes plain, 10–16mm (0.4–0.6in) long: **C. intaminatum**

19. Anthers not aristate; tubers corky, rooting from all over the base: corolla glandular, the lobes entire – **20**
or Anthers aristate; tubers velvety, rooting only from the centre of the base; corolla rarely glandular, the lobes usually somewhat toothed   **– 21**

20. Mouth of corolla 10–13mm (0.4–0.5in) diameter; corolla pale rose-pink to whitish; leaf-lamina angled but not toothed: **C. libanoticum**
or Mouth of corolla 3–6mm (0.12–0.24in) diameter;

corolla pink to magenta-purple; leaf-lamina toothed but not angled: **C. pseudibericum**

21. Blotch at base of the corolla-lobes with a pair of paler 'eyes'; flowers generally unscented   **– 22**
    or Blotch at base of corolla-lobes solid or consisting of close, more or less parallel, lines; flowers sweetly scented   **– 23**

22. Leaves kidney-shaped to suborbicular with an entire to somewhat indented margin; corolla-lobes 8–20mm (0.32–0.78in) long, obtuse: **C. coum**
    or Leaves heart-shaped with a scalloped margin and subobtuse to subacute apex; corolla-lobes 18–25mm (0.6–1in) long: **C. elegans**

23. Leaf-lamina marbled or variously patterned above, somewhat toothed, generally patterned; corolla-lobes 9–13mm (0.4–0.5in) long, generally more or less horizontal, twisting through only 90°, the blotch solid: **C. alpinum**
    or Leaf-lamina plain, more or less entire, plain green; corolla-lobes 4–11mm (0.16–0.4in) long, often erect, twisting through 180°, the blotch consisting of close lines: **C. parviflorum**

TERMINOLOGY

I have attempted in the following account to keep botanical jargon to a minimum: after all, this is a book intended for gardeners and horticulturists as well as botanists; however, some terms have had to be employed out of necessity:

Auricle – a small ear-like process at the base of the petal where it folds back; present in only some of the species.
Corolla – a collective name for the petals.
Depressed-globose – a phrase often employed to describe the tuber; round as seen from above but oval in cross-section, the upper surface of the tuber often being rather flattened.
Hastate – spear-shaped; often used to denote the shape of the leaf pattern.
Pedicel – the flower stalk.
Petiole – leaf stalk.
Sinus – the gap in the leaf-blade where it joins the petiole.

SUBGENUS *PSILANTHUM*

(*Cyclamen repandum* Group)
C. repandum, C. r. var. *repandum, C. r.* var. *repandum* forma *album, C. r.* var. *barborense; C. peloponnesiacum, C. p.* subsp. *peloponnesiacum* and forma *albiflorum,* susbp. *vividum,* and subsp. *rhodense; C. balearicum; C. creticum, C. c.* forma *pallide-roseum*

The members of this group delight the gardener in the spring when they come into flower with their finely twisted petals and sweet fragrance. *C. repandum*, which is the best-known and most widely grown of the four of species, is very variable, with a distribution from southern France to Yugoslavia, a distribution almost as wide as that of *C. coum* which, in contrast, is primarily confined to Asia.

Cyclamen repandum and its allies have relatively small, smooth and velvety tubers that root from the centre below. The rather thin leaves are often angled and toothed, while the corolla is without auricles and has no marking around the mouth.

The leaves of this group are consistently thinner than those of other cyclamen and for this reason the members tend to be shade-lovers, or plants at least of semi-shaded places. Leaf size can vary greatly within the species, sometimes within a single population. In general it can be said that those growing in deep shade in moist leafy soils at the lower altitudes tend to have the largest leaves, while those growing in thinner soils or in more open habitats, especially at the higher altitudes, tend to have the smaller leaves.

Cyclamen repandum and its allies are the last species to come into flower in the spring and they can be said to complete the cyclamen calendar. They are among the loveliest of plants with their elegant twisted petals and the sweet fragrance of their blooms. Their leaves are the last to emerge, pushing through the soil surface and expanding long after their cousins, shy to expose themselves before the warmer days of the late winter and early spring arrive. Sometimes they emerge so late in cultivation that one begins to have doubts as to whether or not they are still alive. In the wild the leaves start rather earlier into growth, especially in the mild regions close to the Mediterranean.

The group in fact has a wide distribution (see map 1) in southern Europe from France to south-eastern mainland Greece, including all the larger Mediterranean island from the Balearics, to Corsica and Sardinia, to Sicily, Crete and Rhodes, although they are absent from most of the other Greek islands.

The Repandum Group presents the botanist with one of the more complex problems of classification found in the genus. Some see a single variable species with ill-defined subdivisions, while others have distinguished several species and more clearly defined subdivisions. I adhere to the latter school of thought and I would urge anyone interested in these plants to study them in the wild or to study cultivated plants of known wild origin where hybridization has not been allowed to muddle and obscure the picture of natural variability.

Admittedly, the flowers and foliage have a lot in common but this is, after all, what holds the group together. Ignoring the occasional pure white (albino) forms of *C. repandum*, only *C. balearicum* and *C. creticum* have pure white, or occasionally very pale pink, flowers. In *C. peloponnesiacum* the flowers are either pale pink with a deep pink rim to the corolla or mid- to deep magenta-pink, while in *C. repandum* itself, the flowers are also deep maganta-pink.

It is perhaps in the foliage that most of the differences can be observed and once one is acquainted with the various elements in the group it is quite possible to distinguish them by their leaf characteristics alone. Used in conjunction with the characters of the flowers, then little confusion is likely to occur, although anyone who has studied wild populations will quickly observe that in almost every group which they have studied, non-conformists can be found; it is the overall characteristics that need to be evaluated. The overall differences can be summarized as follows:

- **C. balearicum**: leaves heart-shaped, longer than wide, with an obtuse to subobtuse apex and undulate, scarcely toothed or lobed margin which is often somewhat turned downwards, grey-green overall with a pale grey or silvery marbling, or a more or less well-defined hastate pattern; flowers white with greyish or very pale greyish-pink veins, small, the corolla-lobes only 9–16mm (0.35–0.62in) long.
- **C. creticum**: leaves narrow heart-shaped, longer than wide, with an acute or subacute apex and with a scalloped, distantly toothed margin, grey-green overall with a greyish or grey-green, rather ill-defined hastate pattern and/or speckles; flowers pure white or very pale pink, intermediate in size, the corolla-lobes 15–26mm (0.6–1in) long.
- **C. peloponnesiacum**: leaves broadly heart-shaped, as long as wide or rather wider than long, with a scalloped and often distinctly toothed margin, green, with or without a hastate pattern in grey, cream, white or silver, but generally the leaf sparsely or densely overlain with speckles or dashes in one of the colours outlined; flowers pale to deep pink or rich magenta-purple, the corolla lobes 20–32mm (0.8–1.2in) long.

The subspecies of *C. peloponnesiacum* can also be similarly distinguished:

Subsp. *peloponnesiacum*: leaves as wide as long or wider, with a shallowly scalloped margin and a well-defined hastate pattern and speckling, or only speckling; flowers pink with a deep rim to the mouth of the corolla

Subsp. *vividum,* as subsp. *peloponnesiacum* but leaves generally speckled and more rarely with a hastate pattern and flowers deep magenta-pink or crimson-magenta.

Subsp. *rhodense*: leaves slightly longer than wide, with shallowly scalloped to coarsely toothed or almost lobed margin, often with a well-defined hastate pattern and speckling, or only speckling; flowers white or pale pink with a deeper rim around the mouth of the corolla.

- **C. repandum**: leaves heart-shaped, sometimes very broadly so, longer than wide, the apex acute to subacute, the margin generally deeply scalloped to lobed or angled to rather coarsely toothed, mid- to deep green overall, with a well-defined hastate pattern, in grey, grey-green or silver, very occasionally plain; flowers deep magenta-pink, the corolla-lobes 16–21mm (0.6–0.8in) long.

Cyclamen balearicum Willk.

Cyclamen balearicum is a rather underrated and often overlooked species in the *C. repandum* complex and even among the collections of cyclamen addicts it often takes very much of a back seat. This is unfair, for it is a pretty little plant despite the fact that some dismiss it for its 'small anaemic flowers'. True *C. balearicum* has the smallest flowers in the complex but they make up for size by producing an intoxicatingly sweet scent, adding to the belief that if you cannot make an impression by bulk then you might as well do it by smell.

26 *Cyclamen balearicum* in cultivation; a form with attractively marked foliage.

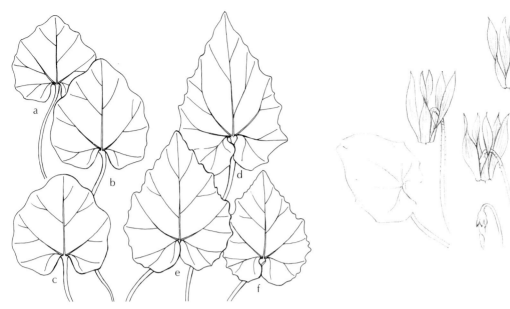

Typical leaf shape of *C. balearicum* (a–c) and *C. creticum* (d–f).

Cycalmen balearicum.

Cyclamen balearicum can be distinguished in leaf as well as in flower. The leaves are roughly similar in shape to those of *C. repandum* but have a less markedly lobed margin which is often somewhat down-turned, while the surface is greyer and more strongly marbled; in some forms the leaves are beautifully marked with silvery-grey or pure silver; indeed they can possess some of the loveliest leaves in the group. The flowers are relatively small and white, or rather off-white, with distinctive very pale pink veins which give the flowers, like those of *C. intaminatum*, a slightly etched look; this off-white flower colour is in contrast to the pure white found in typical *C. creticum* or the rare white forms of *C. repandum* that are occasionally found in the wild.

Cyclamen balearicum was thought to be endemic to the Balearic Islands for many years but it was subsequently found in southern France (in fact its existence there was recognized as long ago as the 16th century, but overlooked by most authors subsequently). It seems certain from recent research (see M. Debussche and J.D. Thompson in the *Journal of the Cyclamen Society* 23:52–55, 1999) that *C. balearicum* is truly native to southern France. It does not overlap in the wild with *C. repandum* in France so that the chance of hybridization does not occur. If they did, then, knowing the propensity of members of this group to hybridize, one might well expect to find hybrids in the wild: after all the two species hybridize freely in some gardens. However, more recent work in Corsica has indicated populations of possible hybrid origin between *C. balearicum* and *C. repandum*. This certainly complicates the picture and requires further investigation. Debussche and Thompson report that *C. repandum* populations on Corsica show mixed characters with some populations with a very small percentage of white-flowered plants while others are much higher (reaching 15 per cent in one instance). In addition, some white-flowered plants bore a ring of carmine around the mouth (reminescent of *C. peloponnesiacum* subsp. *rhodense*), while other plants with *C. balearicum*-type leaves but typical *C. repandum* flowers could be identified. Other mixed characters are described. They conclude – 'What is happening at this site remains a mystery: either we are witnessing the divergence of a new *C. balearicum*-like taxon from *C. repandum* on Corsica; or perhaps (following the speciation of *C. balearicum* from *C. repandum*), a relict population of *C. balearicum* remained on Corsica, introgression with *C. repandum* then produced a mixed population with many hybrid forms. Only future work using genetic markers will allow us to discriminate between these hypotheses.' The paper concludes with an extensive list of references most of which are not included in the bibliography at the end of this book.

Cyclamen balearicum was first featured in Johnson's 1633 edition of Gerard's 'Herball' under the name *Cyclamen vernum album*, or the White-flowered Sowbread, where there is a woodcut which is unmistakably that of the species in question. Gerard's *Cyclamen vernum*, or Spring Sowbread, which is also illustrated, is *C. repandum* as we know it today; apparently the close affinity of the two species was recognized even at this early date.

DESCRIPTION *Tubers* depressed-globose, up to 3cm (1.2in) diameter eventually, occasionally larger, the surface smooth with a thin greyish-brown skin, rooting from the centre beneath. *Leaves* appearing in late autumn and winter; lamina broadly heart-shaped, 2.4–8.5cm (0.9–3.3in) long, 2–9cm (0.8–3.5in) wide, with a rather shallow basal sinus with the lobes not or only slightly overlapping, the margin shallowly and remotely toothed or slightly angled, especially towards the base, bluish-green or greyish-green, with a grey, silver or whitish marbling above, generally in the form of a wide hastate pattern, purplish or reddish beneath; petiole 4.5–11.5cm (1.8–4.5in) long, grey-green, often flushed with purple or red. *Pedicels* 9.5–14.5cm (3.7–5.7in) long, coiling from the top downwards as the young fruits develop. *Flowers* appearing with the mature leaves, strongly fragrant; corolla white with greyish or pinkish translucent veins, the corolla-lobes twisted, narrowly elliptic to lanceolate, 9–16mm (0.35–0.62in) long. *Style* not or only very slightly protruding.

HABITAT Growing in shaded or semi-shaded places, beneath trees and bushes, particularly of *Pinus* and *Quercus*, growing amongst the tree roots or rocks, or in rock crevices, sometimes in gullies or ravines, or along stream banks; sea-level to 1,443m (4,700ft) altitude.

DISTRIBUTION Balearic Islands (Majorca, Menorca, Ibiza, Cabrera and Draponera) and in a limited area in southern France; March–May (see map 1).

The French distribution is fragmented with five isolated populations across the Languedoc-Rousillon region (Basse Cévennes, Hérault River Gorge, Minervois, north of Nîmes and Pyrénées), presumably relicts of a wider distribution in former times. In these areas the plants always seem to inhabit areas on limestone, particularly on north-facing slopes with evergreen oak, *Quercus ilex*, and at the base of cliffs. The effects of the last ice ages and the human factor, particularly deforestation, have undoubtedly restricted these populations.

CULTIVATION Less seen in cultivation than it truly deserves this charming little species is worthy of our attention. It is generally grown in pots in the alpine house or planted out in frames. The foliage can be damaged quite easily by heavy frosts but these are unlikely to kill the plant unless prolonged freezing occurs. Like the other members of this group, all of which have rather thin leaves, the foliage can be scorched by bright sunlight, so plants thrive best in dappled shade; an ideal place is beneath the staging in the alpine house, provided enough light reaches the plants. Plants should never be allowed to dry out completely, even during the dormant season,

although they should not be kept over-wet when resting.

In mild districts this species can certainly be tried outside. Desmond Meikle (Minehead, Somerset) has managed to keep it growing outside for a number of years and each season it puts up a few flowers. Tubers, as with *C. repandum* and *C. creticum*, should be deep-buried; this applies to those grown in pots as well as those in the open garden. Hybrids will occur spontaneously if *C. balearicum* is grown in close proximity to any other members of subgenus Psilanthum.

Plants generally flower in their third season from sowing but it is not until they are about five years old that they begin to reveal their full flowering potential.

AWARDS
• A.M. 1977

Cyclamen repandum Sm.

One of the loveliest of all cyclamen, sweet-scented and floriferous, *C. repandum* is widely grown in our gardens, where it is sometimes found in wonderful and satisfying drifts.

The species has been cultivated for at least 300 years. In his famous 'Herball' of 1597, Gerard describes it as the "Spring Sowbread", giving it the name *C. vernum* long before the days of Linnaeus.

Linnaeus in fact throws no light on the species whatsoever. In his 'Species Plantarum' of 1753 (the starting point of modern taxonomy: only Latin binomial names for plants are accepted from that date onwards by the international rules of botanical nomenclature) he lists only two cyclamen, the mysterious *C. indicum* and *C. europaeum*. Today we know that *C. europaeum* is an ambiguous name

Typical leaf shapes of *C. repandum* (a–b), *C. peloponnesiacum* subsp. *peloponnesiacum* (c–d) and *C.p.* subsp. *rhodense* (e).

27 *Cyclamen repandum* var. *repandum* in cultivation.

that encompasses several distinct species including *C. coum*, *C. balearicum*, *C. hederifolium*, *C. purpurascens*, *C. repandum* and *C. persicum*.

Cyclamen repandum is widespread in southern Europe and it is therefore surprising that it was not referred to more often in early literature. Phillip Miller in the eighth edition of his 'Gardener's Dictionary' makes no mention of the species under any name. Miller knew the species of cyclamen in cultivation at the time very well and he can, in many ways, be said to have laid the foundations for *Cyclamen* classification. Even in the 1797 edition of his book, after various adjustments had been made to the initial names proposed by Miller, there is no reference to the species under any name.

As a result it was not until 1806 that Sibthorp and Smith in their remarkable and magnificent 'Flora Graeca' described and figured the species under the name that we accept today. It might be assumed that the plant illustrated in the 'Flora Graeca' would be of Greek origin. However, the plant depicted, which has been taken to represent the type of the species, does not match the mainland Greek plant at all. If it did then the Greek plant would be *C. peloponnesiacum*. The plant in fact closely matches our present-day concept of *C. repandum* (which is not found in Greece at all). The reason for this is quite clear: Sibthorp died before the completion of his master work and many of the plates subsequently drawn depicted the equivalent plant in Italy or elsewhere. The cyclamen we know was drawn from an Italian plant and it was generally assumed at the time that the Greek plant matched it in detail.

In the first editon of this work the Greek plant was recognized as a separate subspecies (subsp. *peloponnesiacum*), as was the plant from Rhodes (subsp. *rhodense*). Both these taxa are isolated not only from one another by the Aegean Sea but from *C. repandum* by a

considerable distance. It is interesting that none of these are to be found in mainland Greece (with the exception of the Peloponnese, which is almost an island), nor for that matter in central and southern Yugoslavia; in effect *the Greek plants* are isolated from *C. repandum* by the Adriatic Sea.

Recent DNA research by James Compton (to be published) has shown that in fact *C. peloponnesiacum* is more closely related to *C. balearicum* than to *C. repandum*. This and the more obvious morphological differences have convinced me that species recognition was probably the best way to treat the Greek plants (including subsp. *rhodense*). However, before I was able to upgrade the taxon formally it has been done recently by Kit Tam in the 'Endemic Plants of Greece (The Peloponnese)', without the knowledge that DNA sampling has subsequently provided. No doubt this was done in order to bolster the number of endemic species in Greece, yet I and others have thought for a number of years that this taxon should perhaps be elevated to species level.

In cultivation *C. repandum* can make a very fine plant. Naturalized in some gardens, drifting down glades between trees or tumbling down a grassy embankment, it can look ravishing. Yet this is not always the easiest species to grow in the open garden, taking to some sites while disliking others. The reasons for this are not clear although the species dislikes cold places and exposed gardens where the foliage may get scorched and plants weakened as a result. As with the other members of the group it also greatly resents dry conditions, so sunbaked

28 *Cyclamen repandum*: cultivated form with paler flowers than normal, but showing the characteristic leaf shape.

Cyclamen repandum var. *repandum*.

corners of the garden are not appropriate, however sheltered. A sheltered site with dappled shade and a moist leafy soil are probably ideal conditions for it. The tubers should be placed well down in the soil (10–15cm(4–6in)) and the plants given an annual top-dressing of leaf mould. In a woodland glade they will probably receive a leafy mulch by natural processes.

 Cyclamen repandum also makes a fine pot plant; pots are preferable to pans which are too shallow. The tubers should be placed about halfway down the pot. It is a good plant for growing under the glasshouse staging, preferring the extra shade there, rather than the brighter conditions on top of the staging, where the foliage will often wilt in strong sunlight.

 Cyclamen repandum, and indeed *C. peloponnesiacum* and its allies, make excellent subjects for planting out permanently in frames, where they can be protected during severe cold periods by placing fleece, bubble plastic or even sacking overhead (on top of the glass). This should be removed the moment the weather relents, and the frames aerated at all times except when frosts threaten. Once settled in, plants will generally seed around. If two or more of the species or subspecies are grown in the same frame they will undoubtedly hybridize. Some of the resultant hybrids will be most attractive.

DESCRIPTION *Tubers* depressed-globose, to 6cm (2.3in) diameter, sometimes larger, velvety and deep chestnut brown but becoming somewhat corky with age, rooting from the centre of the lower surface. *Leaves* with a heart-shaped lamina, (2.2–) 4.3–9.3 (–15.2)cm long, (1.8–) 3.7–8.9 (–14.8)cm (wide, longer than wide, with a narrow and rather deep sinus at the base with the basal lobes converging and often slightly overlapping, or somewhat diverging, the margin usually angled and lobed, especially in the lower half, as well as distinctly toothed, deep green or grey-green above and often shiny, rarely plain, with a hastate pattern in a paler often greyer green, cream or silver, the pattern often fragmenting into blotches, dashes or spots, the leaf surface sometimes without a hastate pattern but instead covered all over with streaks and dots, pale green beneath and often flushed with reddish-purple; petiole 6–20cm (2.3–7.8in) long, distinctly elbowed in the middle or in the lower half, green or purplish. *Pedicels* 10.5–21cm (4.1–8.3in) long, elbowed in the lower half, greenish or brownish-purple, coiling from the top downwards as the young fruits begin to develop. *Flowers* appearing with the mature or semi-mature leaves, sweetly scented; corolla deep pink, often with a deep pink or purplish-red zone around the mouth, to deep carmine-magenta; petal lobes narrow- to broad-elliptical, twisted (sometimes up to three revolutions), 17–31mm (0.7–1.2in) long, without auricles at the base. *Style* protruding by 1–2.5mm.

DISTRIBUTION The *Cyclamen repandum* Group reveals a rather complex picture of variability but, unlike some of the other widespread species such as *C. hederifolium*, the Group has a fragmented range with many sites in southern Europe south to Sardinia and Corsica and Sicily, but with isolated populations in the Greek Peloponnese and on the island of Rhodes. Although the Group as a whole shows a great range of differences in leaf shape and patterning, as well as flower colour, the mainland Greek and Rhodes plants can be clearly separated out and are now recognized as a closely related yet separate species, *C. peloponnesiacum*. In my monograph of 1988 I distinguished three subspecies of *C. repandum*, with the one from the Peloponnese, subsp. *peloponnesiacum*, further divided into two forms based on flower colour. Various writers, particularly Jim Archibald (1990), have questioned the validity of these subdivisions but at the time I had no hesitation in maintaining them. I would be the first to admit that not every wild specimen conformed neatly to the divisions but the majority do and it would be foolish to lump all plants into a single variable species. The picture is further clouded in cultivation as all the plants freely interbreed, muddling the divisions as they are seen in wild populations. Map 1.

 This is a group in which divergence is still occurring. One has to accept a certain amount of variation, even within the different species. The presence of plain-leaved forms in *C. peloponnesiacum* and its subspecies are perfectly acceptable within the circumscription of the species, as are

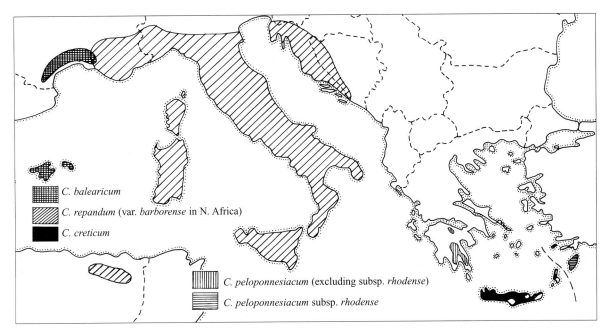

Map 1: Distribution of *C. balearicum, C. creticum,*
C. repandum and *C. peloponnesiacum.*

the occasional plants which bear wholly silvered or
pewtered leaves. Look at the overall statistics of the species
and subspecies rather than being misled by the occasional
plant that does not seem to conform in one particular or
another: such non-conformists turn up in almost every
species I have ever looked at, in a host of different genera.

Strangely, the existence of *C. repandum* on the south
side of the Mediterranean in Algeria has been overlooked
by me and other authors. Its presence there is by no means
unexpected as *C. repandum* grows on the islands of
Corsica, Sardinia and Sicily, the latter only 600km (373
miles) distance from the Algerian localities, in an area with
a decidedly moist Mediterranean climate (800–2000mm
/32–80in of rain per year, mostly during the winter). In fact
the presence of the species in Africa has been noted since
1880 when it was discovered by Doumet-Adanson on the
northern slopes of the Djebel Babor, a mountain in the
Petite Kabylie, and later recorded by Battandier and Trabut
in their *Flora of Algeria and Tunisia* of 1902. Apart from
one or two additional sitings, little has been seen or written
about the Algerian plant in the intervening years. In these
years a great deal of deforestation in the region, as well as
overgrazing, has undoubtedly affected the populations and
this interesting outlier must be considered to be at

considerable risk. To add to this, the political situation in
Algeria in recent years has precluded any further research
in the region. The differences between the varieties can be
summarized as follows:

VARIETIES OF *C. REPANDUM*

Corolla diameter at mouth 4–7mm (0.2–0.25in), the petal
lobes (12–)15–21 (–26) x 5–7mm: **var. *repandum***
Corolla diameter at mouth 6–8mm (0.25–0.3in), the petal
lobes 20–30 x 7–11mm (0.8–1.2in) : **var. *barborense***

Var. *repandum*. *Leaves* deep green with a grey-green or
silver hastate pattern, but no flecking or very little, always
with a broad plain green marginal area; lamina longer than
wide, with a long apex, generally green flushed with pink
beneath. *Flowers* deep carmine-pink or carmine-magenta,
rarely pure white, the colour more intense around the
mouth but not as a distinct zone as in *C. peloponnesiacum*
s.l.; corolla-lobes (12–)15–21 (–26)mm long.

29 *Cyclamen repandum* var. *repandum* forma *album,* the
rather rare pure white form of the species.

30 *Cyclamen peloponnesiacum* subsp. *peloponnesiacum* foliage in the Taigetos Mountains; Langada Gorge west of Mistras.

31 *Cyclamen peloponnesiacum* subsp. *peloponnesiacum* beneath plane trees, *Platanus orientalis*, in the Taigetos Mountains, west of Sparta.

HABITAT Primarily a plant of dappled shade, growing in deciduous or pine woodlands, olive groves, sometimes in maquis, usually growing in deep leaf litter, in rock crevices or in the mossy areas at the base of trees; sea level to 1,200m (3,900ft) altitude. *C. repandum* sometimes forms very extensive colonies in the wild.

DISTRIBUTION *C. repandum* is found in southern France, Corsica, Sardinia, southern Switzerland, Italy, Sicily and the western Yugoslavian states, as well as north Africa (Algeria, Petite Kabylie). Reports of it from Albania and the island of Corfu appear to be erroneous. March–May.

In cultivation subsp. *repandum* is rather uniform and many plants seem to come from the same source, long cultivated and propagated. Little has been done to try and introduce other forms into cultivation, with the exception, that is, of the pure white form, forma *album*.

- **Forma *repandum*.** *Flowers* deep carmine-pink to magenta-purple. Found throughout the range of the variety.
- **Forma *album*.** *Flowers* pure white. Occasionally found from time to time in the wild and not uncommon as albinos in most other *Cyclamen* species, being particularly common on Corsica (see also under *C. balearicum*).Found throughout the European range of the species.

Var. *barborense* Debussche & Quézel. As for var. *repandum*, but corolla diameter at mouth 6–8mm (0.25–0.3in), and the petal lobes 20–30 x 7–11mm (0.8–1.5 x 0.25–0.8in).

DISTRIBUTION NE Algeria: Petite Kabylie in deciduous oak (*Quercus canariensis* and *Q. afares*) woodland, at 400–1,800m (1,300–5,900ft).

In addition, there is evidence that on average the leaves of var. *barborense* are somewhat larger than the European plant and that the leaf margin has a greater number of teeth. However, there is some overlap with Corsican plants and this requires further investigation.

AWARDS
- *C. repandum* subsp. *repandum* forma *album* A.M. 1952
- *C. repandum* subsp. *repandum* forma *repandum*: A.M. 1959; F.C.C. 1973; A.G.M.

Cyclamen peloponnesiacum (Grey-Wilson) Kit Tan

Formerly *C. repandum* subsp. *peloponnesiacum*, this taxon has now been raised by Kit Tan (2001) to species level and I concur with this view. Var. *vividum* now becomes subsp. *vividum*. In addition, *C. repandum* subsp.

32 Above left: A drift of *Cyclamen peloponnesiacum* subsp. *peloponnesiacum*; Mani Peninsula, Peloponnese, SW of Gythio.
33 Centre left: *Cyclamen peloponnesiacum* subsp. *peloponnesiacum* in the Taigetos Mountains west of Sparta.
34 Below left: An unusually pale form of *Cyclamen peloponnesiacum* subsp. *peloponnesiacum*: Taigetos Mountains west of Sparta.
35 Above right: Another pale form of *Cyclamen peloponnesiacum* subsp. *peloponnesiacum* with particularly well-marked foliage.

rhodense has been transferred to *C. peloponnesiacum* as a third subspecies.

DESCRIPTION *Tuber* details like *C. repandum*, generally not exceeding 5cm (2in) diam. *Leaves* with a broad heart-shaped lamina, (2.5–)4.4–9.4 (–15)cm long, (2–)5–10.2(–14.8)cm wide, generally wider than long, with a narrow basal sinus, the basal lobes generally converging but not overlapping, the margin shallowly lobed and toothed, sometimes slightly angled, especially in the lower half, mid-green to dark green, occasionally plain but generally with speckles and dashes in grey, cream or silver, covering much of the leaf surface densely in some forms, in addition sometimes underlain by a weakly to

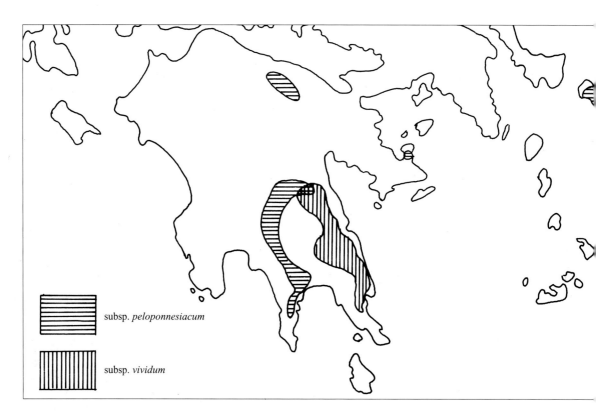

Distribution of *C. peloponnesiacum* in the Peloponnese.

subsp. *peloponnesiacum*

subsp. *vividum*

strongly defined hastate pattern, generally in grey-green, green to reddish-purple beneath; petiole 5–20cm (2–8in) long, distinctly elbowed near the middle or in the lower third, green or purplish. *Pedicels* 10–20cm (4–8in) long, occasionally longer, elbowed like the petioles, greenish or brownish-purple, coiling from the top downwards as the young fruits begin to develop. *Flowers* appearing in spring with the mature or semi-mature leaves, sweetly scented; calyx lobes ovate, 2–4mm (0.1–0.2in) long, entire or slightly toothed; corolla white with a pink mouth, to pale or mid-pink with a deeper mouth, or uniformly deep carmine-magenta; lobes narrow to broad-elliptical, twisted, 20–31mm (0.75–1.75in) long, 4–8mm (0.2–0.3in) wide, without basal auricles. *Style* protruding, generally by 2–3mm (0.1in).

DISTRIBUTION Greek Peloponnese, confined primarily to the eastern half of the region, as well as the island of Rhodes and Cos (for further information and habitats see under the three following subspecies).Maps 1 and 2.

SUBSPECIES OF *C. PELOPONNESIACUM*

Subsp. *peloponnesiacum*. *Leaves* grey-green, very occasionally plain, but mostly with a narrow hastate pattern in grey-green or silver which fragments in spots and dashes to the leaf margin, or the whole leaf surface sometimes speckled but without a regular pattern, generally green beneath, though sometimes flushed with

pink or purple; lamina as wide as long or often wider, with a short subacute to subobtuse apex, generally rather shallowly and evenly lobed. *Flowers* pale to mid-pink with a deeper carmine-pink zone around the mouth (at

Cyclamen peloponnesiacum subsp. *vividum* (a) and subsp. *peloponnesiacum* (b).

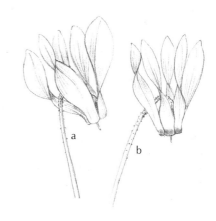

a

b

least 2–3mm [0.1in] deep); corolla-lobes 20–31mm (0.8–1.2in) long.

The wooded valleys and gorges to the west of Sparta are alive with this charming plant in the spring, the plants thickly carpeting the ground in places, the flowers dancing in the slightest breeze like myriad small pink butterflies above the foliage. In the autumn they are often replaced by *C. hederifolium* and, in some places, also by the autumn-flowering snowdrop, *Galanthus reginae-olgae*.

HABITAT Subsp. *peloponnesiacum* is a plant of cool dappled shade, relishing the moist leafy soils and rocky soil pockets usually well inside the woodland, often in the valley bottoms beneath large old plane trees, *Platanus orientalis*, but also in mixed deciduous woodland or beneath large bushes, occasionally on river banks or at the base of cliffs; 350–1,200m (1,100–4,000ft), although it has been found once as high as 1,500m (4,900ft) in the central Taigetos Mountains.

DISTRIBUTION It is confined to the central and southern areas of the Peloponnese except for the bare treeless regions close to the Mediterranean. Most of the known localities are to the west and north-west of Sparta, particularly on the east flanks of the Taigetos and the mountains south of Tripolis. There are also some extensive colonies in the northern Mani Peninsula, particularly between Gythio and Aeriopoli, with one or two small outlying populations further south. In addition, there is a small outlier of this variety in the northern Peloponnese close to Mt Chelmos, not far from the town of Kalavrita. Recently (see Kit Tan, 2001) it has been verified as occurring on the Methana Peninsula (east of Epidavros in the east Peloponnese) and on two Greek islands, Andros and Tinos, in the Cyclades; reports of its occurrence on the islands of Ikaria and Samos cannot be substantiated; March–May. Map 2.

In recent years the members of the Cyclamen Society have reported seeing pure white forms of this variety in the Greek Peloponnese. Since the last edition of this work Brian Mathew has formally described the white-flowered plant as forma *albiflorum* (*Journal of the Cyclamen Society* 23: 50–51, 1999): forma *albiflorum* (Mathew) Grey-Wilson, see p.207.

36 *Cyclamen peloponnesiacum* subsp. *vividum*: a selection of leaves from a single colony from the wild found on the western slopes of the Parnon range, east of Sparta.
37 *Cyclamen peloponnesiacum* subsp. *vividum* growing beneath pine trees in the Parnon range, Peloponnese.
38 *Cyclamen peloponnesiacum* subsp. *vividum*; form with evenly speckled leaves.

39 *Cyclamen peloponnesiacum* subsp. *vividum* east of Sparta; form with a well-defined leaf pattern.
40 *Cyclamen peloponnesiacum* subsp. *vividum* east of Sparta; form with plain leaves.
41 *Cyclamen peloponnesiacum* subsp. *vividum*; form with particularly intense flower colouring.

Subsp. *vividum* (Grey-Wilson) Kit Tan. *Leaves* generally deep red beneath, but not consistently so, and they can be almost plain above or marked with a mass of flecks, these sometimes overlaying a weak hastate pattern; the flecking, which can cover the entire upper leaf surface, is sometimes in a contrasting and striking silver, although it is generally rather more muted in this particular subspecies. *Flowers* deep carmine-magenta, even deeper and more intense than those of the related *C. repandum*.

Unlike subsp. *peloponnesiacum*, this subspecies, which has no rival for the intensity of its blooms, inhabits more open rocky areas often in the full sunshine in places where one might expect to see *C. graecum*.

HABITAT Subsp. *vividum* particularly favours rocky gullies, open scrub and sunny banks, sometimes growing close to woodland, but occasionally making extensive colonies in dry open pine woodland. It is sometimes found growing in hot sites beneath prickly, drought resistant shrubs. This is unusual for all the other members of the *C. repandum* group favour the coolness and shade of trees and bushes, growing in moist leafy soils. I have observed it on a number of occasions on Parnon in flower in April growing in open rock gullies and in rather exposed places. It is common in the mountains to the NW of Monemvasia, where it tends to grow in rocky scrub in very dry exposed places, but often in part shade and shielded from the midday sun; 400–1,400m (1,300–4,600ft) altitude.

DISTRIBUTION It is restricted to the eastern Peloponnese, particularly the region around Mt Parnon (Oros Parnon) and the Mandara Mountains, with most of the known localities to the south of Astros and east of Sparta, but it also found extensively to the NW of Monemvasia and in isolated pockets well to the south of the town; March–May. Map 2.

In the north-west of its range it overlaps in distribution with subsp. *peloponnesiacum*, but the subspecies appear to remain distinct, despite the fact that they must have the opportunity to hybridize.

The tubers of subsp. *vividum* are often deep buried, protected from the harsh conditions by a deep layer of rock fragments, whereas those of subsp. *peloponnesiacum* after often found to be fairly shallow in the soil.

Subsp. *rhodense* (Meikle) Kit Tan. *Leaves* grey-green with a broad, often fragmented, hastate pattern in paler grey-green, grey or silver, sometimes two-toned, with spots and dashes, especially in the marginal zone, occasionally the whole leaf surface more or less pewter or silver; lamina rather longer than wide or as wide as long, with a short apex, often pronouncedly and rather unevenly lobed. *Flowers* white or very pale pink, always with a pink zone around the mouth (coloured zone mostly 0.5–1.5mm deep); corolla-lobes 20–32mm (0.8–1.2in) long.

HABITAT Hill and mountain slopes, often growing beneath *Pinus brutia* or scrub in shaded and semi-shaded places, especially amongst rocks and tree roots, or along stream sides; 35–500m (115–1640ft) altitude.

DISTRIBUTION Greece: long thought to be restricted to the island of Rhodes (quite widespread on the island but particularly common in the Salakos, Mt Philerimos and Mt Prophitis Elias areas); found in recent years in SE Cos; March–April.

The discovery of subsp. *rhodense* on the island of Cos in recent years is surprising if not entirely unexpected. Surprising, because the island is fairly well known botanically, while not unexpected because Cos lies not far to the NW of Rhodes. It might perhaps also be expected to grow on the neighbouring part of SW Turkey (Muğla Province). Its discovery on Cos was made by Dr David Thomas of the Biology Department of Cardiff University in 1996. It is generally found at low altitudes on Cos, not higher than 260m (850ft).

All the known forms of *C. peloponnesiacum* so far investigated reveal the same chromosome number of 2n=20. Although hybrids have occurred (mostly spontaneously) in cultivation between the subspecies (and indeed with the closely related *C. balearicum*, *C. creticum* and *C. repandum*), no methodical or detailed formal hybridization has been carried out. This is a pity because the species as a whole reveals a great deal of variability and there is a huge potential for the development of new garden forms. *C. peloponnesiacum* is less hardy in the garden than *C. repandum*, but it shows exciting variations in leaf shape and patterning as well as flower colour, and some of these desirable characters bred into hardier forms would seem to be a very worthwhile objective, provided that is, that the identity of the parents is not swamped by a mass of hybrid offspring, something that has already occurred unwittingly in some cultivated collections.

It has been suggested by Richard Bailey (*The Cyclamen Society Journal* 15:46, 1991) analysing the results of the Society's Expedition to Rhodes and Karpathos in 1991 that: "Considering the results of this expedition it is possible to suggest that subsp. *rhodense* is as distinct from the other subspecies of *C. repandum* as it

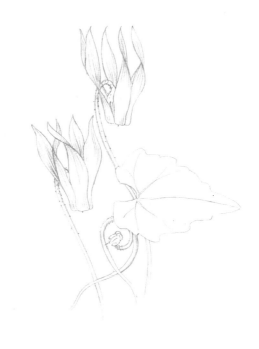

Cyclamen creticum.

is (and they are) from *C. balearicum* and *C. creticum*, and no less uniform than those species – in which case it would justify specific status." I am not quite sure what raising this subspecies to specific status would achieve. It clearly comes closest to subsp. *peloponnesiacum* subsp. *peloponnesiacum*, differing primarily in small details of the leaf shape and flower colour and, more importantly, in geography. As subspecies, the close relationship can be more readily evaluated, besides *C. balearicum*, *C. creticum* and *C. repandum* differ in rather more obvious details of leaf and flower and one must not forget that these species have plain, unmarked flowers, leaving aside albino forms of *C. repandum* subsp. *repandum*.

In summation, if the leaves are longer than broad and have a hastate pattern but no speckling and the flowers are deep pink then the plant is *C. repandum*. If the leaves are as broad as long or broader and speckled in part and the flowers white, pink or deep carmine with a deeper colour zone around the mouth then the plant is *C. peloponnesiacum*. Beware, however – cultivated plants will hybridize freely when grown in close proximity to one another, so expect hybrids with intermediate characters between the species and subspecies to show up. In some forms of subsp. *peloponnesiacum* the flowers are noticeably larger than the other subspecies.

Cyclamen peloponnesiacum is certainly less hardy than *C. repandum*, although it has been grown outside successfully by some growers. I have grown subsp. *rhodense* outside in a sheltered peat bed for more than six years in my former garden in Suffolk, although it has never self-sown but flowers each season. The leaves are readily damaged by slugs. Subsp. *peloponnesiacum* and subsp. *vividum* are less easy, I find: the typical form (subsp. *peloponnesiacum*) will succeed outdoors in similar conditions to subsp. *rhodense* but I have had no success with subsp. *vividum*. This latter, as has been discussed above, grows in the wild in far more open and sunnier situations and it may well require such conditions in cultivation. A few years ago I placed some three-year-old tubers in a sunny frame together with *C. graecum* and *C. libanoticum* to see whether they would fare better, but cannot report any great success; although the plants survived, they did not thrive.

Cyclamen repandum and its allies can be flowered from seed in their third season, but are generally rather slow to build up to a peak flowering performance. The elegant flowers and attractive perfume are incentives enough to want to grow and increase this species in the garden.

AWARDS
• *C. repandum* subsp. *rhodense* (as var. *rhodense*); now *C. peloponnesiacum* subsp. *rhodense*: A.M. 1965

Cyclamen creticum (Dörfler) Hildebr.
This charming and sweetly scented species was thought for a number of years to be endemic to the island of Crete, but in recent years it has been discovered on the neighbouring island of Karpathos to the east, where other Cretan 'endemics' such as *Paeonia clusii* have also been discovered. In spring it is one of the loveliest sites in the wooded vales and gorges of Crete, especially at the extreme western end of the island. A colony in full flower can bear many thousands of flowers, their scent wafting through the air over a considerable distance.

The plant was described in 1905 by Dörfler, not as a species but as a variety of *C. repandum*, but it was raised to species level the following year by Hildebrand in Germany.

The affinity of *C. creticum* to *C. peloponnesiacum* and *C. repandum* cannot be disputed, but in the wild the two species are readily distinguished. The leaves have an overall grey-green appearance, with a well-defined hastate pattern, speckling, or both. In form they are

42 *Cyclamen creticum* growing in a wooded gully near Spili, Crete.
43 *Cyclamen creticum* showing the typical long rather narrow heart-shaped leaves; W Crete, near Spili.

44 *Cyclamen creticum* growing in a rock crevice in woodland near Spili, Crete.
45 *Cyclamen creticum* photographed near Prina, E Crete, showing the common white form, forma *creticum,* and the scarcer pink-flowered forma *pallide-rosea*.

mostly rather narrowly heart-shaped with a pronounced acute apex. The flowers are plain white or very pale pink but without a darker zone around the mouth.

It used to be thought that *C. creticum* possessed only pure white flowers and indeed this is so for the vast majority of plants found in the wild. However, in some populations very pale pink-flowered forms can be found, though all-pink colonies do not occur to my knowledge. The presence of these pink-flowered forms (now distinguished as forma *pallide-rosea*) gave rise to speculation that *C. repandum* itself was to be found on Crete, but this does not appear to be so, despite its record by Sfikas ('Wild Flowers of Crete', 1987). *C. repandum* has flowers that are mid- to deep pink, often of a vivid deep magenta-pink hue. In *C. peloponnesiacum.* subsp. *rhodense* the flowers are white or pale pink but they have a pronounced pink rim around the mouth of the corolla. On the island of Karpathos, where *C. creticum* is rather rare, most plants bear pure white flowers, although in some a hint of palest pink can sometimes be recognized.

The leaves appear in the late autumn in the wild and are usually fully developed by late winter when plants start to come into flower. They are generally greyer than those of *C. repandum* and *C. peloponnesiacum*, with a more pointed apex and certainly with more muted markings.

One of the great delights of the Cretan spring is to come upon glades of *C. creticum* in full flower. In late March and April they are to be seen at their best, especially in woodland and along the banks of streams and rivulets where the scent, reminiscent of lily of the valley, wafts down the slopes. They relish the deep leaf litter among the trees and rocks. At higher altitudes plants can be sometimes seen in more open situations growing in rock crevices or even on screes, but nearly always in places that are shaded for at least part of the day.

It is perhaps surprising that this little gem is not more often cultivated, but the grander and more colourful forms of *C. peloponnesiacum* and *C. repandum*, which are generally more hardy species, tend to dominate in gardens, both in the open and under glass.

DESCRIPTION *Tubers* depressed-globose, to 4cm (1.6in) diameter, rarely larger, smooth, with a thin grey-brown skin, rooting from the centre of the lower surface. *Leaves* heart-shaped, generally rather narrowly so, the lamina 4.7–15.7cm (1.9–6.2in) long, 3.8–11.5cm (1.5–4.5in) wide, with a narrow and rather deep basal

sinus, the margin rather scalloped, somewhat lobed or with distant shallow to coarsely dentate teeth, the apex acute or subacute, grey-green, with generally a rather subdued hastate pattern in paler grey-green or grey, occasionally silvery-grey, with or without speckling, the leaf surface sometimes speckled all over but rarely without a defined hastate pattern, usually purplish-red beneath; petiole 11–25cm (4.3–9.9in) long, generally with a distinct elbow towards the base. *Pedicels* 11–23cm (4.3–9.1in) long, grey-green, often flushed with brown or purple, coiling from the top downwards as the young fruits begin to develop. *Flowers* appearing with the mature leaves, sweetly scented; corolla usually white, occasionally very pale pink or white flushed with pink; corolla-lobes 15–26mm (0.6–1in) long, narrow-elliptical, twisted, without auricles at the base. *Style* not protruding or only protruding for up to 1.5mm (0.06in).

HABITAT Woodland gullies, particularly beneath *Platanus orientalis*, but sometimes beneath pines or *Pistacia lentiscus* and other shrubs, or in olive groves, shrubby maquis, rock fissures, banks, along stream banks and in rocky gullies, often in shade or semi-shade, but at the higher altitudes sometimes in more exposed, sunnier positions; sea level to 1250m (4063ft) altitude, possibly as high as 1500m (4875ft) in the White Mountains (Lefka Ori) of western Crete.

DISTRIBUTION Crete, widely distributed, especially in the western half of the island but more locally common in the east; also central Karpathos where it is restricted to a few sites, particularly on the east side of the island; February–May. Map 1.
- **Forma *creticum***. *Flowers* pure white. Found throughout the range of the species.
- **Forma *pallide-roseum* Grey-Wilson**. *Flowers* very pale pink; found more or less throughout the range of the species in populations of the pure white form; commoner in the east of the range.

In the wild *C. creticum* grows in association with a variety of other plants including *Arisarum vulgare, Arum concinnatum, Geranium lucidum, Mercurialis annua, Orchis quadripunctata, Primula vulgaris* subsp. *vulgaris* (occasionally), *Ranunculus ficaria* s.l., *Ruscus aculeatus, Umbilicus erectus, Valeriana asarifolia*.

On Crete *C. creticum* exists at two chromosome levels 2n=20 and 2n=22. The latter condition is widespread on the island and must be assumed for the majority of populations of the species. However, in the region of the White Mountains (Lefka Ori) at the western end of the island most populations that have been investigated have 2n=20. The significance of this is not properly understood.

It is interesting to note that *C. graecum* on Crete shows morphological differences which are correlated with its distribution in the same region and a distinct variety, subsp. *candicum*, is found there. The situation is different in *C. creticum* because no observable morphological differences can be detected between the 2n=20 and 2n=22 chromosome populations of *C. creticum* and they are therefore treated as a single entity here.

The taxonomic separation of *C. creticum* is given added weight by the study of Professor Greilhuber from the University of Vienna (see *The Cyclamen Society Journal* 13,2:57, 1989) who examined the taxonomic relevance of the karyotype structure in the *C. repandum* group. Of the occurrence of the two chromosome numbers on Crete he states: "The question arises about the relationship of these karyotypes and the taxonomic bearing of this finding. Lepper (1975) was explicit about this: Cretan cyclamen with 2n=20 have the same distinct karyotypes as the plants from Rhodes (i.e. *C. peloponnesiacum* subsp. *rhodense*), and are morphologically much alike. He proposed to treat them as one species, so that on Crete two species of the subgenus are to be found, namely, *C. rhodium* with 2n=20 and *C. creticum* with 2n=22.

"This view is not supported by the present results. These metacentrics in *C. peloponnesiacum* subsp. *rhodense* and *C. repandum* from other localities are the same in shape. If there is a difference to be found in the plants from Rhodes, it is a slightly larger short arm of the nucleolar chromosome, while the corresponding short arm is minute in all Cretan plants. Moreover, although the karyotypes are not dramatically different in *C. repandum* and the Cretan plants with 2n=20, it is not difficult to match the karyograms in detail. On the other hand, the shape of the nucleolar chromosome common to both chromosomal groups on Crete indicates their distinctiveness from other taxa in the subgenus and argues for their close relatedness … which is so strongly indicated by their external characters. In conclusion there is no argument for lumping Cretan 2n=20 plants with the plants from Rhodes. Neither are their karyotypes the same, nor do they appear the same in external traits.

"It is of course a different problem that there is a cryptic, karyological differentiation within *C. creticum*. This requires further analysis, especially with regard to the exact structural rearrangements which led to different chromosome numbers in *C. creticum*, but also with regard to the detailed distribution of 2n=20 populations, the stability of variability of this karyotype in shape, the occurrence of hybrids and mixed populations, and the effectiveness of the different chromosome numbers as a barrier for gene flow. Then, the question of a taxonomic separation should become topical."

For general cultivation see under *C. peloponnesiacum, C. repandum* and *C. balearicum*; this species needs very

46 *Cyclamen coum* subsp. *coum* in cultivation.
47 *Cyclamen coum* subsp. *coum* glistening in morning dew; this form is typical of many of those found at the western end of the range of the species.
48 A form of *Cyclamen coum* subsp. *coum* with lustrous, unmarked foliage.

similar conditions. It greatly dislikes prolonged frosty weather but will succeed in the open garden in mild districts, given a sheltered niche. It has been known to hybridize with *C. repandum* in the open garden. Hybrids between it and *C. balearicum* have not been substantiated to date.

AWARDS
• *C. creticum* forma *creticum* A.M. 1972

SUBGENUS *GYROPHOEBE*

SERIES PUBIPEDIA
(*Cyclamen coum* Group)
C. alpinum; *C. coum*, *C. c.* subsp. *coum*, *C. c.* subsp. *coum* forma *albissimum* and forma *pseudoalbum*, *C. c.* subsp. *caucasicum*; *C. elegans*; *C. parviflorum*, *C. p.* subsp. *parviflorum* and subsp. *subalpinum*

This group is centred on Turkey and the Caucasus Mountains and contains the most widespread of all cyclamen species, *C. coum*, which is a popular and easy garden plant and one of the great delights of the winter months. In fact the four species are winter- or early spring-flowering in gardens, although the high-altitude *C. parviflorum* may be found much later in flower in the wild. The section is characterized by having relatively small, rather velvety tubers that root only from the middle of the base. The leaf-margins are not angled, although they may occasionally be somewhat lobed. The calyx-lobes are 3–5-veined in contrast to the previous subgenus in which they are 1-veined. The corollas are without auricles, but the corolla-lobes have a dark blotch at their base. In addition the anthers are aristate.

Cyclamen coum Miller
Cyclamen coum is one of the gems of winter and early spring. No garden should be without it, for during the harshest period of the year this hardy little plant reveals its cheerful little flowers as if to say "not so long now, spring is on its way". There the little flowers sit, pink or red or white, through the rotten days of winter to raise our spirits, resisting all that the weather can throw at them – wind, rain, snow and frost. The flowers can be buried in snow for several weeks only to appear after the

snow has melted unaffected by the event. During heavy frost the plants lie limp and sad, bejewelled by ice crystals, only to perk up after the frost has gone, delighted to have overcome the ordeal. Together with *C. hederifolium*, *C. coum* is the hardiest species in our gardens and the easiest to grow. Neither require the closet comfort of frame or alpine house to keep them growing and, once established, they will seed around freely. A large drift in full flower can be a most arresting site, especially mixed with the little tommies (*Crocus tommasinianus*) of late winter. *C. coum* is as easy as *C. hederifolium* but less robust and mixed colonies in the garden rarely work, as the latter will nearly always overwhelm the former. Whereas *C. hederifolium* can live for very many years and the tubers eventually become enormous, such is not the case with *C. coum* which is probably rather short-lived. However, because it so freely sows itself around it is often difficult to say just how old a particular tuber is and there appear to be few authenticated examples of them exceeding 20 years or so.

There is little I can say on the cultivation of this species that has not been said already. In the open garden it is equally at home in a sunny as well as a semi-shaded position, and mature plants will soon be surrounded by a host of seedlings. The leaves appear in the autumn and are generally fully developed by the onset of winter. Peer beneath the leaves and you will see the croziered buds, already with some colour, nestling in a cluster close to the 'heart' of the plant. They sit there for many weeks until they begin to expand, generally not coming into bloom before Christmas, although the odd flower or even the odd plant may do so. The related *C. elegans* (previously *C. coum* subsp. *elegans*), which is rarely grown in the open garden, differs in coming into flower in November.

Cyclamen coum in its many forms makes a very fine plant for growing in pans or pots. They can be grown as single specimens but can also be very effective when several plants are placed in large shallow pans. It is best to keep to a single form or cultivar per pan as they tend to look better when evenly matched. Few plants make such a bold display over so many weeks in the depths of winter and the alpine house can be a welcome refuge from the inclement winter weather when they come into flower. On warm winter days, when the oblique watery sunshine catches them, an occasional bumblebee may venture out to visit the flowers.

Many seedlings will flower in their second season and nearly all will have flowered by the time they are three years old, with the exception of *C. elegans* which seems to be a tardier plant and needs rather more careful nurturing if it is to succeed. It is certainly not so frost hardy and few growers risk their plants to the rigours of the open garden; it is by no means common in cultivation as either subsp. *coum* or subsp. *caucasicum*.

Reginald Farrer in the 'English Rock Garden' was not over-impressed by *C. coum* saying of it: "In autumn appear the small rounded leaves, of a sullen and leathery dark green, black and leaden in effect, and unlivened by the smallest touch of white. They are followed all the winter through by a profusion of little fat-looking flowers of a heavy magenta – though perhaps this judgement is not so harsh when they are seen bejewelling the January days with little glowing sparks of colour upon the dead earth. There is a much more attractive white form, but the shape of the small blossom always lacks the usual grace of the family … the sure absolute sign is the unrelieved darkness of the Soldanella-shaped foliage"; and of *C. hiemale* (now *C. coum* subsp. *coum*) he states: "is perhaps one of the plants that passes for *C. coum*; for its foliage is of the same size and shape, but blotted with white marblings instead of being uniformly dark."

Today our garden 'coums' are far more variable in leaf variations and flower colour and one wonders whether Farrer would have been more entranced by them. Clearly he was not wholly won over by this little gem. What is interesting is that today it is the great variations in leaf colouring and patterning which attract the gardener, as well as the range of flower colours, a range not available earlier in the 20th century. In the garden it is the mixtures of flower colours, the whites, pinks, roses, magentas and near crimsons that make these such appealing and desirable plants in the depths of winter, offset by a mat of attractive leaves, some plain, others variegated, some silvered or pewtered or variously variegated, that carry on long after the display of flowers is over.

Of all cyclamen species *C. coum* presents the taxonomist with the greatest problems of interpretation. It is an immensely variable plant over its range with numerous, often subtle, variations in flower and leaf size and colour. The main problem is the fact that there are no neat and clear discontinuations to allow easy separation within this species. "Why bother," one might say, but the fact is that to do nothing is just as unsatisfactory as producing a complex system of subdivisions. By the very act of describing species the taxonomist is imposing a system of classification upon a group of related species, in this case cyclamen (this problem could equally well apply to many thousands of different genera). The taxonomist soon learns that some species are easy to define, uniform and without obvious subdivisions, while others have an ordered and easily observable pattern of variations that can be neatly divided into subspecies or varieties. However, in some species a range of variation is observable but these variable characters are without an obvious pattern or, at least not one that is clear cut, and the species cannot be readily divided. Where the pattern of variability follows a more or less continuous sequence over the range of the species (for instance from west to east or from low to higher altitudes) then the species is said to be a cline. *C. coum* is one such cline.

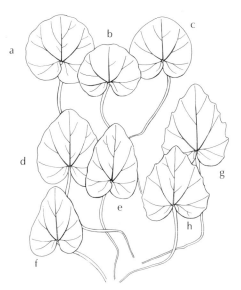

Typical cyclamen leaf shapes in: *C. coum* subsp. *coum* (a–c), subsp. *caucasicum* (d–f) and *C. elegans* (g–h).

Cyclamen coum is distributed along northern Turkey to the Caucasus Mountains, with southern outliers in south-east Turkey (Amanus Mountains) southwards to the Lebanon and northern Israel, as well as a western extension of its range into Bulgaria. It is by far the most common and widespread species in Turkey and the Caucasus region (see map 3).

The leaves range from kidney-shaped to rounded to heart-shaped, and the surface may be plain green or variously marbled with silver, white or grey-green. The farther east one goes the more the heart-shape lamina dominates, so that most Caucasian plants are like this. In addition, eastwards the leaf-margin becomes noticeably toothed. Along the Turkish Black Sea coast there is a more or less gradual transition between the rounded and heart-shaped leaf forms.

The flowers may be small and dumpy with short rounded petals or larger with more pointed petals and these latter become more common the farther east one travels. In addition the 'eyes' at the base of the petals are white in the west but become pink in the east of the range.

So from west to east (excluding the southern populations, southern Turkey to Israel) four prime trends can be observed:

1. To the west leaves rounded to kidney-shaped; to the east leaves heart-shaped.
2. To the west leaf-margin untoothed: to the east leaf-margin toothed or scalloped.
3. To the west petals short: to the east petals longer and rather less rounded.
4. To the west 'eyes' at base of petals white, occasionally pale pink; to the east 'eyes' variable but often pink, sometimes as deep pink as the rest of the petals.

Clines can be divided, although the divisions may sometimes seem somewhat arbitrary, but such divisions help in the understanding of the species. It also recognizes the fact that some 'species' have not reached a stage in evolution where the characters have become more or less fixed but they are still in a state of flux. We have to accept that while the majority of individuals fit comfortably within one taxon or another, some elements (groups or individual plants) may not comply with the proposed divisions. What do you call the non-conformists? There is no simple answer to this but perhaps *C. coum* sensu lato (in the wide sense) would suffice or *C. coum* intermediate form for those determined to apply a label at all costs. As far as subsp. *coum* and subsp. *caucasicum* are concerned they should be viewed as good, if somewhat 'untidy', subspecies.

But how does all this affect the gardener? In cultivation *C. coum*, in the broad sense, encompasses a wide range of forms, especially as regards flower colour and size and leaf patterning. These, fine and exciting as they are, confuse the picture rather than help, for many represent forms and hybrids that have arisen in cultivation. The gardener sees *C. coum* as a confusing mish-mash, but these plants are mostly derived from Turkish forms of the species with the more extreme eastern forms missing. Some of these come true from seed whereas others produce highly variable offspring; nearly all have considerable garden merit. To understand this complex it is necessary to look at *C. coum* in the wild.

49 *Cyclamen coum* subsp. *coum*: the rare small, matt-leaved form from the Crimea formerly described as *C. kusnetsovii*, but doubtfully distinct.

50 *Cyclamen coum* subsp. *caucasicum* in cultivation; an authenticated first-generation selection from material gathered in the Georgian Caucasus.
51 As Pl. **50** showing particularly clearly the heart-shaped leaves characteristic of the subspecies.

Cyclamen coum subsp. *caucasicum.*

SUBSPECIES OF *C. COUM*

Leaves rounded to kidney-shaped, as long as wide or wider than long; corolla-lobes 8–14mm (0.3–0.6in) long, with white, occasionally very pale pink 'eyes':   **subsp.** *coum*
Leaves heart-shaped, longer than broad; corolla-lobes 12–25mm (0.5–1in) long with pale to deep pink 'eyes', rarely white: **subsp.** *caucasicum*

C. coum **subsp.** *coum*. *Leaves* are kidney-shaped to rounded with an entire to somewhat crenate margin. *Flowers* tending to be on the small side with rounded petals 8–14mm (0.3–0.6in) long and the 'eyes' at the base of each petal are usually white.

This is the most usual manifestation of the species seen in gardens and it is very variable, especially in leaf size and patterning. However, the key characters are reasonably uniform.

HABITAT Subsp. *coum* inhabits woodland or forests, particularly of *Abies*, *Pinus brutia*, *Quercus* or *Fagus*, scrub (including *Rhododendron*) and plantations, particularly of hazel (*Corylus*), generally growing in shaded or semi-shaded places in deep leaf litter, amongst the roots of trees or in rocky gullies or on rock ledges, more rarely in open fields; December–April.

DISTRIBUTION Found in eastern Bulgaria, the Crimea, northern (generally on the northern slopes of the Pontus Mountains) and probably south-eastern Turkey (Amanus Mountains), western Syria, the Lebanon and northern Israel; possibly also the northern Caucasus Mountains, but this requires further investigation; from sea level to 2,150m (7,100ft) altitude. The rare Crimean plant has been described as *C. kusnetsovii* (by Kotov & Czernova in 1958) but, apart from being a generally squat plant with small mat leaves, it fits well within the circumscription of the subspecies. Map 3.

Over the years subspecies *coum* has gathered a host of synonyms and some of these persist in horticultural literature (especially in nursery catalogues) to this day; most important are *C. hyemale* (*hiemale*) and *C. orbiculatum*.
- **Forma** *coum*. *Flowers* pink to magenta, with dark markings at the base of each corolla-lobe. Throughout the range of the subspecies.
- **Forma** *albissimum* **Bailey** *et al*. *Flowers* pure white without any markings. Rare in the wild. Described from a plant found in south-eastern Turkey (between Topbogazi and Belen Amanus Mountains) in March 1980 by Manfred Koenen, and also by the Cyclamen Society in northern Israel. Plants derived from the Turkish source are cultivated as 'Tilebarn Fenella' and those from Israel as 'Golan Heights'.

- **Forma *pallidum* Grey-Wilson**. *Flowers* white or very pale pink with a deep marking at the base of each corolla-lobe. Occasionally found in the wild, almost throughout the range of the subspecies. Both this and the previous forma have been described from cultivated rather than wild material.

C. *coum* subsp. *caucasicum* (K. Koch) Schwarz. *Leaves* characteristically heart-shaped with an obvious crenate margin; they are normally marbled above but sometimes plain. *Flowers* tending to be rather larger with more elliptical petals, 12–20mm (0.5–0.8in) long, and the 'eyes' at the base of each petal are often pink, sometimes deep pink, though they can be white as in subsp. *coum*.

Subspecies *caucasicum* is far less often seen in gardens.

In the Caucasus a medley of different forms exist sometimes side by side but also as discreet colonies, and botanists working in the region have described many species in this complex, though few would uphold these today as distinct elements; the synonyms include *C. abschasicum*, *C. adzharicum*, *C. caucasicum*, *C. cicassicum*, *C. ibericum* and *C. vernum*.

HABITAT Similar to subsp. *coum*; (late November) December–April.

DISTRIBUTION Subspecies *caucasicum* occupies similar habitats to subsp. *coum*. It is distributed in north-eastern Turkey, the Caucasus and Trans-Caucasus; sea level to 1,350m (4,390ft) altitude, occasionally higher. Map 3.

In cultivation subsp. *caucasicum* is certainly less common than subsp. *coum* and is said to be both slower to flower from seed and rather less hardy. This latter fact may certainly be true of some forms of subsp. *caucasicum* but such statements are without any real evidence to prove them one way or the other. Reports that they are hardy or less hardy are meaningless unless they are backed up first by substantiated data and, more importantly, by confirmation that the plant or plants are correctly named in the first place. The fact that subsp. *caucasicum* is far rarer in the open garden, despite numerous introductions over the years, perhaps indicates that the subspecies is less hardy but this requires further investigation. Some of the forms are very handsome with their attractively marked leaves and with larger flowers than many an average subsp. *coum*; the various shades of pale and mid-rose are particularly appealing.

So far I have rather ignored the southern populations of *C. coum*, those found in south-eastern Turkey (Amanus Mountains in Hatay Province), western Syria, the Lebanon and northern Israel, included in subsp. *coum* avove. Strangely these are far more uniform in leaf and flower

52 *Cyclamen coum* in the Amanus Mountains of S Turkey; the southern forms of the species do not happily fit into either subsp. *coum* or subsp. *caucasicum* and require further investigation.

characters, plants having somewhat heart-shaped leaves and small flowers with rather short and rounded petals. One interesting feature that many plants show is a shallow scalloping of the leaf margin. Most have rather dark flowers, generally with white eyes though occasionally with pink. They are misfits for they do not conform neatly with the other subspecies: indeed they appear to bear characters from each (the small flowers of subsp. *coum*, the more heart-shaped leaves of subsp. *caucasicum*) but in none of these is the particular character as pronounced as it is in the relevant subspecies; a tricky dilemma for the taxonomist.

The southern 'coums' represent an isolated outlier sealed off from the far more extensive northern populations by the great dry expanses of the Anatolian Plateau. Evolution has treated them in a rather different way, but the populations do not appear to reveal any single character whereby they can be 'safely' separated from their brethren. Even in this southern area the various populations are often widely separated with stands in south-eastern Turkey (primarily the Amanus and Anti-Taurus region, with large colonies in the Dörtyol region), north-western Syria, the Lebanon and northern Israel. It grows in shrubby habitats, often beneath evergreen oaks, sometimes venturing out into rocky places or onto screes; growing in association with *C. pseudibericum* in several localities in southern Turkey, with *C. libanoticum* in the Lebanon and, in one locality, with *C. persicum* in Israel.

In Israel the prime colonies are to be found in the Golan Heights, on Mt Hermon a scattered colony on Mt Meron, where they grow above 1,000m (3,250ft) beneath trees. However, a more remote colony has been found some 20km (12 miles) further south on Mt Harashim at 850m (2763ft). This relict colony, consisting of only about 50 individuals, grows in a very exposed rocky habitat and marks the southernmost known limit of the distribution of the species. Interestingly, it is found at the southern locality in association with *C. persicum*.

These populations clearly require further study and analysis; they may well be treated as a variety or even varieties of *C. coum* in future accounts of the genus. Overall their characters can be described as follows:

Leaves ovate, rarely rounded, often with a somewhat scalloped margin and with a slightly notched apex. Flowers small and generally deep pink to magenta-pink, usually with pink eyes at the base of each corolla-lobe. Petals (6–)8–13mm long, rounded rather than elliptical (especially in population in Israel and the Lebanon), sometimes densely glandular on the surface but not consistently so. The presence or absence of glands on the corolla of *C. coum* has been entirely overlooked by researchers and may be of taxonomic interest. Previous classifications of the genus and the cladistic study of Anderberg (1993) have consistently shown the corolla to be glabrous, whereas in *C. cilicium*, *C. mirabile*, *C. intaminatum*, *C. cyprium* and *C. libanoticum*, they are clearly glandular. It is interesting that all these species are eastern rather than western Mediterranean in distribution.

AWARDS
* *C. coum* subsp. *coum* forma *coum*: A.M. 1956; F.C.C. 1975, A.G.M.

Cyclamen elegans Boiss. & Buhse

The status of this taxon has been uncertain for a number of years. This is primarily due to the fact that there was very little material of it about for a detailed analysis. Today, however, live material is available from various sources and the plant is far better known in cultivation than formerly. Live material dates primarily from the 1960s from wild gatherings made in northern Iran by Brian Mathew (Bowles Scholarship Memorial Expedition), Paul Furse and Jim Archibald. Floras and accounts of the time equated this plant with the eastern form of *Cyclamen coum*, subsp. *caucasicum*, another taxon which was rare in cultivation at the time.

The Iranian populations are very isolated from all the known localities of *C. coum*, which does not venture into Iran. Recent work by Chris Clennett (awaiting publication) shows quite clearly that the Iranian plant is distinct from *C. coum* and, as a result, he proposes reinstating the species, which was first described as long ago as 1860. I have no hesitation in following this thorough analysis.

A comparison of living material of *C. elegans* reveals it to be quite distinct from *C. coum*. Apart from the obvious differences in leaf and flower morphology, flowering time is quite distinct with all the cultivated plants (from whatever source) starting to bloom in late October and continuing through to early in the New Year, at about the time when *C. coum* is just coming into bloom. In the wild *C. elegans*, which is primarily a species of low altitude, can be found in bloom from December to March.

Morphological differences can be summed up as follows:
1. The leaves are markedly heart-shaped, often rather oblong-elliptical, and have a pronounced toothed margin that is often somewhat lobed or scalloped, (usually rather unevenly so); they are always marbled above, usually with an attractive narrow hastate pattern. In contrast to *C. coum* the prime lateral veins of the leaf-lamina run to the tips of the teeth or lobes, whereas in *C. coum* they meet the tiny indentations on the margin.

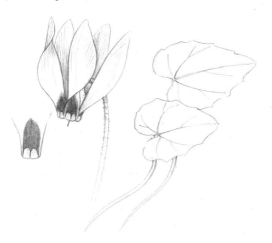

Cyclamen elegans.

53 *Cyclamen elegans* in cultivation.

54 *Cyclamen elegans* showing the typical heart-shaped leaves with a scalloped margin.
55 *Cyclamen elegans* showing the typical long, rather pointed petals.
56 Profile of *Cyclamen elegans* flowers showing the rather pointed petals with an elongated basal blotch and characteristic pink 'eyes'.
57 *Cyclamen elegans*: plant with pewtered leaves derived from BSBE 518.

2. The flowers are larger than those of *C. coum* with elliptical, pointed, petals 18–25mm (0.7–1in) long, and the 'eyes' are pale to deep pink.

In general effect this plant, as its name implies, has an elegant look and the leaves certainly appear to be longer and narrower than those of *C. coum*.

Clennett (to be published) also notes differences in the anthocyanin leaf pigments between *C. coum* and *C. elegans*, the shape of the anther papillae, the type and size of the epidermal trichomes, as well as slight differences in the shape of the style which is somewhat constricted behind the stigma in *C. coum*.

DESCRIPTION *Tubers* generally rather small, rarely exceeding 4cm (1.5in) across, rounded in outline and rather compressed with a smooth and velvety coat, rooting from the centre of the base only. *Leaves* appearing in the early autumn and more or less fully developed by flowering time, the lamina heart-shaped, 2.2–7cm (1–3in) long and 1.6–5.6cm (0.6–2.5in) wide, with scalloped margin, green, generally with a weak grey-green, occasionally silver, hastate pattern, or sometimes plain green, or pewter or silvery overall, pale to mid-purple or crimson and shiny beneath; petiole to 18cm (7in) long. *Pedicels* coiling from the top downwards as the fruits begin to develop. *Flowers* ranging in colour from pale to mid-pink, each petal with an elongated dark crimson-magenta, more or less M-shaped basal blotch with pale to deep pink 'eyes'; corolla-lobes 18–25mm (0.7–1in) long, elliptical, with a pointed (acute to subacute) apex, generally unscented or slightly scented.

HABITAT This reinstated species shares similar habitats with *C. coum*, although in the lush forests of the Elburz Mountains of northern Iran it can often be found growing on the lower mossy trunks and branches of trees; the broad-leaved forests of the region are dominated by oak (*Quercus*) *Parrotia* and *Zelkova*; November to January (–February).

DISTRIBUTION Confined to the region of northern Iran (Persia) bordering the Caspian Sea, primarily between Astara and Chalus; there are also unauthenticated reports of it growing further to the east in the vicinity of Gorgan, where the forests extend to the east of the Caspian Sea. Unlike *C. coum*, *C. elegans* is usually found only at quite low altitudes, rarely above 1000m (3250ft) and mostly below 450m (1460ft). This is a generally rather humid, almost subtropical region close to the influence of the Caspian Sea, where frost is rare and summer rainfall not unknown. Map 3.

CULTIVATION In cultivation this is a rare plant. In the 1960s plants were introduced into cultivation by several expeditions, including those of Paul and Polly Furse and Brian Mathew (Bowles Scholarship Memorial Expedition; including a fine silver-leaved form), Jim Archibald and Per Wendelbo, but the plant proved rather fickle in gardens and there are relatively few genuine plants around at the present time. It is certainly a less hardy plant and, unfortunately, it is rather reluctant to set much seed. Seedlings are fairly slow to reach flowering size and may not do so for three or four years (or more) from the time of germination. This is in marked contrast to *C. coum* (both subsp. *coum* and subsp. *caucasicum*) which can generally be relied upon to flower in the second season, sometimes even in the first. Interestingly, in cultivation, *C. elegans* comes into flower in late October or November, usually well in advance of *C. coum*; this helps prevent their crossing spontaneously in cultivation.

It is undoubtedly a very elegant plant, as its name suggests, with attractively twisted petals which have an elongated dark blotch at the base of each petal. Kath Dryden has several plants in her garden (under glass) originating from Paul Furse, Per Wendelbo and Jim Archibald collections. A particularly fine-leaved form with plenty of silver over the surface was collected by Brian Mathew on the Bowles Scholarship Botanical Expedition under BSBE 518; this is a rare plant today in cultivation and apparently difficult to increase, but well worth persevering with.

Cyclamen parviflorum Pobed.

Cyclamen parviflorum is the smallest and one of the least-known species in the genus and sadly not at all common in cultivation, although a number of growers succeed with it very well indeed. It is essentially a plant of high alpine slopes, often in the open, where it comes into flower in the spring as the snow melts. It is endemic to a relatively small region of the Pontus Mountains in north-eastern Turkey to the south and east of the Black Sea port of Trabzon, the best-known locality being the magnificent Zigana Pass region. At first glance it looks like a squat version of *C. coum* but the sweet scent and solid blotch at the base of the rather short corolla-lobes indicate otherwise.

This charming little plant is generally too small for the open garden but this is a little gem to cherish in the close confines of a pot, trough or raised bed where it should never be allowed to dry out. Some succeed with it outdoors in the corner of a peat bed and Brian Mathew tells me that his plants seed around. Regrettably I have had no such luck to date. In recent years there have been some exceptionally vigorous and floriferous plants exhibited at Alpine Garden Society Shows; plants like these are never found in the wild!

Plants start into growth in the autumn, although some do not appear above ground until well into winter. Under glass the first flower buds can often be seen before Christmas, although few open until the New Year. Watering is rather tricky for pot-grown specimens; too much water and the small tubers may start to rot; too little and they may desiccate. On the whole avoid watering during muggy misty weather as this only invites botrytis to attack the plants. A breezy atmosphere seems to suit them well and the installation of a circulatory fan in a glasshouse may well have beneficial results. However, its chief enemy is summer drought, for in its native habitats it probably never really dries out. Pot-grown plants are probably best removed to a cool, shady place during their summer dormant period and kept just moist, rather the same treatment as for *C. purpurascens*. Planting the tubers quite deep (say 5–10cm/2–4in) can help prevent desiccation and plants do not seem to suffer from such treatment; , they certainly seem to relish such deep burial when planted in troughs or on raised beds in the open garden. There is little doubt that *C. parviflorum* is as hardy as any cyclamen and losses as a result of severe winter cold seem unlikely; losses as a result of winter desiccation seem the more probable.

It has been argued by some authorities that *C. parviflorum* would be better treated as a high-altitude ecotype of *C. coum* and accorded varietal or subspecific rank. I do not agree with this in any way: apart from its small stature and the characters of the flowers themselves, and the

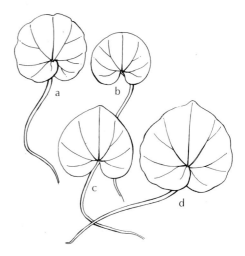

Cyclamen parviflorum leaves: subsp. *parviflorum* (a–b); subsp. *subalpinum* (c–d).

consistently plain green leaves, this is a high-altitude species descending as low as 1200m (3,900ft) in several localities in the Pontus Mountains where it can be found occasionally in close association with *C. coum* subsp. *coum*, but the two do not hybridize and no intermediates have ever been found, a strong indicator that these are two mutually incompatible, yet related, species. In fact the general affinities of *C. parviflorum* appear to be closer to the south-western Turkish *C. alpinum*. In a genus in which a number of species are naturally very variable, then any differences which prove to be consistent and which, furthermore, can be demonstrated readily in a diagnostic key, are best regarded as belonging to distinct species.

The tiny flowers need to be looked at closely to appreciate their real beauty. The petals can be blunt or rather triangular and pointed, but they are often short and stubby. The petals may be strongly reflexed so as to be erect or they may spread outwards like the spokes of a propeller in much the same manner as *C. alpinum*. The blotch at the base of each petal is 'solid' as it is in *C. alpinum*; looked at closely, however, it often consists not of a solid block of colour but of a series of close dark, more or less parallel, lines, some of which are linked.

Surprisingly, although this species was not described until 1946, there is a sheet at the Kew Herbarium marked Gay 1828, linked with two collections made later in the century by Sintenis (nos. 81 and 5451; Gumushane) which are clearly *C. parviflorum*. They appear to have been overlooked and were filed under *C. coum* subsp. *coum*. However, Gay clearly recognized his plant as a separate species.

DESCRIPTION *Tubers* small, globose to depressed-globose, generally not more than 3cm (1.2in) diameter when mature, but occasionally up to 4cm (1.6in), slightly flattened above, smooth, brown and velvety when mature, rooting from the centre of the base. *Leaves* rounded to kidney-shaped, very rarely more or less heart-shaped, mostly 1.4–4.1cm (0.5–1.6in) long, 1.5–4.5cm (0.6–1.8in) wide, occasionally up to 5.6cm (2.2in) long and 6.8cm (2.7in) wide, with a shallow and rather narrow sinus at the base, with the basal lobes converging or somewhat overlapping, the margin untoothed to slightly scalloped, deep plain green above, often slightly shiny, unmarked, usually purplish or carmine-purple beneath; petioles elbowed in the lower half, 2.4–9cm (0.9–3.5in) long, green or purplish-brown. *Pedicels* elbowed in the middle or in the lower half, 2.8–12cm (1.1–4.7in) long, green or purplish-brown, coiling from the top downwards as the young fruits develop. *Flowers* borne close to the ground among or just above the mature foliage, sweetly violet-scented; corolla pale to deep lavender-pink, reddish-purple,

58 *Cyclamen parviflorum* subsp. *parviflorum* in cultivation.
59 *Cyclamen parviflorum* subsp. *parviflorum* showing the typical plain, round leaves, and the flowers with their strongly reflexed petals.
60 Another view of *Cyclamen parviflorum* subsp. *parviflorum*.

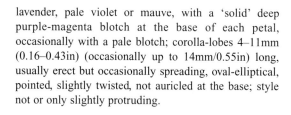

Cyclamen parviflorum subsp. *parviflorum*.

Cyclamen parviflorum subsp. *subalpinum*.

lavender, pale violet or mauve, with a 'solid' deep purple-magenta blotch at the base of each petal, occasionally with a pale blotch; corolla-lobes 4–11mm (0.16–0.43in) (occasionally up to 14mm/0.55in) long, usually erect but occasionally spreading, oval-elliptical, pointed, slightly twisted, not auricled at the base; style not or only slightly protruding.

Note: Interestingly, nectar can often be seen within the corolla bowl, generally represented as five discreet sticky blobs to the outside of the stamens, and these are readily seen with a x10 hand lens. This is in marked contrast to other species in which nectar is generally very difficult to detect at all!

HABITAT *Cyclamen parviflorum* is confined to a relatively small region of north-eastern Turkey where it inhabits grassy slopes (alpine turf), rocky places, gullies, river gravels and fir forests (*Picea orientalis*), often amongst tree roots, though

occasionally on mossy branches, sometimes growing below *Rhododendron luteum*, where it is often found in dark humusy and mossy soils, occasionally in snow hollows. At the higher altitudinal range it is to be found amongst shrubs such as *Rhododendron* and *Vaccinium* or in open alpine meadows, even snow hollows; April to early July.

DISTRIBUTION Confined to a limited region of the Pontus Mountains in north-eastern Turkey (from Giresun to Rize provinces), primarily between the Zigana Pass area and Ikizdere; 1,200 and 2,260m (7,400ft) altitude. At the higher altitudinal range plants may be buried in deep snow during the winter and they will not come into flower until late spring or even early summer, once the snow has melted. Map 3.

CULTIVATION Two 'forms' of *C. parviflorum* exist in cultivation: the most frequently seen has very small flowers with markedly reflexed blunt corolla-lobes while the second has altogether larger flowers with spreading, more pointed, corolla-lobes, the general appearance being that of a small-flowered *C. alpinum*. Both forms have sweetly scented flowers and plain, deep green leaves. Initially I thought that these variations had little meaning but, having studied the available herbarium material, photographs and various reports of field observations, I concede that, whereas the former is exclusively a plant of the higher altitudes, the latter is found primarily at lower altitudes. These differences are here distinguished as subspecies: subsp. *parviflorum* having very small flowers with strongly reflexed corolla-lobes only 4–8mm (0.16–0.31in) long, whereas subsp. *subalpinum* has larger flowers with spreading and more twisted corolla-lobes 8–11(–14)mm (0.31–0.43(–0.55)in) long.

SUBSPECIES OF *C. PARVIFLORUM*
Corolla-lobes small and erect, 4–8mm (0.16–0.31in) long; leaf-lamina rarely more than 2.5cm (1in) wide, not apiculate: **subsp.** *parviflorum*
Corolla-lobes larger and spreading horizontally, 8–11(–14)mm (0.31–0.43(–0.55)in) long; leaf-lamina

61 *Cyclamen parviflorum* subsp. *subalpinum*, showing the somewhat more heart-shaped leaves and the typical propeller-shaped flowers.

up to 6.8cm (2.7in) across, often slightly apiculate: **subsp. *subalpinum***

Subsp. *parviflorum*. At higher elevations (up to 2,400m/7,900ft), plants are often very small with the leaves seldom exceeding 2.5cm (1in) across and often smaller. In the winter the plants will be under a thick blanket of snow and this may not melt off the higher colonies until at least the late spring so that plants may sometimes be found still in flower well into July. I passed over the Zigana Pass in early February 1971 close to several well-known sites of this species and the whole area was deep in snow, judged to be well over a metre deep on average and banked up high on either side of the road by snow ploughs. High-elevation colonies are often found in open situations, especially amongst the fibrous roots of the turf. In contrast, in cultivation they rarely stay in flower longer than early April, generally coming into bloom in February, or earlier. At lower altitudes the species is most closely associated with more densely shaded sites, especially beneath firs and rhododendrons where, presumably, it can avoid the direct hot sunshine of the summer months. Despite this the region as a whole is often misty, the mist drawn up from the humid slopes close to the shores of the Black Sea.

In the wild *C. parviflorum* grows in association with an interesting array of different species. These include: *Ajuga reptans*, *Anemone blanda*, *Bellis perennis*, *Crocus scharojanii* and *C. vallicola* (both autumn-flowering), *Cyclamen coum* (occasionally at the lower altitudes), *Daphne glomerata*, *Gentiana pyrenaica*, *Potentilla micrantha*, *Primula vulgaris* subsp. *vulgaris*, *Sedum reflexum*, *S. spurium*, *Veronica chamaedrys*, *Viola altaica* and many other subalpine species.

Cyclamen parviflorum generally grows in moist sandy, peaty or humusy soils in the wild, often in habitats with a rather low light intensity. Although quite a few people have studied plants in the wild and found that, at the lower limits of its range at least, it often grows in association with *C. coum*, flowering at the same time, no natural hybrid has ever been recorded. This fact, and the fact that these two can be readily told apart at a glance in the field is, in my view, strong and convincing evidence that the two are quite distinct species and there should be no question of uniting them. Even if natural hybrids were to be found in the wild I still see no reason for uniting them.

Subsp. *subalpinum* (Grey-Wilson) Grey-Wilson. This less well-known subspecies may often have larger leaves and the tubers may develop long floral trunks but this requires further close observation in the field; in addition the tubers can become quite large, to 6cm (2.3in), occasionally

62 *Cyclamen parviflorum* subsp. *subalpinum*: a superbly grown, multi-flowered pan representing a single plant.

more, in diameter, whereas those of subsp. *parviflorum* are seldom more than 3cm (1.2in) across. These latter characteristics may be reflected in habitat differences: subsp. *parviflorum* is most frequently a plant of more open habitats such as turf or gullies or around low shrubs such as *Daphne glomerata*, whereas subsp. *subalpinum* inhabits lower altitude woodland (c.(800–)1200–1700m/(2600–)3900–5600ft), often growing in the dense shade of firs or rhododendrons in deep leaf litter.

AWARDS TO *C. parviflorum*
- P.C. 1972 (to var. *subalpinum*); A.M. 1985 (to var. *parviflorum*)

Cyclamen alpinum hort. Dammann ex Sprenger Syn. *C. trochopteranthum* Schwarz

This charming little cyclamen with its characteristic whirligig flowers was quite rare in cultivation at one time but today it is far better known and quite widely available. The specific name of the plant comes from the Greek words for windmill and flower, indicating the propeller-like arrangement of the corolla which is almost a unique feature in the genus.

The whirligig arrangement of the corolla is not unique to the genus as was once thought, for one of the varieties of *C. parviflorum* (var. *subalpinum*) has a similar arrangement. In fact the two species are very closely related, sharing rather similar tubers and sweetly scented flowers in which the blotch at the base of each petal appears to be 'solid'. However, the two cannot be confused: *C. alpinum* is an altogether larger plant with marbled leaves which hails from generally lower altitudes in south-western Turkey, whereas *C. parviflorum* is a

small plant with plain leaves and, in its most characteristic form (var. *parviflorum*) the petals are reflexed rather than spreading. *C. parviflorum* is a high-altitude plant confined to the damper regions of north-eastern Turkey.

Cyclamen alpinum is usually compared with *C. coum* and indeed the two species do form a close alliance, together with *C. parviflorum*. The leaves of *C. alpinum* look more like those of *C. mirabile* in general outline and the scalloping of the margin. the flowers, with their typical propeller-shaped (horizontal and twisted) petals and with a solid basal blotch at the base of each lobe, are very distinctive. In addition, the apex of the petals is more markedly toothed than in *C. coum*, although this is not a constant and reliable feature.

As with several other Turkish species *C. alpinum* has had a rather chequered history in cultivation and indeed its taxonomic position was muddled for many years because of a lack of good authenticated material. In brief the history of this plant can be summarized as follows:

In 1892 Karl Sprenger in Germany received a tuber of a cyclamen from Turkey via the firm of Dammann & Co. and named *C. alpinum*, being described as "The dwarfest and perhaps the most beautiful of all known cyclamen species, with small, kidney-shaped, white-patterned leaves and beautiful flowers, crimson with a basal blotch which is nearly black. It has great beauty. The most rewarding and floriferous of all cyclamen. It grows by the eternal snow in the highest mountains of Asia Minor and is therefore probably completely hardy. Flowers in the spring". Further enquiries revealed that "*Cyclamen alpinum*, named by us [Dammann & Co. sic], is probably nothing but a form of *Cyclamen coum*. It grows in the Cilician Taurus near the snow line, has some red flowers and some white ones and is low-growing". No doubt realising that it was a new species, Sprenger gave it a brief mention in *Gartenflora* (1892:526) under the name *C. alpinum*.

Hildebrand was able to observe the living plants he obtained from Dammann & Co. According to Hildebrand these plants did indeed show the characteristics described and listed by Dammann & Co., but also revealed other features that only a thorough examination of the living plant could reveal. "This," says Hildebrand (1898), "led to the recognition of *Cyclamen alpinum* as a new species,

63 *Cyclamen alpinum* (formerly *C. trochopteranthum*) photographed in the wild in SW Turkey.
64 *Cyclamen alpinum* in cultivation, a two-year-old plant.
65 *Cyclamen alpinum*; a fine form cultivated at Tile Barn Nursery.
66 *Cyclamen alpinum*; flower detail showing the characteristic propeller-shaped corolla with a solid blotch at the base of each petal.

which has only the leaves in common with *C. cilicium* and which is specifically different from *Cyclamen coum* and *ibericum* because of the stigma and the basal blotch of the corolla lobes."

Hildebrand follows with a full and detailed description of the plant in question. This can be summarized briefly as follows:

1. Tubers depressed, covered with stellate hairs, rooting only from the centre of the base.
2. Leaves similar to those of *C. cilicium* (drawing comparing with *C. alpinum*) produced only from the centre of the upper surface, appearing in the autumn before the flowers, with creeping petioles.
3. Leaf-lamina kidney-shaped, apex usually rounded, remaining very small on some individuals, the upper surface dark green with a zone of irregular silver blotches or with a continuous silver zone; lower surface carmine.
4. Flowers appearing after the snowmelt in the spring.
5. Calyx lobes ovate-lanceolate with five parallel veins, sometimes slightly branched.
6. Corolla bright carmine, the tube semi-globose, very constricted at the mouth, the lobes without auricles, ovate-lanceolate twisting at right angles in the fully open flowers and spreading out horizontally, with a solid dark black-red basal blotch.
7. Style red at tip, with a flat papillous stigma, without a collar of papillae.

Detailed drawings accompany the description with comparisons of the prime features with *C. coum* (incl. *C. ibericum* = *C. coum* subsp. *caucasicum*). These clearly show the propeller-shaped corolla, the leaf and tuber details and the other characteristics described.

There is no doubt that *C. alpinum* as described by Hildebrand is one and the same species as the plant we know today as *C. trochopteranthum* (described by Otto Schwarz in 1975). The main question outstanding remains: is Hildebrand's *C. alpinum* the same as that of Dammann & Co. and indeed Carl Sprenger's *C. alpinum*? With the publication of a thorough and accurate translation of Hildebrand's 'Die gattung Cyclamen' by Erna Frank for the Cyclamen Society in 1999, it has been possible to analyse the information in detail.

In my opinion they are all one and the same thing. Having said this, certain points need qualifying.

First, Dammann & Co.'s original brief description of *C. alpinum* reasonably describes the species, as does the geographical location.

Second, remarks stating that plants sold by Dammann & Co. as *C. alpinum* "did not seem to be anything other than a dwarf *Cyclamen cilicium*". In fact these plants can be dismissed as a red herring: they were received as a separate consignment (probably also from the Cilician Taurus) from

Cyclamen alpinum.

Whitall in Smyrna in 1892 and sent to various commercial nurseries in Europe.

Third, Hildebrand clearly states that, although the leaves of *C. alpinum* resemble those of *C. cilicium* (which they do!) it differs in many other respects including flowering time, corolla details and so on, which he describes in detail.

Fourth, early confusion between *C. alpinum* and *C. coum* sensu lato is understandable. The two species are frequently confused today by the non-experts. In fact *C. coum* is not recorded from the region in question, which makes it all the more certain that the original plants imported were in fact a distinct species.

Logically one has to ask what other species this could possibly be confused with from the southern and south-western regions of Turkey. The answer is none. *Cyclamen cilicium*, *C. mirabile* and *C. intaminatum* are all autumn-flowering and have a very different flower shape. *C. coum* is found well to the east and Hildebrand makes it quite clear that it is distinct from *C. alpinum*.

Confusion over the true identity of *C. alpinum* was confounded when, shortly after being fully described, the plant disappeared from cultivation and, worse still, Hildebrand's dried specimens were destroyed, leaving future generations in some doubt about the species. Here matters remained for a number of years until 1956 when Peter Davis and Oleg Polunin collected live material of a cyclamen in south-west Turkey, under the numbers *Davis* 25368 and 25579. When this eventually flowered it was seen to be distinct and at once assumed to be Sprenger's long-lost *C. alpinum*, but doubts remained in some minds. For a while the name could neither be confirmed nor satisfactorily rejected. For this reason Otto Schwarz in 1975 (*Feddes Repert. Sp. Nov.* 86:493) described the Davis and Polunin plant as a new species, giving it the epithet *trochopteranthum* (literally meaning propeller-shaped flowers).

However, Otto Schwarz was not at all sure how to treat Sprenger's original plant (the true *C. alpinum*!). In 1938 he included it under *C. vernum* Sweet as var. *hiemale* forma *alpinum*, but changed his mind in 1955 when he made it a variety of *C. coum* (*C. coum* var. *alpinum*). Later he was convinced that it was no more than one of the many variable forms of *C. coum*.

In addition, in 1959 Doris Saunders described the same Davis and Polunin plant, now well-established in cultivation, as *C. coum* var. *alpinum*, assuming it to be different from Sprenger's *C. alpinum*!

As already stated, with the translation into English of Hildebrand's *Die Gattung Cyclamen* it has been possible to study Hildebrand's description and remarks concerning *C. alpinum* in great detail. It is abundantly clear to any who ponder over that work (both considering the written words and the clear line drawings) that the species is fully and accurately recorded. What is more important is the fact that this accords perfectly satisfactorily with the plant we know today under the name *C. trochopteranthum*. I think that it would be hard to argue against the re-adoption of the name *C. alpinum* and I have no hesitation in doing so. Under the rules of priority therefore *C. trochopteranthum* has to be rejected as a synonym and *C. alpinum* Dammann ex Sprenger reinstated. It is perfectly true that the epithet *alpinum* caused a great deal of confusion in the past, especially amongst gardeners. This stems mainly from the use of the same epithet by Turrill in 1963 informally applied to *C. cilicium* (as *C. cilicium* var. '*alpinum*'). In order to avoid further confusion Desmond Meikle formally described the variety as var. *intaminatum* in 1978; the plant we know today as *C. intaminatum*. In fact *C. alpinum*, and *alpinum* as applied to *C. cilicium*, were never stated to be the same and indeed they represent different taxa, so the confusion was hard to understand.

If *C. alpinum* and *C. trochopteranthum* are not the same species then the question must be asked "What is *C. alpinum*?" We know for a fact that it is a spring-flowering species (both Sprenger and Hildebrand say so) so it cannot be *C. cilicium*; although the leaves are said to be similar, Hildebrand clearly states that it is a distinct species. Could it be a form of *C. coum*: this seems highly unlikely and Hildebrand, and to some extent Sprenger, stress the differences (both in the main text and in the identification key presented by Hildebrand). The only other species from the general region are *C. hederifolium*, *C. intaminatum*, *C. mirabile*, *C. graecum* subsp. *anatolicum* and *C. persicum*. Of these only the last is spring-flowering and was well known to both authors and very unlikely to be confused with *C. alpinum*. This leaves only one other possibility and that is that *C. alpinum* represents a distinct species which we do not know of in cultivation today. The chances of such a species

remaining unrevealed in southern Turkey today are remote. Despite the fact that the region is a large one, it is well explored, scoured by botanists, plant hunters and numerous local gatherers over the past 30 or more years. On the other hand, the chances of it being identical to *C. trochopteranthum* are extremely high and the arguments in favour of this view are very persuasive.

One point remains outstanding and that is typification of the name *C. alpinum*. With the loss of Hildebrand's material there is no actual type herbarium specimen. The name can, however, be neotypified easily on the accurate drawings in Hildebrand's *Cyclamen* monograph and I do so here accordingly: *Cyclamen alpinum* hort. Dammann ex Sprenger in *Gartenflora* 41: 526 (1892). Neotype: Taf. III, figs 45–63 in Hildebrand *Die gattung Cyclamen* L. Jena 1898.

Interestingly, Hildebrand (1898) states that *C. alpinum* has unscented flowers. Whereas most forms in cultivation today have sweetly scented flowers, I do have a form that is unscented. On the other hand Hildebrand also clearly states that that most sweetly scented of all cyclamen, *C. cyprium*, is also unscented, so perhaps his olfactory system was not as keen as it might have been.

On another point, Hildebrand also describes in detail small-leaved forms of *C. alpinum*, something that the Cyclamen Society has been investigating in the wild in recent years. "Some plants distinguish themselves by having only exceedingly small leaves which sometimes do not reach more than 15mm (0.6in) in length and 18mm (0.7in) in width …". Sprenger seems to have been looking at such small-leaved specimens when he called *Cyclamen alpinum* the species "with the smallest leaves and the dwarfest species of all." (Both *C. intaminatum* and *C. parviflorum* were unknown at the time!) Such small-leaved specimens are well known in cultivation and when selfed keep their dwarf characteristics. They appear to be ecotypes from the upper altitudinal range of the species. This fits in well with Hildebrand's comments that the plants (from Dammann & Co.) had originated high up in the Cilician Taurus. In fact he does not describe the larger-leaved variants found at much lower altitudes and well known today.

Cyclamen alpinum has been collected on a number of occasions in recent years both living and as dried (herbarium) material. These collections have shown the species to be more widespread in south-western Turkey than was originally supposed. Living material has certainly also shown the species to be far more variable, especially in the overall size of the plants as well as flower size and colour, and in its various forms it is certainly a very desirable plant to have in any collection.

Recent research in the wild by the Cyclamen Society has shown that *C. alpinum* is locally abundant in the wild in an area at the most some 9,000 square miles (23,000 square kilometeres) in extent. It has an astonishing

67 *Cyclamen alpinum* forma *leucanthum* cultivated by Rod and Jane Leeds; the white-flowered form still bears a dark blotch at the base of each petal.

altitudinal range, growing in some places right next to the Mediterranean Sea but in others high up in the mountains where it is affected by the vigours of winter: Brian Mathew reports that in some of the higher elevations (at 1,400m (4,600ft) on the Kuraova Pass) the tubers were "actually frozen into the soil" (see *Cyclamen Society Journal* 24(1): 13, 2000). This suggests that the species is probably far hardier than formerly supposed and some of the high-altitude selections and their progeny may well prove to be good hardy garden plants in due course. In addition he notes that the flower shape was not always the standard propeller characteristic of the species, some being more like those of *C. coum* or even *C. elegans*, while a few noted in the wild had petals that drooped downwards below the calyx, a phenomenon noted in other species e.g. *C. hederifolium* and *C. repandum*.

DESCRIPTION *Tubers* depressed-globose, to 5cm (2in) diameter, brown, smooth and velvety when mature, rooting from the centre of the base. *Leaves* generally somewhat longer than wide, the lamina oval to broadly heart-shaped, 1.2–9cm (1.5–3.5in) long, 1–9.2cm (0.4–3.75in) wide, with a narrow and shallow basal sinus with the basal lobes usually converging or slightly overlapping, the margin toothed to slightly scalloped, deep dull green above and with a narrow to broad hastate pattern in grey, grey-green, silver or cream, and generally with spots or splashes of similar colour towards the margin, sometimes more or less pewter overall, purple or crimson beneath; petiole elbowed in the lower half, often close to the base, 4.4–14.5cm (1.7–5.7in) long, usually purplish-brown. *Pedicels* elbowed in the middle or lower half, 7–12cm (2.8–4.7in) long, greenish or purplish-brown, coiling from the top downwards as the young fruits develop. *Flowers* borne with the semi-mature or mature leaves, sweetly primrose scented; corolla pale to deep pink, rose-pink or deep carmine-purple, rarely white, with a solid deep purple-magenta blotch at the base of each petal; corolla-lobes spreading out almost horizontally, not erect when reflexed, strongly twisted through 90°, oval, apiculate, 9–14mm (0.35–0.6in) long, slightly to moderately toothed especially towards the pointed apex; style not or only slightly protruding.

HABITAT Coniferous forest (*Cedrus libani*, *Juniperus excelsa* or *Pinus brutia*) or deciduous woodland, particularly with *Liquidambar orientalis*, or in scrub (*Crataegus*, *Prunus* and *Quercus*), often amongst the roots of trees, or rocky slopes, often in the shade of bushes, sometimes in gullies or along stream beds, at the upper altitudinal range in more open places in screes amongst conifers; (sea level–)400–1670m (1300–5450ft) altitude.

DISTRIBUTION Confined to south-western Anatolia, Turkey, from the Marmaris-Datça Peninsula eastwards to Dedegöl mountains (east of Lake Eğirdir), north as far as Denizli, often as fragmented and local colonies, sometimes in abundance; January–April. Map 3.

CULTIVATION When this species first came into cultivation in the 1950s it was thought to be rather uniform with little variation. However, in the past decade or so more recent introductions (especially the mass illegal imports of the 1980s) have shown *C. alpinum* to be far more variable in overall size, the degree of toothing of both leaves and flowers and above all in flower size and colour. Some forms have rather small leaves but large flowers, whereas others may have fewer and larger leaves and flowers in a range of colours from pale pink to deep pink, or carmine-pink. Leaf patterning is also variable and the differences are primarily in the amount and intensity of the marbling which is nearly always rather blotchy, or with a broad hastate pattern with a marginal blotched zone; the central green area, often shaped like a Christmas tree, varies greatly in size from one plant to another and may only occupy the very centre of the leaf blade but, at the other extreme, it may extend to over half the surface area. Some of the leaf forms available today are very beautiful, including some that are wholly pewtered.

In cultivation most plants are to be seen grown in pots or planted out in frames; it is rather rarely seen flourishing in the open garden. A pan-full in flower is an arresting sight, especially where several plants are grown together. In general the species dislikes wild fluctuations in moisture and temperature and these should be avoided if possible. Planting in large pans or pots helps avoid such extremes which, in fact, few cyclamen will tolerate for long.

Although reasonably hardy, *C. alpinum* is less often seen in the open garden that it deserves. Now there is far

68 *Cyclamen pseudibericum* in the Amanus Mountains, Southern Turkey.

more material of this species about it is to be hoped that gardeners will be more adventurous with it. It should thrive in places in which *C. cilicium* or *C. coum* flourish. During frosty weather the foliage becomes dark and limp and looks as though it may have been killed, but the moment temperatures rise it regains its former splendour. Having said this, though, pot-grown plants are best protected from severe winter weather, for both foliage and flowers can be damaged during prolonged freezing and, if the compost is kept too moist, the tubers may perish.

Seedlings generally flower in their third season. The flowers have one of the most pleasing fragrances of any cyclamen, reminiscent of violets, or is it primroses?

It is clear from the original material of *C. alpinum* cultivated by Dammann & Co. in Germany that a white-flowered plant was known, imported from Turkey with the normal-coloured forms. This was described by Sprenger in *Gartenflora* of 1892 (the same year that *C. alpinum* was described), being called var. *album*. In recent years other white-flowered plants have been seen in the wild, as well as those turning up spontaneously in cultivation (see p.148). To conform with the other coloured variants found in the wild the rank of forma would be more appropriate for this taxon. The white-flowered forms are not true albinos and possess the usual dark magenta, almost black, blotch at the base of each petal lobe. They are referable to forma *leucanthum*.

AWARDS
• P.C. 1959, 1962; A.M. 1962

SERIES PSEUDIBERICUM
(*C. pseudibericum*, *C. p.* forma *roseum*)

Cyclamen pseudibericum Hildebrand

Cyclamen pseudibericum is one of the most beautiful, indeed one of the showiest, of the early spring-flowering species and is a must in any collection, even thriving outdoors in some gardens. With its bold, relatively large, flowers of deep purple-magenta borne above a mass of deep green leaves, banded and marked with grey-green or creamy-white above, it makes an arresting sight in full flower. Add to this a powerful and sweet fragrance and a long flowering season, then it is not surprising that quite a few growers list it in their top three favourite species.

The species has a rather strange and chequered history. It was first described by the German botanist Hildebrand in Freiberg in 1901. Hildebrand had been sent flowering material by the Dutch bulb firm of van Tubergen, who had in their turn received a consignment of 'bulbs' from Turkey which were said to have originated in Smyrna (now Izmir). Although Hildebrand clearly thought that it was a distinct species, doubts were expressed as to its origin and Otto Schwarz (*Gartenflora* 1938:14) sank it into synonymy under *C. libanoticum* and then a few years later Schwarz (*Feddes Repert. Sp. Nov.* 58:256, 1955) even went so far as to suggest that the plant had arisen in cultivation as a hybrid. Glasau (*Planta* 30:523, 1939) was of the opinion that it represented a subspecies of *C. libanoticum* and described it as such. Incidentally, the original stock was all said to have originated from a single tuber at van Tubergens.

Here the situation remained until 1952 when the Turkish botanist Dr Demiriz rediscovered it on Duldul Dağ in the Amanus Mountains of southern Turkey. In 1957 Peter Davis in the company of Oleg Polunin collected extensively in south-eastern Turkey. Amongst their many exciting finds was a cyclamen, collected under Davis number 26117, and this turned out to be the mysterious *C. pseudibericum*, proving beyond doubt that Hildebrand was correct in his original diagnosis. Interestingly, Schwarz accepted these findings and in his monograph of the genus produced in 1964 for he formally recognizes *C. pseudibericum* as a species in its own right.

Davis and Polunin had found the plant in the vicinity of Haruniya in the Amanus Mountains where it was growing in open oak woodland together with another fascinating Turkish endemic, *Helleborus vesicarius*. This region is in fact not very far from the Syrian border, as had been originally reported! Today the region is fairly accessible (political troubles permitting) and it is easy to forget that even as late as the 1950s this part of Turkey was remote, little travelled in and scarcely known. Later other expeditions, including Mathew and Tomlinson (at a second site some 20km/12 miles from the original) and Aldbury,

Cheese and Watson, made further gatherings. Among the collections of the latter expedition were plants from a third locality some 60km (37 miles) from the original site and close to the town of Dörtyol. This third colony differed in that some plants bore flowers different from the usual intense colour, being described as "anything from a paleness near to *C. libanoticum* to the usual rich magenta-pink" and these paler plants were introduced into cultivation under the number ACW 6644. In cultivation the pink form has been given the name 'Roseum' (now forma *roseum*) and is listed today by at least three nurseries. It is an attractive plant with flowers best described as warm rose, which although admittedly not as spectacular as the original colour are, none the less, very pleasing and worthy of a place in a collection (see below).

Cyclamen pseudibericum has a limited distribution in the wild, being confined to a small area, perhaps as little as 80km (50 miles) in extent, north to south, in that easternmost region of the Mediterranean just north of the Syrian border, where it is found on the wooded slopes of the northern Amanus Mountains as well as the southern flanks of the Anti-Taurus. This region has a moister climate than adjacent parts of Turkey and this alone perhaps helps explain the presence there of cyclamen and other moisture-seeking plants such as the common primrose, *Primula vulgaris*. The only other cyclamen found in the region is *C. coum*, in one of its more southern outliers, and the two species are sometimes found growing in close association in the wild. Interesting associations of pink or purple *C. pseudibericum* can be found grouped together with pale yellow primroses (*Primula vulgaris*) and blue scillas (*Scilla sibirica*), a combination that can be easily mimicked in the garden.

Interestingly, the next major sites for cyclamen when heading south (with the exception of several coastal sites for *C. persicum* in Syria) are those in central Lebanon where both *C. coum* and *C. libanoticum* are to be found, again in rather a restricted area. Here again it is worth noting that the habitat is notably moister than surrounding regions and these prevailing conditions have effectively isolated as well as limited the spread of these plants in the eastern Mediterranean region. Of course, in former times when the Mediterranean region was far more extensive and the climate generally wetter and less

69 *Cyclamen pseudibericum* in cultivation showing the typical shuttlecock-shaped flowers with a white snout.
70 *Cyclamen pseudibericum* in the Van Tubergen form (forma *pseudibericum*) widely grown in cutivation.
71 *Cyclamen pseudibericum* thriving in a cold frame in David Haselgrove's garden in Hertfordshire.
72 A fine pot of *Cyclamen pseudibericum*, with wider than average petals; cultivated by Rod and Jane Leeds.

Cyclamen pseudibericum.

arid, these cyclamen, or their progenitors, may have been far more widespread in the region as a whole.

The species grows in association with a wide range of plants in the wild including *Anemone blanda*, *Corydalis* species, *Cyclamen cilicium* (rarely), *C. coum* (occasionally), *Primula vulgaris*, *Scilla sibirica* and *Helleborus vesicarius*.

Cyclamen pseudibericum is unquestionably one of the loveliest and boldest of all cyclamen and a plant in full flower can be extremely eye-catching. The big, rather brazen, flowers, especially in their deep magenta-purple form, are almost twice the size of those of an average *C. coum* and are about the same size as its paler cousin *C. libanoticum*. This species makes an excellent pot plant and looks superb when allowed to self-sow in a large cold frame where it will flower for many weeks in the late winter and early spring. The leaves

appear in the autumn and are usually fully developed by Christmas time. The flower buds arise shortly after the leaves but reside nestling below the foliage for much of the winter before they expand into full flower.

Some growers have succeeded very well with it in the open garden, where as might be expected, it requires a sheltered sunny or semi-shaded warm site. It is probably hardier than *C. libanoticum* and certainly a good deal hardier than its other cousin *C. cyprium*.

Plants generally flower in their third season from seed but some will flower in the second.

When grown in pots I find that it requires ample moisture during the growing season and, although the leaves are quite thick, they will wilt on occasions.

Cyclamen pseudibericum has crossed in cultivation with *C. libanoticum*. This chance hybrid was originally reported by Phil Cornish in Gloucestershire and was greeted with some scepticism from other cyclamen growers, especially as cyclamen species are on the whole notoriously difficult to hybridize. However, I have examined a number of plants of this putative hybrid and can confirm that it does fall midway between these two species and there is little doubt in my mind that Phil Cornish was quite correct in his original diagnosis of the plant in question. As a result, I named this hybrid *C.* x *schwarzii*,. Furthermore, it has since arisen elsewhere and a plant received from Peter Moore as *C. pseudibericum* 'Roseum' (now forma *roseum*) is certainly of similar hybrid origin.

DESCRIPTION *Tuber* subglobose to depressed-globose, to 7cm (2.8in) diameter, smooth when young but gradually becoming grey-brown, corky and somewhat fissured with age, rooting from the base. *Leaves* longer

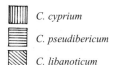

C. cyprium

C. pseudibericum

C. libanoticum

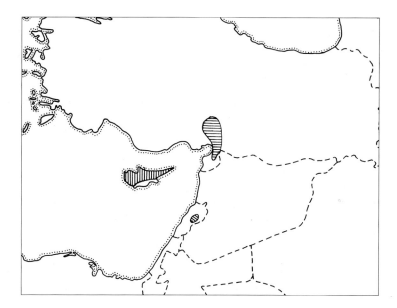

Map 4: Distribution of C. cyprium,
C. libanoticum and C. pseudibericum.

than wide, cordate, often broadly so, lamina 2.3–7.8cm (0.9–3.1in) long, 2–8.2cm (0.8–3.2in) wide, with a shallow and rather narrow basal sinus and a regularly toothed margin, not lobed, dark green and shiny above, usually with a grey-green or whitish hastate pattern and blotching or speckling, shiny and purplish-red beneath; petiole 2–27cm (0.8–10.6in) long. *Pedicels* purplish-brown, elbowed in the lower half or third, 8–27cm (3–10.6in) long, coiling from the top downwards as the young fruits develop. *Flowers* borne with the mature leaves and generally held just above the foliage; corolla deep magenta-purple or rose with a short whitish 'nose' with a chocolate-magenta blotch ('ace-of-spades') mark close to the base of each petal; corolla-lobes erect, somewhat twisted, oval, 18–25mm (0.7–1in) long, not auricled; style not, or only very slightly, protruding.

HABITAT Coniferous forests, particularly of *Pinus brutia*, or deciduous woods or scrub (*Quercus, Fagus* and *Ostrya*), growing among the tree roots in deep leaf litter above metamorphic or igneous rocks, but sometimes in more open rocky situations and screes; March–May.

DISTRIBUTION Endemic to southern Turkey in the Amanus and Anti-Taurus mountains, primarily in Adana, Osmaniye and Hatay provinces, centred on Dörtyol, Duldul Daǧ, Haruniye and Karatepe; 500–1500m (1,600–5,000ft) altitude. Map 4.

    Cyclamen pseudibericum is one of the most striking species in the genus. In the wild it is restricted to a relatively limited area and any over-exploitation of the wild populations would undoubtedly do considerable harm. Although it grows in a rather remote region of Turkey it could become the focus of collectors. There is no need for this, as it is already well-established in cultivation and by no means difficult to raise from seed or to cultivate.

CULTIVATION Here I must just comment again on the inconsistency in the use of names of cyclamen in cultivation. 'Roseum' arose not in cultivation but in the wild and, like the white forms of species such as *C. cilicium, C. coum* and *C. graecum*, deserves formal recognition. I am somewhat loath to alter names around but it seems to me that a standard treatment is a more critical objective. The plant therefore under my system becomes forma *roseum* (see p.167), and a white form, should it become discovered in the wild, would become forma *album, albiflorum, niveum, virgineum* or whatever Latin epithet the author pleases to use in this respect. The occurrence of colour forms of species in the wild is by no means exceptional and although they are of interest they probably do not indicate any evolutionary significance. If I had to start from scratch

73 *Cyclamen pseudibericum* forma *roseum*, showing the typical paler, less boldly marked flowers.
74 Another manifestatioin of *Cyclamen pseudibericum* forma *roseum*.

I would not formally recognize any of these colour variants but rather absorb them into the general description of the species which, after all, often includes other variable factors. Of course, colour forms are of great interest to growers and colour breaks in cyclamen must be expected to excite the cyclamen fanatic, so they need to be identified somehow. Here the world of the botanist and that of the horticulturist are opposed and neither really has a satisfactory remedy to the problem, yet we all admire these plants whatever we call them.

- **Forma pseudibericum**. *Flowers* mid to deep magenta-purple. Found throughout the range of the species.
- **Forma roseum Grey-Wilson**. *Flowers* pale to mid rose-pink. Found occasionally in the wild, especially in the south-eastern range of the species.

AWARDS
- *C. pseudibericum* forma *pseudibericum*: A.M. 1956; F.C.C. 1967; A.G.M.

75 *Cyclamen cilicium* in the wild near Akseki, Taurus Mountains, Turkey.

SERIES CILICIUM

(*Cyclamen cilicium* Group)

C. cilicium, *C. c.* forma *cilicium* and forma *album*; *C. intaminatum*; *C. mirabile*, *C. m.* forma *mirabile* & forma *niveum*

Elegance characterizes the three Turkish species in this association. They are autumn-flowering with rather small tubers that root from the base only. The relatively small leaves are unlobed and the flowers are without auricles, but the corollas are finely glandular, either on the outside or on the inside. The sepals are 3–5-veined. In addition, the anthers are aristate (with a small bristle-like appendage). These popular little species are readily obtainable and easy to grow, being reasonably hardy and prolific flowerers, once established.

Cyclamen cilicium Boiss. & Heldr.

This is another autumn-flowering species which is not seen in our gardens as much as it should be, for it is perfectly hardy in my cold East Anglian garden, and my small patch is now seeding itself around and expanding nicely. I think it is true to say that *C. cilicium* is slower to establish in the open garden than either *C. coum* or *C. hederifolium*, but that should in no way deter us from trying it, for it is a dainty and floriferous species. A sheltered leafy nook between shrubs where it can receive sunshine for part of the day at least seems to favour it well. Young plants seem to adapt to the garden more readily than mature specimens and, once settled in, each plant will produce numerous blooms which appear somewhat in advance of the foliage. In recent years the delightful and equally floriferous and (if

anything) somewhat more vigorous pure white form of the species (forma *album*) has caught the attention and is now freely available. It makes an equally good plant in the open garden and fortunately comes true from seed, so it is easy to build up a small colony of white-flowered plants. Both the ordinary pink-flowered form and the white are excellent in frames and in pots. Being generally less vigorous than *C. coum* and *C. hederifolium*, they prove less invasive in frames or raised beds; *C. coum* will quickly seed all over raised beds, filling every available space at the expense of other desirable and less prolific plants!

Cyclamen cilicium is considered by some gardeners not to be entirely hardy but this is misleading. The species is certainly frost-hardy in all but the severest winters and in my own garden I cannot say that I have ever lost a plant in the open due to severe cold. The fact that *C. cilicium* thrives in some gardens but not in others may have cast doubts on its overall hardiness but other reasons need to be sought for this. Despite its origins in southern Turkey, where it gets long hot summers, this is not a species that relishes being kept bone-dry throughout the summer months. In the wild it often grows in the partial shade of trees, bushes or rocks and will, in all probability, receive at least some moisture throughout that period. The area of my garden where it grows most successfully is often irrigated during the summer but the plants show no resentment of this treatment which, strangely, does not seem to affect the flowering time as it so clearly does with *C. hederifolium*.

Cyclamen cilicium is endemic to southern Turkey in an area centred on the Cilician Taurus and where it is locally common and rather more widespread than was formerly supposed; in fact it is the commonest species in southern Turkey. In the east of its range it just overlaps

Cyclamen series Cilicium leaves: *C. cilicium* (a–b); *C. intaminatum* (c–d); *C. mirabile* (e–f).

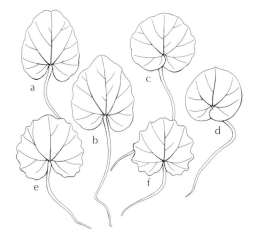

76 *Cyclamen cilicium* naturalized among ivy at the Royal
Botanic Gardens, Kew.
77 *Cyclamen cilicium* in the author's garden.
78 Flower details of *Cyclamen cilicium* showing the
narrow-mouthed flowers with small blotch marks at the
base of each petal.

with *C. pseudibericum* and the two can be found growing
together in at least one site, although they of course
flower at quite different times of the year.

The normal form seen in cultivation, which has been
cultivated for a number of years (and the form most often
sold commercially) has deep green foliage with some cream
or silver markings, forming a rather narrow hastate pattern.
However, offspring of a Peter Davis collection under the
number PD 25889 have bolder, more attractive leaves with a
broader band of silver, and seedlings of this type are
sometimes offered for sale. On the whole *C. cilicium* does
not show the same range of exciting leaf variations as some
of the other species, but it has a quiet charm and no
collection is complete without it.

For many years the flower colour proved to be a
rather pale and uniform pink with deep carmine-magenta
markings around the mouth, but more recently, deeper
pink-flowered forms have come into cultivation as well as
the lovely pure white plant (forma *album*) already
mentioned. It is certainly a species where more serious
selection and hybridization would present an interesting
challenge with the expectation of introducing more
diverse forms into our gardens. In some ways this has
been a neglected species.

The flowers are elegant with their rather narrow and
delightfully twisted petals flaring out from a narrow little
nose and held on delicate stalks. In the wild the flowers
may appear in advance of the leaves, but more often the
leaves are partly developed by the time the first flowers
open: this depends very much on when the first late-
summer/early-autumn rains arrive for, if they are early,
then plants are initiated into growth with flowers and
leaves arising together.

Cyclamen cilicium is readily raised from seed and
young plants will often come into flower in their second
season, although three years is a better average. Once
established in the garden, they will self-sow quite
happily, although not as vigorously as some of the other
hardy species.

Cyclamen cilicium forms a very close alliance with
C. intaminatum and *C. mirabile*. All three species are
endemic to Turkey, occupying distinct niches and
scarcely overlapping in distribution. They are not, to my
knowledge, ever found growing together in the same
localities in the wild. They were at one time much
confused by botanists as well as gardeners, especially the

former two species. However, they differ on a number of readily discernible characters which I have simplified below:

- *C. cilicium*: Tuber with roots arising as a bunch from the centre of the base. Leaf-lamina longer than wide, usually with a distinctly toothed margin, never flushed with pink or red above; corolla pink with dark basal markings (except in pure white forms), with pinkish veins and untoothed or indistinctly toothed corolla-lobes, glandular (often very sparsely so) on the outside (being the inside when the lobes are reflexed).

- *C. intaminatum*: Tuber with roots arising as a bunch from the centre of the base. Leaf-lamina wider than long, the margin untoothed or only very slightly so, sometimes flushed with pink above; corolla without any dark markings, white with greyish veins or very pale pink, untoothed or indistinctly toothed corolla-lobes, glandular on the outside (the inside when the lobes are reflexed).

- *C. mirabile*: Tuber with the roots arising in a distinct ring from the base, not from the centre. Leaf-lamina about as long as wide, sometimes wider than long, with a distinctly toothed margin, often flushed with pink or red above, especially when young; corolla pink with dark basal markings (except in pure white forms), with distinctly toothed corolla-lobes, glandular (often densely so) on the inside (the outside when the lobes are reflexed).

More technical details of the glands on the corolla and tuber details reveal other differences between these species (see p.98).

Cyclamen cilicium.

All three species share the same chromosome number of 2n=30 yet, despite this, there are no authenticated hybrids reported between them. Their reasonably close association in the wild may indicate that they have an inbuilt incompatibility mechanism which prevents hybridization from taking place but this requires further investigation. Having said this, however, reported pink-flowered *C. intaminatum* plants in cultivation may in fact represent hybrids between *C. cilicium* and *C. intaminatum*, but I have not had the opportunity to examine such plants in detail.

DESCRIPTION *Tuber* small and depressed-globose, to 5.2cm (2in) diameter eventually but often smaller, smooth and velvety at maturity, rooting from the centre of the base. *Leaves* longer than wide, oval to suborbicular, the lamina 1.4–6cm (0.6–2.3in) long, 1.2–4.8cm (0.5–1.9in) wide, with a narrow and rather shallow sinus at the base, the margin scarcely toothed to shallowly and rather remotely scalloped, deep green above with an irregular hastate pattern in grey, grey-green or creamy-white, pale green suffused with purple or crimson-magenta beneath; petiole slightly elbowed in the lower half, 5–20cm (2–8in) long. *Pedicels* 6–12cm (2.3–4.7in) long, with a slight elbow towards the base, generally purplish or purplish-brown, coiling from the top downwards as the young fruit develops. *Flowers* appearing with the young or semi-mature leaves, moderately sweetly honey-scented usually; corolla pale to mid-pink, occasionally deep rose, with a magenta-crimson blotch at the base of each petal; corolla-lobes narrow-elliptical to elliptical-lanceolate, twisted, 14–19mm (0.6–0.7in) long, sparsely glandular on the inner surface (the outer surface when the lobes are reflexed), generally with an untoothed margin; style slightly protruding.

HABITAT The species inhabits light woodland, particularly of *Cedrus*, *Pinus* and *Abies*, often growing in the shade of bushes or rocks, but sometimes venturing out onto screes in more exposed places. Occasionally growing in olive groves or on banks surrounding fields or orchards, or even along roadsides, but generally in dappled shade; September–November.

DISTRIBUTION *C. cilicium* is distributed in southern Turkey in a narrow arc from more or less the vicinity of Antalya and Isparta eastwards to north of Adana in the region of the Cilician Gates, generally following the arc of the Taurus Mountains, at an altitude between 600 and 2,000m (1,970–6,500ft), although it is commonest in the altitudinal range 700–1500m (2,300–4,900ft). Reports of its occurrence on Cyprus, apparently in a dried stream bed in the Troödos range, have not been proven and seem

wholly unlikely unless the species has at some time been introduced to the island. Map 5.

- **Forma *cilicium*:** flowers pale to deep pink with dark markings at the base of each corolla-lobe. Throughout the range of the species.
- **Forma *album* Frank & Koenen:** flowers pure white without any markings. Once found in the west of the range of the species.

Forma *album* was discovered in Turkey by Erna and Ronald Frank in the company of Manfred Koenen (under the number Koenen 8210) in October 1982 between Murtici and Akseki in southern Anatolia, a well-known area for this particular species. Like most of the albino cyclamen found in the wild it is rare, being found as an isolated individual among many other plants of the normal pink colour. Diligent propagation by the discoverers has meant that this charming plant is now freely available. It has proved a prolific seeder and the seedlings all produce white flowers, although the leaf patterning varies somewhat from plant to plant. Some growers have reported the white form to be a "better garden plant", being generally more vigorous, although I have not found this to be the case. However, it does make a superb plant for a frame or pot in the alpine house in my experience.

AWARDS
- *C. cilicium* forma *cilicium*: A.M. 1952; F.C.C. 1975; A.G.M.
- *C. cilicium* forma *album*: A.M. 1988

Cyclamen intaminatum (Meikle) Grey-Wilson

With its dainty white or very pale pink flowers charmingly marked with pale grey veins and its small and neat stature, this little gem of a cyclamen is a 'must' in every collection; it is the smallest known species next to *C. parviflorum*. Although it is perfectly hardy in the garden and quite the equal of its close cousin *C. cilicium* in this respect, its smallness makes it generally unsuitable for the open border. However, it is ideal for frames, raised beds and troughs, where it can more readily be appreciated when it comes into flower. Its paleness requires a dark background if the flowers are to be seen

79 A fine pot of the normal form of *Cyclamen cilicium*, forma *cilicium*.
80 The pure white form of *Cyclamen cilicium*, forma *album*, is rather more vigorous than forma *cilicium*, and makes a good plant in the garden, or for pot culture.
81 *Cyclamen cilicium* forma *album*, now well established in cultivation.

82 *Cyclamen intaminatum*, perhaps the daintiest of all cyclamen species.
83 *Cyclamen intaminatum*; a form with a pink flush overlying the young leaf markings.

C. alpinum. The latter name was never validly published, yet, even so, it caused immediate confusion because the epithet had already been used by Sprenger in 1892. Sprenger described his *C. alpinum* from a living plant but subsequently all the material was lost and since then botanists and horticulturists have wondered what the plant was. Professor Schwarz, who had in fact seen specimens of *C. alpinum* before they were destroyed, stated quite categorically that they were no more than a form of *C. coum*. However, this is not surprising as at a casual glance *C. coum* and *C. alpinum* do seem very similar. In any event Sprenger's *C. alpinum* has nothing to do with Turrill's plant. The epithet *alpinum* has therefore to be rejected for the plant in question, for being a latter homonym besides not having been correctly validated.

The plant had to wait until 1978 before receiving a name and then only being recognized as a variety of *C. cilicium*. Desmond Meikle in preparing a paper in advance of his account in the 'Flora of Turkey' named it var. *intaminatum* (meaning literally 'pure, without blemish'). However, many horticulturists were sceptical about the varietal status of this plant. In the meantime further material was seen and photographed in the wild by various people and more material was brought into cultivation. Whilst preparing my monograph of the genus, published in 1988, I had the chance to look at the material in more detail and decided that the plant differed in at least four characters from ordinary *C. cilicium* and, as a result, I raised the variety to specific level as *C. intaminatum* and this move has gained general acceptance. The prime differences are in the general stature of the plant, the leaf shape and the colour and size of the flowers, see p.92.

Much of the early confusion, I suspect, stems from E. K. Balls's locality for his original collection of the species, under number EKB 669a, and said to come from Burujik. Burujik (variously spelled Burujek, Buruçek and Buruk) lies in the Taurus Mountains in the region of the Cilician Gates Pass, in fact between the small town of Pozanti and the Cilician Gates (formerly close to the old road, although a modern motorway now sweeps up over the pass through the former site of Burujik). *C. cilicium* is certainly found in the area but *C. intaminatum* has never been found there since. In fact all the known localities are well to the west and north-west. E. K. Balls was a methodical collector and his detailed notes of collections and journeys as he criss-crossed the country were quite meticulous. Balls in fact only collected

at their best and this can generally be achieved by giving plants a top-dressing of dark rock chippings, or perhaps pine bark would produce a more 'natural' effect.

This plant has been known to the outside world since 1934 when E. K. Balls collected it in June of that year, reportedly from the vicinity of Buruk (= Burujuk), under the number EKB 669a. This number, not to mention the status of the plant, caused considerable confusion over the following 50 years or so. At first this distinctive little plant was referred to as "*C. cilicium* var." and as such it was written up by William Turrill in *Curtis's Botanical Magazine* (New series, t. 307, 1957) and later as

C. intaminatum, as we know it today, under one other number and that was 628a from north-west Turkey and in all probability in the vicinity of Eskişehir where the species is well known to occur. It seems highly likely to me that Balls's live collections were in part muddled and that no plants of *C. intaminatum* were ever collected in the Burujik area. Weight is given to this argument by Balls himself who, commenting on the number in question in the *Gardener's Chronicle*, states that "A form of *Cyclamen cilicium*, which Dr Goulay and I collected both at Namrun (B 185) and at Burujik (B 669a), flowered last winter most persistently from November to March. Its rounded pink flowers in constant succession drew attention to the plant, as being of exceptional value for winter display, especially as it flowered so freely out of doors. Throughout the Taurus range this plant wedges its tubers into limestone outcrops or hides under the shade of dense shrubs". This description certainly in no way brings to mind either *C. cilicium* or *C. intaminatum* but would be fine for *C. coum*. The common cyclamen of the Taurus region is in fact *C. cilicium*. We have seen that *C. intaminatum* has only been confirmed as inhabiting regions to the west and north-west, while *C. coum*, which is widespread in some parts of Turkey, is not known from the Taurus, although it is found to the east in the Amanus Mountains. Quite clearly a muddle was made. The fact that we know that Balls collected *C. intaminatum* from another (confirmed) locality adds weight to this argument. Squabbles over the precise localities of these species and where the plants were originally collected are bound to continue, yet the species in question are quite distinct and unlikely to be confused in the garden.

The original EKB 669a plants, or at least plants under that number, had small deep green unmarked leaves, but later collections often had larger leaves attractively marbled with cream or silver. More recently plants with pinker and somewhat larger flowers have been discovered to the east of Ulu Dağ in north-western Turkey and these broaden our former conception of this interesting species.

In cultivation today both white and pink forms with plain leaves as well as silvered leaves can be seen. Most are prolific flowerers and set seed in profusion for so small a plant. In some the unmarked nose of the flowers has a flush of pale green. The subtle veining of the petals is more obvious in the white- rather than the pink-flowered forms of the species. The plain green-leaved forms tend to come true from seed, though those with leaf variegations tend to produce rather mixed progeny, but this requires further investigation.

Some of the more vigorous-looking forms available commercially today, with rather more oval leaves and larger, deeper pink flowers, may represent hybrids with *C. cilicium*, though this is far from certain: it is not even

84 *Cyclamen intaminatum* showing the characteristic greyish veins running the length of the petals.

known at the present time whether or not the two will hybridize.

DESCRIPTION *Tuber* small and depressed-globose, to 3.5cm (1.4in) (much larger eventually in cultivated plants) diameter eventually, smooth and velvety at maturity, rooting from the centre of the base. *Leaves* slightly wider than long, the lamina suborbicular, 1.7–3.8cm (0.7–1.5in) long, 2–4.2cm (0.8–1.7in) wide, with a shallow and narrow sinus at the base with the basal

Cyclamen intaminatum.

lobes often converging or slightly overlapping, the margin scarcely toothed to shallowly and remotely scalloped, matt green to deep green above, plain or marked with a narrow to broad, irregular, hastate pattern in grey-green or pewter, occasionally silvery and sometimes flushed with pink when young (especially over the hastate pattern), pale green beneath, sometimes flushed with purple; petiole elbowed in the lower half, 5–9.5cm (2–3.7in) long. *Pedicels* somewhat elbowed in the lower half, 5–16cm (2–6.3in) long, green or purplish-brown, coiling from the top downwards as the young fruits develop. *Flowers* small, appearing with the semi-mature or mature leaves, not scented; corolla white (occasionally suffused with pink) or pale to mid-pink, generally with pale grey veins but without a basal blotch to each petal, often flushed with pale greenish-yellow, occasionally white, around the mouth; corolla-lobes elliptical to slightly oblong, only slightly twisted when reflexed, 10–16mm (0.4–0.6in) long, usually shallowly toothed or undulate towards the apex, densely glandular on the outer surface (the inner surface when the lobes are reflexed); style not, or only slightly, protruding.

HABITAT The species is primarily a plant of dryish deciduous oak (*Quercus*) woodland, where it grows amongst roots and rocks in the partial shade, sometimes beneath bushes, often in leaf-litter. In its more northerly localities it is sometimes found growing in association with *C. coum* and *Crocus speciosus* as well as various *Colchicum* species; (September–)October–November.

DISTRIBUTION *Cyclamen intaminatum* is known from a handful of localities in western and north-western Anatolia. It is found in particular to the west of Eskişehir

and just south of Ulu Dağ (centred on the boundaries where Bilecik, Kütahya and Eskişehir provinces meet) and in a few scattered localities southwards as far as Honaz Dag; 700–1,100m (2,300–3,600ft) altitude. Map 5.

It also reportedly grows with *C. alpinum* in one locality to the south of Ulu Dağ, although this has not been confirmed and, in any event, this would be a considerably northward extension of the range of that latter species. *C. intaminatum* is one of the most restricted and localized species. Fortunately, the fact that it is not as spectacular as some of the other Turkish species probably gives it some protection from marauding collectors. Nevertheless its survival in the wild needs careful monitoring.

I cannot apply forma names to the pink- and white-flowered manifestations of the species as every intermediate can be found and it is sometimes difficult to tell whether some are white or the very palest pink; often a hint of pink vanishes as the flowers mature.

AWARDS
• P.C. 1976 (as *C. cilicium* var. *alpinum* 'Album'); A.M. 1983

Cyclamen mirabile Hildebrand

Once an extremely rare species in cultivation, *C. mirabile* is now widely available and an exciting addition to any collection of the species. In flower it is very similar to *C. cilicium*, although the petals have a more obviously toothed margin. In leaf, however, the species are very different: in *C. mirabile* they are rounded with a pronouncedly toothed margin, while in *C. cilicium* they are oval, or more or less so, and with less pronounced

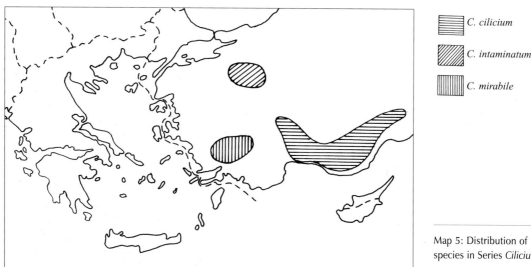

C. cilicium

C. intaminatum

C. mirabile

Map 5: Distribution of species in Series *Cilicium*.

marginal teeth or no teeth at all. *C. mirabile* is often noted for the flush of pink or red on the upper surface of the young (often well-marked) leaves; this is often said to be a prime diagnostic feature of the species and indeed, from a gardener's point of view, it is a highly desirable one, but it is not common to all the plants, even within one colony in the wild. The leaves can be very variable in their patterning: some have a thin hastate pattern in grey, cream or silver, others a broader band. In the most striking forms the leaves have a broad silvery band that extends to the leaf-margin, which is overlain by glowing crimson or raspberry-red when they are young. As the leaves expand and mature the crimson fades to reveal the silver beneath. Mature leaves rarely have any hint of the red coloration. The degree of leaf colours varies greatly from plant to plant, both in the wild and in cultivation. Seedlings may not reveal their true potential for two or three years and they become more striking in succeeding years as the number of leaves per plant increases. The species name *mirabile* literally means wonderful, refering to the amazing leaf coloration that is often apparent on the young leaves.

Incidentally, the red coloration is not confined solely to *C. mirabile*, although it is most pronounced in that species; some forms of *C. hederifolium* and *C. intaminatum* can also display pink on the upper surface of the young leaves.

The history of *C. mirabile* is as confused and as controversial as any in the genus. At the end of the last century the Dutch bulb firm of Messrs van Tubergen of Haarlem received some tubers of a cyclamen in a consignment of 'bulbs' exported from Smyrna in western Turkey (the plants were said to have come from the vicinity of Smyrna, now Izmir). Smyrna was at that time, and had been for many years, one of the chief ports where goods of diverse sorts were exported from Asia Minor to Europe. In 1901 van Tubergen sent some tubers of this cyclamen to Professor Friedrich Hildebrand in Freiburg, Germany. When these eventually flowered they proved to be an unknown new species which Hildebrand described as a new species, *C. mirabile*, because of the characteristic red zone on the upper surface of the young leaves. Subsequently the cultivated material perished and Hildebrand's type specimen (upon which he based his description of the species) which was housed in the great herbarium in Berlin was unfortunately destroyed during the severe blitz that the city received during the latter stages of the World War II. The species was thus temporarily lost to science.

The situation remained the same for some years and in 1955 when Otto Schwarz published his monograph of the genus he had no alternative but to relegate it to '*species non statis nota*'.

However, the very next year, in March 1956, Peter Davis, in the company of Oleg Polunin, collected a solitary tuber in the Vilayet of Muğla, between Çine and Yatagun in south-western Turkey. This tuber was subsequently grown on at the Royal Botanic Garden at Edinburgh and proved to be Hildebrand's long-lost *C. mirabile*. Subsequently Davis collected a large number of tubers (under the number Davis 41498), between Gokbel and Çine at an altitude of only 400m (1,300ft).

Despite this, the species remained rare in cultivation until well into the 1970s when tubers began to appear in Britain and western Europe in alarming numbers from wild collections made somewhere in western Turkey. Mass importations followed, the plants (and many other 'bulbs') finding their way into department stores where they were often unwittingly sold under the name *C. hederifolium* (or *C. neapolitanum*) or *C. cilicium*. This started the conservation alarm bells ringing in various quarters, especially at the Royal Botanic Gardens at Kew. The truth was that during the late 1960s and 1970s Turkish commercial collectors started a systematic exploitation of the 'bulb' wealth of the country in order to satiate the greedy western European market. Vast numbers of 'bulbs' were exported to Germany and Holland in particular, including many cyclamen tubers. To give an idea of the scale of this export: in 1976 the number of cyclamen tubers exported was 256,000; by 1979 it rose to 1,099,725, by 1982, 2,350,000 and in 1985 a staggering 6,632,000. The great majority of these tubers had been stripped from the wild. A high proportion of the tubers sold in Britain were packeted in Holland and many proved to be *C. mirabile* when they came into flower, although many of these scrubbed and dormant tubers perished without ever coming into growth. Clearly such a trade could not be allowed to continue in the interests of the species in the wild; absolutely nothing is worth such decimation of wild populations! This all proved to be a key factor in alerting

85 *Cyclamen mirabile* in cultivation.

conservation organisations to the gross exploitation of plants in the wild, particularly 'bulbs' from places like Turkey. Under the CITES agreement of 1986 this mass exploitation was stopped, see p.208.

Today *C. mirabile* is well-established in cultivation and there are some beautiful and varied forms around. It is more often grown in pots or on raised beds than in the open garden. However, there are some fine colonies in mild gardens where winter frosts are never too severe. The species is not quite as hardy as either *C. cilicium* or *C. intaminatum*; this is not surprising as many of the forms in cultivation come from very much lower altitudes. Having said this, however, plants will put up with a good deal of frost in the garden, but like most cyclamen they dislike freezing, desiccating winds. The foliage in fact stands up to mild frosts remarkably well.

Plants are readily grown from seed and generally come into flower in their third season.

Many forms of this species have scented flowers. Scent is of course a very subjective sense but if asked I would say that the nearest to which I could describe the scent would be coconut perhaps with the merest hint of primroses.

Besides the general differences noted above under *C. cilicium* (p.92) other differences can be noted. In *C. cilicium* and *C. intaminatum* the mature tuber has a smooth surface and the roots arise from the centre of the undersurface. In *C. mirabile*, on the other hand, the surface of the tuber is corky and the roots arise from various points on the undersurface. In addition the corolla of *C. mirabile* are very much more glandular than those of the other two

---

Cyclamen mirabile.

species, with the glands particularly prominent on the inner surface (outer when the petals reflex); these glands can be readily observed using a x10 hand lens.

Another difference can be seen in the disposition of the leaves. In *C. mirabile* the leaf-stalks rise directly from the tuber, whereas in both *C. cilicium* and *C. intaminatum* they spread out sideways initially to a distinct 'elbow' before being raised upwards. These are small points but they help to enable accurate identification of the species even when they are out of flower.

The flower colour of *C. mirabile* is rather uniform mid-pink, sometimes darker or paler and, until recently, no albino was known, see below.

It has been argued that *C. mirabile* would be better considered as a subspecies of *C. cilicium* but this would hardly improve the general taxonomic position and such a move would undoubtedly annoy horticulturists. In any case there are sufficient differences to distinguish the two species, both in leaf and in flower. Furthermore, the two do not occupy the same localities in the wild, occupying different geographical locations; *C. mirabile* in fact overlaps in the wild with the distantly related *C. alpinum*, though the two have different flowering seasons.

DESCRIPTION *Tubers* depressed-globose, up to 6cm (2.3in) diameter eventually, rarely larger, the surface rather corky and rather fissured when mature, rooting irregularly from the lower surface. *Leaves* generally as wide as long, but sometimes wider than long, the lamina broad heart-shaped, 1.5–4.2cm (0.6–1.7in) long, 1.4–4.5cm (0.6–1.8in) wide, with a shallow and rather narrow sinus at the base with the basal lobes usually converging or slightly overlapping, the margin shallowly toothed, dark green above with a narrow to broad, irregular, hastate pattern in grey-green, cream or silver, often (but not always) flushed with pink or red when young, purplish-red or carmine-purple beneath; petiole ascending, usually not elbowed, 5–16cm (2–6.3in) long, purplish or purplish-brown. *Pedicels* ascending, occasionally somewhat elbowed towards the base, 5–13.5cm (2–5.3in) long, purplish or purplish-brown, coiling from the top downwards as the young fruits develop. *Flowers* often fragrant (reminiscent of coconut), appearing with the very young or semi-mature leaves; corolla pale to deep pink, with a magenta blotch at the base of each petal; corolla-lobes elliptical, pointed, with an irregularly, sometimes pronouncedly, toothed margin, especially towards the apex, densely glandular on the inner surface (the outer surface when the lobes are reflexed); style slightly protruding.

HABITAT *C. mirabile* is primarily a plant of *Pinus brutia* woodland and hill slopes with maquis, particularly that dominated by Kermes oak, *Quercus coccifera*, on various rocks including limestones and granites. In some localities the species is confined to fragmented limestone rocks beneath *Quercus coccifera* or to cliff-crevices in the dappled shade of trees, generally where goats cannot reach them (over-grazing may well have severely limited this species!); September–November.

DISTRIBUTION The species is endemic to south-western Anatolia centred on the Muğla, Aydin area, but in recent years it has also been found in a number of localities to the north of that general area and is certainly more common than was formerly supposed. In addition there is an isolated outlier just to the west of Lake Eğirdir. Associated plants in the wild include *Euphorbia rigida* and *Spiranthes spiralis*; 330–1,600m (1,100–5,200ft) altitude. Map 5.
- **Forma *mirabile*:** flowers pale to deep pink with dark markings at the base of each corolla-lobe. Found throughout the range of the species.
- **Forma *niveum* Grey-Wilson & J. White:** flowers pure white. Only found once – see below.

Forma *niveum* is distinguished from the normal form (forma *mirabile*) by having pure white flowers without any markings. In October 1993 Jill and Colin White travelled around various cyclamen localities in south-western Turkey. By the 13th of that month they had arrived in one of the best regions for *C. mirabile*, between Yatagan and Çine, where under an olive tree at 330m (1,100ft) altitude they spotted, amongst a host of ordinary pink *C. mirabile*, a plant with pure white flowers. It was growing in grass among metamorphic rocks together with *Scilla autumnalis*, which was also in flower, and the fruit heads of a *Fritillaria*. The flowers were pure white and unmarked and the leaves with a green inner and outer zone but with a broad hastate pattern in pink. Most of the ordinary pink-flowered forms were in fact growing not beneath olive trees but among bushes of prickly *Quercus coccifera*.

The plant has subsequently been named forma *niveum* rather than *album* to distinguish it from the albino forms of the other cyclamen species which have mostly been called *album*. The plant was brought into cultivation and a number of young seedlings have resulted, although it is not known at this stage whether forma *niveum* will come true from seed, although the few seedlings so far raised look very similar in leaf characteristics to the parent plant. It is to be hoped so, for the albino plants will undoubtedly make an interesting and desirable garden plant.

AWARDS
- *C. mirabile* forma *mirabile* A.G.M.; P.C. 1968; A.M. 1976

86 *Cyclamen mirabile* forma *niveum*; the pure white-flowered form is very rare in cultivation at present.

SUBGENUS *CORTICATA*

C. cyprium; *C. libanoticum*

This subgenus contains two isolated eastern Mediterranean species, one confined to Cyprus, the other to the Lebanon. They are characterized by corky tubers that root only from the base, sometimes to one side, by angled or toothed leaves and by glandular corollas in which the corolla-lobes have a distinctive blotch close to the base. The corollas are distinctly or rather indistinctly auricled. In addition, as with the *C. coum* group and the *C. cilicium* group, the calyx-lobes have 3–5 veins.

This grouping formerly included the south-eastern Turkish *C. pseudibericum* but this has now been moved to the closely allied subgenus *Gyrophoebe*. At first glance they would seem to have little in common except for their eastern origins, for they look so very different in both leaf and flower that they are unlikely to be confused: one, *C. cyprium*, has rather narrow pale flowers with distinctive auricles, while *C. pseudibericum* has dark flowers with a narrow snout and no sign of auricles, while the third, *C. libanoticum*, has pale flowers with very broad petals with only the merest hint of auricles. Yet these three species share in common corky tubers that root only from the base and the same chromosome number (2n=30). Interestingly *C. libanoticum* has been hybridized in cultivation with the other two, although the three-way cross (*C. cyprium* x *C. pseudibericum*) has yet to be achieved. As no other crosses have been made

87 *Cyclamen cyprium* in cultivation.
88 *Cyclamen cyprium*.
89 *Cyclamen cyprium* showing the typical flowers with rather narrow petals and well-spaced auricles.

between these three cyclamen and any other cyclamen species one must conclude that, despite their different appearances, these three species do perhaps reveal a secret kinship.

In fact the chromosome number of 2n=30 is shared between these species and the members of both the *C. coum* series and the *C. cilicium* series (in fact all the members of subgenus *Gyrophoebe* and subgenus *Corticata*). Chromosome numbers may reveal an affinity but more detailed cytological studies are required before further judgements can be made. In addition, all the inherent morphological and anatomical features of the species have to be taken into account, for it is easy to be persuaded by just one or two characters, rather than an overall assessment of the gross morphology. A character may be estimated to be of evolutionary importance or not and what may prove to be an important feature in one group or association may not be so in another. For instance, it might be assumed that the presence or absence of corolla auricles is of great importance, but is it? Auricles are one of the most useful features in identifying cyclamen species but useful features such as this may not be of great evolutionary significance, especially if they are unlinked to any other feature. In fact the presence of auricles in cyclamen species is closely associated with the width of the corolla mouth; those species with pronounced auricles having particularly wide mouths compared to those without, while those with poorly marked auricles (*C. libanoticum* and *C. rohlfsianum*) also have relatively wide mouths in proportion to the rest of the flower.

There is, however, no general agreement as to the affinities of these species. In his monograph of 1964 Schwarz divides the genus into subgenera and series.

These three species come together under his scheme with *C. mirabile* based on the corky nature of the tuber and a shared chromosome number; however, more recent research by Clennett and separately by Anderberg place *C. pseudibericum* closer to *C. coum*. This emphasizes the danger of using single characters in isolation when trying to reveal affinities between species, for *C. mirabile* in its overall morphological floral characteristics, distribution and flowering time shows a clear affinity to *C. cilicium* and *C. intaminatum* and not to *C. pseudibericum* and its allies.

Cyclamen cyprium Kotschy

This attractive and sweet-smelling species is endemic to the island of Cyprus being found growing most frequently in mountain woodland, especially in the Troödos range, although it is in fact widespread in most of the island except for the south.

Cyclamen cyprium was first collected in 1862 by Kotschy who described it three years later from material cultivated in Vienna. No botanist has since doubted the validity of this species; indeed it has a very distinctive appearance.

The auricled flowers have led some botanists in the past to associate this plant with *C. hederifolium* but the presence of auricles is certainly not an important clue to close affinity in this instance. In their cytological details the auricled species are extremely diverse with *C. hederifolium* and *C. africanum* with 2n=34 or 68 chromosomes, *C. graecum* with 2n=84 normally and *C. rohlfsianum* with 2n =96. All the auricled species possess corky tubers but they root in different ways. *C. cyprium* is particularly unusual, as detailed below.

The foliage is generally rather lobed or angled and the general colour olive green, marked or variously splashed with grey, deeper green or pewter. In many plants the leaf colours are rather muted, even sombre, but in some forms found in the wild (also in cultivation) they are strikingly splashed and blotched with silver.

The flowers are rather smaller and have a distinctly thin look. This is due to the rather narrow and twisted petals which do not overlap one another, even at the auricled mouth. The characteristic purple or magenta M-shaped mark at the base of each petal has been likened to a bird in flight.

In cultivation *C. cyprium* has been hybridized artificially with *C. libanoticum* to produce the hybrid *C.* x *wellensiekii* (see p.194). Incidentally, *C. libanoticum* has also formed a spontaneous liaison with *C. pseudibericum* (see *C.* x *schwarzii*, p.192). The third cross in the trio, *C. cyprium* x *C. pseudibericum*, has not yet been produced but I feel it is only a matter of time before it appears. The cross would have to be made artificially by storing pollen of the former, as their

Cyclamen cyprium.

flowering seasons do not usually overlap.

Cyclamen cyprium is a splendid plant when well grown and a mature plant may sport many flowers. It is one of the least hardy species, unfortunately, and I personally have never found it particularly easy to grow. The flowers and foliage are very susceptible to frost and need to be protected carefully. When they die down in the spring they are best given a complete summer rest by withholding all water, as with *C. africanum* and *C. rohlfsianum*. Some growers advocate giving the plants a little water occasionally during the summer months, especially if the weather is hot. After their summer dormancy, plants are often difficult to coax back into growth. Too much water applied at this time may well cause the tubers to start rotting. Once growth is 'in full swing' then more generous helpings of water can be applied.

A good plant will start to flower in September and continue right through to Christmas time, very occasionally pushing forth one or two late flowers after that date.

One of the most curious and unique features of this species is obvious to all those who have cultivated it and that is the strange, often asymmetric, rooting of some tubers, with all the roots being produced in a bunch on one side of the base. Plants sometimes appear to capsize, especially when newly planted, as the roots pull the tuber over.

Cyclamen cyprium makes a fine pot plant for a cool, frost-free, sunny windowsill in the house and can be treated in much the same way as *C. persicum*. This asymmetric rooting is unique in the genus.

DESCRIPTION *Tuber* subglobose to depressed-globose, to 10cm (4in) diameter, often less, generally with a rough, corky, greyish skin when mature, but sometimes smooth, with the roots borne on the lower surface sometimes from the centre, sometimes from one side,

90 *Cyclamen libanoticum* in the wild in the mountains of the Lebanon.

often forming a small ring. *Leaves* usually somewhat longer than wide, the lamina broad heart-shaped, (3–)4–14cm/(1.2–)1.6–5.5in long, (2–)3.8–11cm /(0.8–)1.5–4.3in wide, with a deep and narrow sinus at the base and an untoothed to coarsely toothed, somewhat lobed, margin, usually grey-green above and marbled with pale or deep grey-green or olive green, pewter or silver, the markings often in the form of a broken or unbroken hastate pattern, flushed with purple or crimson-purple beneath; petiole usually elbowed, 6.5–22cm (2.6–8.7in) long. *Pedicels* 5.5–19cm (2.2–7.5in) long, brownish or purplish, coiling from the top downwards as the young fruits develop. *Flowers* appearing with the partly mature leaves or in advance of the leaves, but sometimes a few late flowers borne with the mature foliage, strongly and sweetly scented; corolla white, or very pale pink at first but then soon fading to white, with a conspicuous M-shaped magenta blotch at the base of each petal; corolla-lobes narrow and twisted, narrow-oblong, 14–21mm (0.6–0.8in) long, with marked auricles at the base; style slightly protruding.

HABITAT Generally found growing beneath trees (*Pinus* in particular) and shrubs on both limestone and igneous formations, growing in shaded places, stony places, along stream banks, or occasionally in vineyards, or on screes at the higher elevations; near sea level to 1,200m (3,900ft) altitude.

DISTRIBUTION Endemic to Cyprus, particularly to the west and north of the island; it is especially abundant in the Troödos Range; late September to January, generally flowering at the higher altitudes first. It is absent from the low-lying areas in the south of the island. Map 4.

In the Troödos Mountains, which dominate the centre of the island, *C. cyprium* can sometimes be found

in association with the delightful *Colchicum troodii*, another endemic to the island.

AWARDS
• A.M. 1949

Cyclamen libanoticum Hildebrand

This is one of my favourite species but, regrettably, not one that I find particularly easy to maintain in cultivation for any length of time.

Cyclamen libanoticum is endemic, as its name implies, to the Lebanon where it was discovered in 1895 by E. Hartman, who found it in a number of localities to the north-east of modern-day Beirut. Tubers were sent to Hildebrand in Freiburg, Germany, who described the species three years later. Two other species are also to be found in the Lebanese mountains, *C. persicum* at rather lower altitudes, and one of the southern outliers of *C. coum* which is sometimes found growing with *C. libanoticum* in the wild, although the two species flower at different seasons.

Cyclamen libanoticum has rather large and floppy flowers which have been likened to 'drowsy butterflies'. They have very broad petals which generally overlap at the base and are scarcely twisted. Botanists and gardeners have long argued over whether the corolla of this species bears auricles. The species is generally keyed out among species without auricles and certainly in the mature flower there is rarely a hint of auricles, although they can sometimes be detected. However, as the corolla opens and the petals bend backwards a hint of rudimentary auricles can often be detected but these are generally lost as the petals expand fully. Hildebrand in his original description assigns auricles to this species but few have followed him. This may all seem rather technical and unimportant but the presence of rudimentary auricles does help to show the affinity of this species.

Cyclamen libanoticum is often said to be a relict species without any obvious close affinities but I think this is wrong. Earlier authorities generally thought that the species was closely allied to *C. pseudibericum* which is found to the north in southern Turkey. Some earlier authors clearly linked the two species: Schwarz in 1938 reduced *C. pseudibericum* to a synonym of *C. libanoticum* and in 1939 Glasau recognized it as a separate taxon but as a subspecies of *C. libanoticum*. Today few would argue that these two entities were not distinct species in their own right but their affinity is strengthened by the fact that a hybrid (*C. x schwarzii*) between the two has arisen in cultivation (they share the same chromosome number, 2n=30). The prime differences are seen in the angled, greyer, untoothed leaves of *C. libanoticum* and the paler flowers with their broad petals with 'flying bird' mark at the base of each. In contrast *C. pseudibericum* has bright green, non-angled but toothed, leaves and deeper pink (often vivid magenta) flowers with rather narrower petals which have a characteristic 'ace of spades' mark at the base. *C. libanoticum* has a strange scent which is best described as peppery (some say 'acetylene') and not particularly pleasant. *C. pseudibericum* has a rather sweeter scent but there is, at the same time, an underlying hint of pepper.

Recent cladistic analyses (Anderberg *et al* 2000 and Clennett 2001) place *C. pseudibericum* nearer to *C. coum* and its allies, with *C. libanoticum* and *C. cyprium* forming a rather closer liaison: this is the approch that I have more or less followed in this new account of the genus. The narrow corolla mouth and lack of auricles in the flower of *C. pseudibericum* are features shared with *C. coum*; however, the lack of aristate anthers, the corky rather than velvety tubers, and the entire margined corolla-lobes are features it shares with both *C. cyprium* and *C. libanoticum*.

The affinity of *C. libanoticum* with *C. cyprium* is more problematical. Certainly the two do not look at all similar in their overall morphology. *C. cyprium* has slender flowers with narrow petals and pronounced auricles, as well as a powerful and sweet fragrance, and the leaves are both more pronouncedly angled and more boldly marked. However, the two share the same chromosome number, corky base-rooting tubers and the glandular nature of the corolla, which they also have in common with *C. pseudibericum*. For this reason the three species are often grouped together in a loose alliance. It is perhaps not without significance that all three are isolated from one another in limited areas of the extreme eastern Mediterranean and that *C. libanoticum* hybridizes with the other two species in cultivation (see *C.* x *schwarzii* and *C.* x *wellensiekii*).

The presence or absence of *C. libanoticum* in southern Turkey is a problem that has vexed various enquiring minds. Chris Clennett writes on it at length in the *Journal of the Cyclamen Society* (23: 49–50, 1999). The first and only mention of its occurrence in Turkey stems from Professor Otto Schwarz who did much fine work on *Cyclamen* taxonomy. This finding was dismissed by subsequent researchers who generally concluded that the plant in question was in fact *C. pseudibericum*. The confusion is based on a single sheet in the Haussknecht Herbarium in Jena, Germany, dated 27th February 1865, collected near Beilen (Belen today) in southern Turkey, an area where *C. pseudibericum* and *C. coum* (in its southern form) are known to occur. The specimen in question is clearly not *C. libanoticum*, for it has a narrow mouth to the corolla as well as narrow lobes. This fact clearly dismisses any notion that *C. libanoticum* occurs in Turkey; it would

be a considerably northward extension of its distribution if this were the case! The question remains: "What is the identity of the plant on the Belen sheet?" Clennett argues that the sheet is a mixed one with flowers of *C. pseudibericum* and a stray leaf of *C. coum*. This of course could be feasible as both can grow in mixed colonies and it would be quite possible for the non-observant to collect leaves and flowers of one species and a stray leaf of the other. However, none of the material matches either species, so it is not surprising that when Clennett laboriously added the measurements and details of the specimen to a data matrix designed to test the closeness of relationships within Schwarz's subgenus *Gyrophoebe* (containing *C. coum, C. cilicium, C. pseudibericum,* as well as *C. libanoticum* and *C. cyprium* following his cladistical analysis) the comparative analysis (phenetics: designed to test the relationship between taxa based on their morphology) showed a severe distortion in *C. pseudibericum* when the details of the mystery sheet were added. This distortion could, according to Clennett, be explained by bad disfigurement of the specimen (there is no such sign!), a mixed gathering of *C. pseudibericum* and *C. coum* (but neither are on the sheet!), the possibility of aberrant forms of *C. pseudibericum* in the Belen area possibly constituting a distinct variety (no such specimens have ever been found in the wild, despite numerous forays in the region by various individuals, including botanists!) and finally, and most implausibly, that this specimen represents a new and hitherto undescribed species of *Cyclamen*.

The explanation is, I fear, far less exciting and altogether more mundane, in fact an old-fashioned muddle. It is probable that the specimen arrived at Jena loose in folded paper and was then mounted on a sheet with tapes. At some stage in the handling a mix-up occurred and the sheet received the wrong field notes (such muddles do unfortunately happen from time to time: I saw several blatant examples over the years when I worked in the Kew Herbarium, and they can lead to a great deal of confusion and time wasting). The Belen collection in fact *is C. peloponnesiacum*, so it would have come from the Peloponnese (Greece) or the island of Rhodes: the broad, scalloped-margined leaves, the narrow corolla-lobes and the exserted style are all very diagnostic. If Clennett's analysis had stretched outside subgenus *Gyrophoebe* then I am sure the problem would have been quickly resolved. There remains one outstanding problem and that is where is the Belen specimen. Of course, the original specimen may not have been a cyclamen at all: if it were then I would wager that somewhere in the Haussknecht Herbarium there is a sheet of a Turkish cyclamen with Greek field data. The probability is that, as in most herbaria, large numbers of specimens are being processed and if a muddle does occur then it is often extremely difficult to resolve.

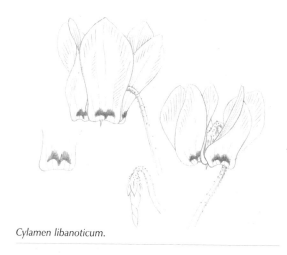

Cylamen libanoticum.

In passing, it is perhaps worth mentioning that in his *Canadensium Plantarum Historia* of 1635, Cornuto describes a 'Cyclamen e monte libani'. The suggestion has been made that this in fact refers to *C. libanoticum*. However, Cornuto's description suggests rather *C. persicum*, which is also found in the same mountains.

After its original discovery little more was seen of *C. libanoticum*, although it was introduced into general cultivation in 1929, and it was assumed to have become extinct in the wild. However, in 1961 it was rediscovered in the Lebanon and more material was introduced into cultivation as a result. Today we know that the species exists in just a few scattered localities in the mountains, north-east of Beirut. It is certainly not common in its restricted localities and is probably

Cyclamen leaves: C. libanoticum (a); *C. pseudibericum* (b–c); *C. cyprium* (d–e).

(together with *C. rohlfsianum*) the most endangered species in the wild and needs careful protection.

DESCRIPTION *Tuber* subglobose to depressed-globose, velvety brown when young but becoming somewhat corky and slightly fissured when mature, to 4.5cm (1.8in) diameter, often less, rooting primarily from the centre of the base. *Leaves* with a heart-shaped lamina, 4–8cm (1.6–3.1in) long, 3.8–7.3cm (1.5–2.9in) wide, somewhat longer than wide, generally with a somewhat angled, untoothed or slightly toothed, margin and with a narrow sinus at the base, dull greyish- or bluish-green above with rather indistinct marbling in grey or whitish, rarely with more distinct patterning, purplish-red or green flushed with pink or purple beneath; petiole usually elbowed, 6–18cm (2.3–7.1in) long, purplish-brown or green with a purple tinge. *Pedicels* elbowed like the petioles with the flowers appearing away from the centre of the plant, 8–15cm (3.1–6in) long, usually purplish-brown, coiling from the top, downwards as the young fruits begin to develop. *Flowers* appearing with the mature leaves, with a rather peppery smell (often described as peppery-acetylene); corolla at first white but gradually turning pale or rose pink, or mauve-pink, with an irregular crimson-magenta blotch towards the base of each petal with a central stripe extending into the mouth, occasionally the blotch very faint and almost absent; corolla-lobes broad-oval, 16–25mm (0.6–1in) long, slightly twisted normally, with the bases slightly overlapping but not noticeably auricled; style not or only very slightly protruding.

HABITAT Growing among rocks and tree roots, particularly in the shade of trees and shrubs, sometimes in more exposed and open situations; 750–1,400m (2,500–4,600ft) altitude.

DISTRIBUTION Lebanon in a few scattered localities 60–70km (37–43miles) to the north-east of Beirut. Reports of the species being found in south-eastern Turkey (Amanus Mountains) are apparently erroneous but see also above; late February to April.

CULTIVATION In the wild, *C. libanoticum* is a plant of the mountains growing in regions subjected to winter frosts and snow. It used to be thought of as a tender species but evidence from the wild contradicts such notions and in cultivation seedlings have been known to survive temperatures as low as –12°C (11°F) quite unaffected, and there are a few growers who have succeeded in growing it outdoors quite successfully, especially in the south and south-west of Britain. I fear I am not one of them. In fact I can safely admit to having

91 *Cyclamen libanoticum* makes a fine specimen for pot cultivation, but greatly dislikes strong light, especially direct sunshine.

92 *Cyclamen libanoticum* showing the typical broad, dumpy flowers with overlapping petal bases and poorly defined auricles.

93 *Cyclamen libanoticum*; a form with scarcely any markings at the base of the petals.

grown it rather badly in the past; plants would produce only a few leaves and flowers and the leaves were always turning a sickly yellow. Then a kind friend, Jack Elliott, suggested I both alter my compost and shade the plants, so they went into a slightly acid compost and the pots were put below the staging in the alpine house and there they have thrived. In fact *C. libanoticum* is far happier in dappled shade. In the open garden a sheltered place with dappled shade is ideal; for instance at the base of a wall or hedge. This has the added advantage of keeping the plants relatively dry which is an important consideration during the winter months when too much moisture can prove fatal. A sheet of glass placed overhead will provide similar shelter.

Cyclamen libanoticum makes a very fine pan plant for the cold glasshouse and is a delight in full flower early in the year and it is always a good subject for some of the earlier flower shows. On the whole it seems to prefer a rather loamier compost than many other cyclamen (one similar to that for *C. repandum* or *C. purpurascens* will suit it well enough). Some growers add pine needles to the compost and swear that it increases the glowing pink of the flowers. Several tubers can be planted in a single pan and they will look uniform because plants tend to have rather similar leaf markings. I have also found that it does better (both in pots and frames) if the tubers are buried some 5–6cm (2–2.3in) into the compost, though not everyone will agree with me on this and most plants one sees seem to be planted on the surface, like most cyclamen species. The tubers tend to be on the small side, even in mature flowering plants, and the roots often arise slightly to one side of the tuber base, but not as eccentrically as those of *C. cyprium*.

Plants should be rested from June to September and then given ample moisture to start them back into growth. Plants are quite susceptible to an erratic watering regime and will soon indicate this when the leaves begin to yellow prematurely. On the other hand, they are best kept on the dry side if severe frosts are expected, but this applies to all cyclamen grown under cold glass.

Seedlings grow quite rapidly and when well grown can be expected to flower in their second season, although perhaps three years is a better average. The tubers increase in size very slowly, but even quite small ones only 1.5cm (0.6in) across can produce a good flower display. The flowers last in pristine condition for longer than most other species. Hand-pollination will help fruit set, though many growers find this a waste of time and get enough seed when plants are left to their own devices.

AWARDS
• A.M. 1901; F.C.C. 1958; A.G.M.

94 *Cyclamen persicum* in the wild in the Lebanon, inhabiting soil-filled pockets on a rocky slope.
95 *Cyclamen persicum* in its most common form in the wild, forma *persicum*; Lebanon.
96 *Cyclamen persicum* forma *persicum*; the flowers which have a pink snout, often open white before turning pink; Lebanon, near Boruk.

SUBGENUS *PERSICUM*
(*Cyclamen persicum* Group)
C. persicum, C. p. var. *autumnale, C. p.* var. *persicum* forma *albidum, persicum, puniceum* & *roseum*; *C. somalense*

This subgenus contains the popular florist's cyclamen, *C. persicum*, which is so much more elegant and refined in its wild manifestations. The two species in this group have rather large and corky tubers that root from the base only and shuttlecock corollas with attractively twisted petals which are without auricles or glands of any sort. Unique to this group are the pedicels which do not coil in fruit but simply arch downwards and thicken. The wild forms of *C. persicum* find a ready niche in a collection of cyclamen but the purist growers shy away from the grosser cultivars. Despite this, the florist's cyclamen, which comes in a huge variety of colours and flower size, is an extremely popular house plant and an important crop on the Continent, especially in Holland, Germany and Italy.

Cyclamen persicum Miller

This species is one of the best known of all cyclamen, yet it is as a pot plant that most people know it. In its wild form it is one of the most elegant, floriferous and sweetly perfumed species, with the flowers held elegantly on slender stalks well above the foliage. The leaves are typically heart-shaped and unlobed, with a finely beaded margin. They show quite a lot of variation in patterning in the wild, although green with paler or darker markings, often in the form of a hastate pattern, seem to dominate. However, forms in which the veins are picked out in yellow-green or pewter are found in the wild, as well as those in which the leaves are patterned in varying amounts of pewter, silver or even cream. Occasionally plants are found with a more or less completely pewter or silver lamina, often with a deep green margin or, alternatively, with a shield-shaped pattern in deeper green, pewter or silver in the centre of the leaf.

In the wild the most common flower colour in *C. persicum* is white or very pale pink, both with a deep pink nose, and such forms are common in places like Cyprus, southern Turkey and Israel. Pure white flowers are occasionally found in populations of the more widespread colour, as well as deeper pinks and even purples, but the vivid magentas, reds, scarlets and orange of some cultivated varieties are unknown in the wild to my knowledge.

In the wild the leaves are produced during the autumn and are generally fully expanded by late winter. The flower buds are initiated at the same time as the developing leaves but do not expand and open until the late winter or early spring in most instances. However, there are populations in Israel that are autumn-flowering.

The arching and thickening of the pedicels as the fruits develop is interesting to watch and highly distinctive in this species.

Various forms of *C. persicum* have been described in the past: *C. vernale* Miller was a name given to what was little more than a colour variant of *C. persicum*; *C. punicum* was a name given to the outlier of the species in Tunisia; *C. aleppicum* was described from Syria; *C. latifolium* Sm. was described from Greece, a plant with particularly large and broad leaves. However, none of these variants are considered worthy of recognition today and are all lumped under *C. persicum*.

Although the species is an eastern Mediterranean one it does not grow in Persia (now Iran) as the specific epithet implies. However, in recent years there has been an unconfirmed report of its occurrence in Iran, but this has yet to be substantiated.

Cyclamen persicum has a decidedly eastern Mediterranean distribution but with outlying stations in eastern Algeria and neighbouring Tunisia. However, it is from the eastern Greek islands, western and southern Turkey round to western Syria, the Lebanon and Israel, as well as Cyprus, that it has its prime distribution. Its occurrence in eastern Crete and in places like the Athos Peninsula may be spurious as in such places it is closely associated with monasteries or is found adjacent to monasteries: it may well have been introduced there by the monks in ancient times, perhaps for medicinal purposes or because they simply liked its sweetly perfumed flowers, or again, it may have been introduced to such places by accident. Today it is almost impossible to tell and a great deal of time can be wasted on conjecture. In none of these outlying places does its presence in any way throw doubt on the general taxonomy of the species.

Cyclamen persicum is widely grown in cultivation but primarily as a house plant and as the large-flowered florist's forms (see p.169). The wild plant is well worth growing in a collection and its elegant flowers will scent the air when they come into bloom (generally shortly after Christmas). In addition, the wild forms make very good house plants, requiring a cool but light windowsill where they will flower over many weeks. They generally dislike the dry, hot conditions of the living room (as do all cyclamen) and an unheated though frost-free room will suit them best. Many find that plants watered from below (by steeping pots in tepid water for an hour or so once or twice a week) last longer and flower better than those watered from overhead. The plant will soon indicate its unhappiness if conditions are not correct by yellowing of the foliage and abortion of the young flower buds. Placing the pot within a bowl filled with grit is a useful method of

97 *Cyclamen persicum* forma *persicum* photographed near Kyrenia, Northern Cyprus, where it is a common wild plant.
98 *Cyclamen persicum* forma *persicum* often grows among rocks or beneath bushes in the wild, as here in Northern Cyprus; the flowers are powerfully scented in the wild forms.

ensuring an even supply of moisture around the plant and as long as the grit is kept moist all should be well. Under no circumstances must the pots be allowed to stand in water for any length of time: this will result in the gradual death of the vital roots.

Wild forms generally have white flowers with a pink nose or pink flowers with a deeper pink nose, but they can occasionally be deep pink all over or mauve, or pure glistening white. The leaf size and markings can, as already discussed, be very variable and there are some very beautiful forms to be seen in the wild.

The wild forms are certainly easier to maintain and certainly hardier than many of its cultivars, except for some of the smaller-flowered types that more closely resemble the wild species. They are all best grown in a cool but frost-free glasshouse with ample light and moisture during the growing season. Plants tend to dry out quickly because of the large number of fleshy leaves and require more water than most cyclamen. Most wild forms come into flower in the New Year but some may not start until well into March. Hand-pollination of the best forms, either selfing or crossing, will ensure a good fruit set.

The old, often blowsy, greenhouse forms and cultivars of *C. persicum* have given many gardeners the impression that this is a temperamental and tender species. It is certainly true that these leafy large-flowered plants, cosseted in warm glasshouses for the pot-plant trade, are quite difficult to maintain in the home environment. However, many of the smaller types, now widely available in a wide range of colours, are very much easier. Some of the small modern cultivar series such as the Miracle Series are much more resilient and are often

Cyclamen persicum.

seen planted in tubs and window boxes in the city environment where they can withstand low temperatures, although not freezing. With the development of new 'cell-cultured' hybrids between *C. persicum, C. hederifolium* and *C. purpurascens* it is possible that, in the next few years at least, a new wave of hardy *C. persicum* lookalikes will become available for the outdoor garden. One can imagine them being used for late summer bedding or for containers.

Cyclamen persicum (wild forms) generally flower in about eighteen months from seed, although some forms may take longer.

Plants require a long summer rest once the leaves begin to die down. They should not, however, be baked and a little moisture given occasionally is advisable; under very dry conditions the tubers will shrivel. Dormant plants can be placed under the staging of the glasshouse or alpine house in a sand plunge that is kept just moist.

The small-flowered types widely sold at garden centres and florists have been derived in the main by back-crossing certain diploid cultivars with their wild counterpart, to produce elegant floriferous plants in a wide range of colours, some of which (especially the white) are well perfumed. These are often grown in peaty composts and I find that purchased plants of this kind are often difficult to keep for more than a year or so; the tubers shrivel away to nothing if allowed to dry out. To overcome this I now repot plants immediately into my standard cyclamen compost and keep them growing for as long as possible, feeding them occasionally to build up a large and more persistent tuber. Some of my plants are now more than five years old.

DESCRIPTION *Tuber* depressed-globose, with a rough, somewhat fissured and corky surface when mature, to 15cm (6in) diameter, though often smaller, rooting from the lower surface, especially from the centre of the base. *Leaves* heart-shaped, the lamina 2.5–14cm (1–5.5in) long, 2.5–13.5cm (1–5.3in) wide (occasionally as large as 21.5mm/0.9in long by 15.5cm/6.1in wide), ascending to erect, often as wide as long, with a rather narrow sinus at the base and a finely toothed, slightly cartilaginous, unlobed margin, plain mid- to deep green or grey-green above, with a paler or darker irregular hastate pattern which is sometimes cream or silvery, rarely with most of the surface silvered, pale green and often flushed with pink or purple beneath, rarely deeply flushed; petiole 5.8–24cm (2.3–9.4in) long, green or purplish-brown. *Pedicels* erect to ascending, 13–32cm (5.1–12.6in) long, green to brownish-purple, curving downwards and thickening as the young fruits begin to develop but not coiling. *Flowers* appearing with the mature leaves, sweetly fragrant; corolla white to pink, mauve or more rarely deep red or carmine, the paler forms often with a pink or purple zone around the mouth; petal lobes variable in shape from oblong, to elliptical or narrow-lanceolate,

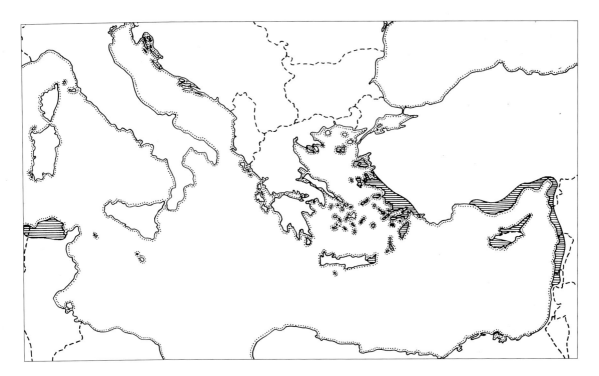

moderately to markedly twisted, 20–37mm (0.8–1.5in) long (much longer in some cultivars), without auricles at the base; style slightly protruding.

HABITAT Open woodland and scrub, maquis and garrigue in sunny or semi-shaded places, growing amongst the tree roots or rocks, sometimes in or beneath rock walls or in rock crevices, olive groves, orchards or abandoned cultivation, occasionally in sandy coastal soils in the part shade of low bushes; sea level to 450–(1200m)/1460–(3900ft) altitude.

DISTRIBUTION South Greece (Karpathos and the eastern Aegean islands, north-east Crete, Rhodes), west, south and south-east Turkey, north and south Cyprus, west Syria, Jordan. Lebanon, Israel, Algeria and north Tunisia. Isolated localities in North African and Cretan localities are often associated with areas around monasteries or graveyards and the species may well have been introduced to such areas initially. It is undoubtedly native to the extreme eastern Mediterranean region. Reports of it from the Athos Peninsula in northern Greece are apparently erroneous; December to May. Map 6.

Some plant associations in the wild include *Barlia robertiana*, *Cistus incanus*, *C. salvifolius*, *Erodium* species, *Orchis* species, *Ophrys* species, *Pistacia* species.

During February 1990 the Cyclamen Society made an expedition to Israel to look for *C. persicum* and *C. coum* in the wild. They found, as elsewhere, that *C. persicum* was

Map 6: Distribution of *Cyclamen persicum*.

not particularly variable in the wild with the common white- and pink-flowered forms with a deeper pink nose predominating. However, they also saw plants with attractively silvered leaves and unusual flower markings. Most notable were several plants collected at an altitude of 1,200m (3,900ft) (under the numbers 90560 and 90561) and it is hoped that plants from such a high altitude will prove hardier than those at present in cultivation. There is some reason to think that this might prove so, as they were growing together with *C. coum*, *Iris histrio* and *Hyacinthus orientalis*, all of which are very hardy in temperate gardens. The high altitude of the Israeli plants is very exceptional, for in most parts of its range *C. persicum* is a low-altitude species, often being found close to the coast.

More interesting still were reports of an autumn-flowering form of the species which the expedition located finally at Duma Junction to the north-north-east of the city of Jericho. In the area most plants were in flower (February) but some, 'in a very restricted area', were long past flowering and in fruit. Plants and seeds were collected under the numbers 90650 to 90654 and the plants have proved to be autumn-flowering in cultivation, commencing to flower in September. Apart from their early-flowering characteristic these cannot be distinguished from any other wild *C. persicum*. At the same time they are worthy of recognition and I have accorded them the name var. *autumnale*.

99 *Cyclamen persicum* forma *persicum*; a particularly fine and floriferous form in cultivation.
100 *Cyclamen persicum* forma *albidum* has pure white flowers; here in cultivation.

- **Var. *persicum***. *Flowers* borne in the late winter and spring. Throughout the range of the species.
- **Var. *autumnale***. *Flowers* borne in the autumn. Known only from Israel.

In addition, various colour forms of *C. persicum* var. *persicum* can be distinguished:

- **Forma *persicum***: flowers white or very pale pink with deep pink round the nose. Throughout the range of the species; by far the most common form seen in the wild.
- **Forma *albidum* (Jord.) Grey-Wilson:** flowers pure white. Found throughout the range of the species but never particularly common.
- **Forma *roseum**:** flowers mid- to deep rose pink, uniformly coloured or rather deeper around the nose. Occasionally found in the wild, especially at the eastern end of the range of the species.
- **Forma *puniceum* (Glasau) Grey-Wilson:** flowers red to carmine. Very rare in the wild but only said to be known from Syria and the Lebanon.

* *Not formally described as no authenticated wild source material is available at the time of writing.*

Awards
- *C. persicum* forma *album*: F.C.C. 1959
- *C. persicum* forma *persicum*: A.M. 1935; F.C.C. 1974

Cyclamen somalense Thulin & Warfa

The various species and subordinate taxa of *Cyclamen* have been known now for quite a few years and although not everyone would agree on the delineation of the various elements (species, subspecies, etc.) there is general agreement on distribution and the range and complexities of variation found in nature. *Cyclamen* is a markedly Mediterranean genus in distribution, extending eastwards to the Caucasus Mountains and the Elburz of northern Iran. It therefore came as a total surprize, even a shock, when in 1986 a Swedish friend from Uppsala University, Mats Thulin, reported finding a cyclamen in northern Somalia.

Cyclamen fanatics that I mentioned this to were at first wholly unbelieving; one even accused me of making it up and another said that if it were true it would prove to be *C. persicum* and to have been introduced to the region.

Mats eventually turned up at Kew with specimens and colour slides and one glance told me that this was in fact a new and unknown species to excite the cyclamen world. This proved very timely as I was just completing my first monograph on the genus *Cyclamen* (1988) and was able to include a provisional description in the book. It was subsequently formally described as *C. somalense* in *Plant Systematics and Evolution* 166, 249–252 (1989).

Mats Thulin discovered the new species in the company of a Somali botanist Ahmed Mumin Warfa while they were exploring the Al Miskat Mountains of north-eastern Somalia in November 1986. Although it was found in a very inaccessible area, the discoverers decided wisely, in the interest of the survival of the species, not to reveal its precise locality. I cannot do better than quote from the original paper on the distribution and habitat of this recent addition to the genus:

"*C. somalense* is known only from the type locality where a few populations, each with a fair number of individuals, were seen at 125–1600m altitude. The plants were growing in crevices in more or less north-exposed limestone rocks in the mist zone. At the end of November the plants were in full leaf but only a few flowers and young fruits were seen. The climate in the area is generally hot and dry during the summer and fairly cool and with frequent mists and showers during the winter when the night temperature may drop to 5°C."

What perhaps is most interesting about the habitat details is that it is so similar to that of other cyclamen species such as *C. rohlfsianum*, *C. libanoticum*, *C. cyprium* and of course *C. persicum*. This region of Somalia has a typical Mediterranean-type climate. Although the vegetation of the region has a marked Mediterranean element, it is mixed with a tropical element. However, associated plants with a primarily Mediterranean distribution or affinity include *Anemone somalensis*, *Brassica somalensis*, *Juniperus procera*, *Olea europaea* subsp. *africana*, *Pistacia falcata*, *Salvia somalensis*, as well as the fern *Cheilanthes catanensis*. It is believed that the disjunct Mediterranean element to which *C. somalense* belongs is a relict of Tertiary origin, indicating that the Mediterranean Basin and its associated flora was far more extensive in former times, being restricted as increasing aridity moved northwards, extending the Saharan region right to the coast of northern Africa.

The nearest known cyclamen locality to this new discovery is that of *C. persicum* in Israel, some 2800km (1700 miles) to the north-west. It is in fact with *C. persicum* that *C. somalense* appears to have the closest affinity. I say *appears* because, until living material in flower and chromosome details of *C. somalense* are closely examined, it is impossible to be absolutely certain. *C. somalense* has a distinctive look, however, and is unlikely to be confused with any other species.

It has in common with *C. persicum* the non-auriculate corolla and the bending but non-coiling of the flower-stalks (pedicels) as the fruits develop; previously this unique feature was confined to *C. persicum*. However, *C. somalense* differs in a number of important respects. First, the tubers are small, not more than 3cm (1.2in) diameter in those examined and the tuber itself is subglobose to somewhat elongated. Second, the leaves are broader than long and often somewhat angled along the margin and are relatively coarsely toothed. Third, at flowering time the pedicels are only as long as the leaves, and flowers are not held above the foliage as in *C. persicum*. Finally the flowers are smaller, the corolla lobes not more than 15mm (0.6in) long.

Cyclamen somalense.

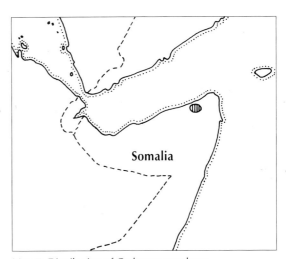

Map 7: Distribution of *Cyclamen somalense*.

DESCRIPTION *Tuber* subglobose to 3cm (1.2in) diameter, or elongating to 6cm (2.3in), with 2–3 rounded to oblong swellings, covered in rough corky skin and rooting from the base of the tuber. *Leaves* generally wider than long, heart- to kidney-shaped, lamina 3.5–10.5cm (1.4–4.1in) long, 4–12cm (1.6–4.7in) wide, with a somewhat angled, somewhat horny, coarsely toothed, margin, deep green above with a prominent silver hastate pattern in the centre, with the silver running outwards along the veins almost to the leaf-margin; petiole 3.5–7cm (1.4–2.8in) long. *Pedicels* erect to ascending, 7–12.5cm (2.8–4.9in) long, elongating, thickening and curving downwards as the fruits develop but not coiling. *Flowers* borne with the mature leaves and

101 *Cyclamen hederifolium* subsp. *hederifolium* in the wild, south of Stupa in the Peloponnese, Greece. Forms like these are widely cultivated in gardens.

held at the same height as or just above the foliage; corolla pale pink suffused with carmine around the mouth; corolla-lobes narrow-elliptical, twisting, 14–15mm (0.5–0.6in) long, not auricled.

HABITAT Limestone rock crevices in shaded north-facing exposures; 1,250–1,600m (4,100–5,200ft) altitude.

DISTRIBUTION Somalia: Bari Region in the Al Miskat Mountains where it is known only from a single locality to date; late September to November. Map 7.

The fruit capsule and seeds of *C. somalense* are unknown at the present time; however the size of the pollen grains is very similar to that of *C. persicum* and this may indicate a similar chromosome number (wild *C. persicum* normally has 2n=48).

CULTIVATION *Cyclamen somalense* is an autumn-flowering species, flowering earlier than most forms of *C. persicum* in the wild. It is not known whether the flowers are scented or not. It is easy to speculate on its hardiness but *C. somalense* is unlikely to receive any frost in the wild and one would guess that it would only tolerate conditions similar to *C. africanum*, *C. persicum* and *C. rohlfsianum*, being generally intolerant of frost, or at least long periods below freezing.

Its attractive foliage alone will make it a desirable plant for cyclamen collections in the future. At the present time there are only three plants in cultivation and these are located in Sweden where they have grown each year since being introduced, producing foliage annually but only a single flower to date. This is a great pity because at present there seems little prospect of getting seed from the wild and the best hope is to get the cultivated plants to flower and fruit. Wild collected tubers of cyclamen often sulk for a number of years in cultivation and there is no doubt that seed, however produced, is the best means of getting this plant into greater circulation. In the meantime we must all

show a good deal of patience and trust that the future will bring this desirable plant into our gardens.

Although it would clearly be exciting to have *C. somalense* in collections, the species also holds some promise for breeding purposes, particularly if it is proven to have the same chromosome number as *C. persicum*, for this increases the likelihood of the two being hybridized artificially. To date *C. persicum* has never been crossed (except by recent cell implant techniques) with any other cyclamen species (although gene implants in Japan using *C. persicum* and other species have produced some interesting results in recent years). The modern trend for an ever-increasing range of cyclamen types, including dwarf or miniature plants for pot culture, makes the use of *C. somalense* in a breeding programme highly desirable from a commercial point of view. First of all, though, it is important to establish the species in cultivation without detriment to the fragile wild populations of this unique species.

Since writing the first edition of this monograph one tuber of the original collection in Uppsala has been passed on to Gothenburg Botanic Garden, where it is growing but scarcely flourishing. A plant flowered at Uppsala but failed to set seed. There is a general agreement that if seed can somehow be procured then the species will quickly become established in cultivation. For some reason no chromosome count has yet been made.

SUBGENUS *CYCLAMEN*

SERIES CYCLAMEN
(*Cyclamen hederifolium* Group)
C. hederifolium, *C. h.* var. *hederifolium* forma *albiflorum*, *C. h.* subsp. *confusum*; *C. africanum*

The species of Series Cyclamen are readily distinguished by their tubers which root primarily from the top and sides, by the often angled leaves and by the presence of well-marked auricles on the corolla. In addition, the base of each petal (in the mouth region) is marked with a more or less V-shaped blotch. In the allied *C. purpurascens* and *C. colchicum* (in the following series) the area around the mouth is unblotched, although the colour of the petals may be more intense in that area. The sepals are 1-veined in all members of the subgenus. This series contains the most widely grown, and arguably the most popular, of all cyclamen, *C. hederifolium*.

Cyclamen hederifolium Aiton

If I could grow only one cyclamen in my garden then it would without doubt be *C. hederifolium*. Easy, dependable, floriferous, long-lived and adaptable, it never fails to excite when the first flowers begin to appear at the end of summer. Once established, plants will often seed themselves around in profusion, often sowing themselves thickly so it is soon possible to extend beds and have plenty of young plants to give away. It is an amazingly resilient species; during periods of heavy and prolonged freezing the leaves look dark, floppy and dismal but the moment the temperatures lift the foliage brightens and loses its limpness as though nothing had happened.

Cyclamen hederifolium looks at its best in drifts, in borders devoted to it, or scattered among shrubs or naturalized beneath deciduous trees. A large drift in full flower can be simply breath-taking, especially when the various shades of pink are mixed with the white forms.

When most gardeners talk about the hardy cyclamen in their gardens it is primarily this species to which they are referring and, apart from the housebound *C. persicum*, *C. hederifolium* must surely be the best known of all the species. Plants often live to a good age and at least one venerable tuber has been recorded as being in excess of 130 years old. Mature plants may bear well in excess of 100 flowers over a period of five or six weeks. Because different forms have staggered flowering times, the species can be in bloom for three months. Some of the hybrids between it and *C. africanum* extend their flowering period right up to Christmas.

The species has been cultivated for many years. It was certainly grown in England prior to 1597 when Gerard recorded it in his famous 'Herball' with the inscription "Cyclamen folio Hederae"; this is backed up by a wood engraving which is indisputably that of the plant known today as *C. hederifolium*. In 'Miller's Gardener's Dictionary' of 1768 there is reference to *C. europaeum* as 'hederae folio' and this is again directly referable to *C. hederifolium*.

That famous and flamboyant writer of alpines Reginald Farrer was somewhat confused over his cyclamen. In 'The English Rock Garden' (1928 edition) he lists both *C. europaeum* (now *C. purpurascens*) and *C. neapolitanum* (now *C. hederifolium*) correctly. However, in the preamble he states that they "scatter their seeds with such profusion and success that *C. europaeum* (at least) long claimed to be an English native on the strength of its abundance in certain woods in Kent". This muddle no doubt stems back to the old confusion in the use of the epithet *europaeum* for Farrer clearly means what we now consider to be *C. purpurascens*. In fact *C. purpurascens* has never become naturalized in Britain. On the other hand, *C. hederifolium* has become thoroughly at home from southern England to southern Scotland as well as the Channel Islands. In his recent 'New Flora of the British Isles' Clive Stace points out that *C. hederifolium* has been known in Kent woods since 1778; clearly this is the plant to which Farrer refers.

102 *Cyclamen hederifolium* subsp. *hederifolium* is widespread in the Balkans, where it is generally a plant of shaded banks, open woodland or shrubby places.
103 *Cyclamen hederifolium* subsp. *hederifolium* in association with *Crocus goulimyi* in the Mani Peninsula, north of Ariopoli, Greece.
104 A fine form of *Cyclamen hederifolium* subsp. *hederifolium* growing in an olive grove near Amfissa, mainland Greece.

Farrer, however, extols the virtue of *C. hederifolium* (as *C. neapolitanum*): "The plant is of delicate beauty, and extreme freedom of flower; making solid clumps of soft flesh-colour or carmine in an open, sunny gravel path, no less than thriving heartily, if not with such condensed ferocity of floriferousness, in places not so inhumane." He also says that "its leaves are very variable in size and shape; typically they are exactly like some ivy-leaf, rather long from base to point; they are dark and waved and marbled, while the beautiful flowers begin to appear before the heyday of the foliage …".

Cyclamen hederifolium presents no real problems in cultivation. In most gardens it is rarely necessary to raise new plants from seed as seedlings generally appear in plenty, although not always where they are wanted. In my garden, ants transport the ripe seeds to many corners of the garden so that I find young seedlings appearing in the cracks in paths and paving, among the rocks on my scree beds, where they were never planted, and even in the middle of the lawn.

It makes a reasonably good pot plant but requires a large pan as the leaves and flowers tend to spread to the perimeter of any container. After just a few years the tubers get too large for most average pots or containers and plants are then best relegated to the open garden. Tubers as large as 36cm (14in) diameter have been recorded (see *Cyclamen Society Journal* 3,2, 1984). Plants with especially fine foliage markings or colours are often grown in pots so that they can be observed more closely and allow the grower to self-pollinate the plants readily in order to obtain authenticated seed, although seedlings cannot all be expected to be as fine as the parent plant – some may be even better. Even in the absence of flowers, *C. hederifolium* can make a very handsome pot plant.

As with some of the other hardy species, especially *C. cilicium* and *C. coum*, the tubers often come proud of the soil surface after a few years. Copious annual mulches, especially of leaf mould, will help to overcome this problem. If it becomes too severe then plants tend to lose vigour and fail to flower so well. They are then best lifted and replanted, having replenished the soil with fresh compost and a scattering of bone meal.

In most gardens the pink- and white-flowered forms seem to be equally abundant. Only some of the whites breed true; many bear pink or white offspring and many of the whites will be found, on close examination, to have pink in the mouth, especially around the auricles.

Seedlings can often flower in their second year from seed, although most will wait until their third season. The peak flowering period in cultivation is September and early October but some plants often start to flower in August and occasionally as early as mid- to late July, but this depends very much on the season.

Cyclamen hederifolium is extremely variable in leaf size, shape and patterning. Gardeners have accentuated this variability by selecting out the more unusual shapes and patternings or colours, often propagating these at the expense (particularly in recent years) of the more normal forms with their typical marbled, ivy-like foliage. Despite this, it is somewhat surprising that botanists have not alighted upon this species and split it into more categories; the species in fact has a short synonymy. But many colonies in the wild do not in my experience show a huge range in variation and I have examined many a colony in former southern Yugoslavia (especially in Bosnia, Hercegovina, Krajina and Yugoslavian Macedonia) and Greece in which the plants have been satisfyingly uniform, that is to say where I have not been perplexed by the variation present. At the same time, it is often difficult to find two plants with exactly the same leaf-patterning. Of course, in large colonies one is bound to find a certain amount of variation and from region to region other variations can be detected but none of these are in any way exceptional save for the tetraploid form occasionally found in the south of the species range (see p.116). So within a colony plants are likely to show some variation in the patterning and shape of the foliage and the depth of pink of the flowers which may be scented or unscented. Pure white-flowered forms are rare in the wild, though they are common in cultivation. The same is true of silver- or pewter-leaved forms and leaves without any pattern at all. The overall variation found in the species as a whole is primarily in the shape and patterning of the leaves but there is certainly no regional variation that can be readily detected, even if leaf-patterning could be more clearly defined, and one is left to conclude that the species is more or less indivisible.

Of course, *hederifolium* is a particularly apt epithet for this species as the leaves do resemble those of the common ivy, *Hedera helix*, but herein lies another confusion, for *C. repandum* is also often referred to as the "Ivy-leaved Cyclamen". It too, particularly in subsp. *repandum*, has foliage that can be remarkably ivy-like. Early writers (including Gerard in 1597 and Miller in 1768), however, were quite clear as to which species they were describing as "Cyclamen folio Hederae" or "hederae folio" and that is the plant that we today call *C. hederifolium*, so if a common name has to be applied then this must become the Ivy-leaved Cyclamen.

The leaves may appear with the flowers, although rarely maturing until after the flowers have faded, or they may appear later. This is in some respects due to seasonal fluctuations, even in the wild, but some plants at least consistently flower before their leaves appear. In the wild the onset of early rain in late summer often promotes leaves and flowers at the same time, whereas the more normal dry end to the summer appears to promote flowers at the expense of the leaves, the latter developing later.

The typical *C. hederifolium* leaf is heart-shaped with an angled margin, often with five short lobes. The overall colour is deep green upon which there is a hastate pattern in another shade of green or grey. In other forms the leaves may be spear-shaped or arrow-shaped, with or without lobing. Leaf colour can range from plain green, sometimes with the veins picked out in another shade of green, to plain pewter or silver (especially in cultivated forms), or green with the pattern picked out in silver or pewter, occasionally with a pink overlay when young. Forms with brighter green, often lustrous, leaves are also found in the wild and in cultivation. This variation has, as with *C. coum* and *C. repandum*, given the gardener a wealth of interesting plants with plenty of scope for hybridization within the species and the chance to select and develop new forms; for the connoisseur of subtle differences, they are ideal plants to grow and will provide countless hours of pleasure.

In the garden, plants also vary in flowering time and I have several clones which are consistent from one year to another in coming into flower as most of the others are fading. This helps to extend the flowering season by several weeks.

Most plants in cultivation are unscented but scented forms are found in gardens. In my experience scented forms come true from seed provided both parents are scented so it is perhaps best to isolate scented plants to their own patch in the garden. Mixed with non-scented plants all seedlings seem to come non-scented. The scent, as with most cyclamen, is strongest on warm, sunny days and least effective in dull, cool or wet weather.

The white-flowered plant often seen in cultivation has been generally referred to as var. *album* or 'Album', but the former has never been validly published and the reader may think that it would be the name to choose in validation; white-flowered forms are found in the wild from time to time, always in mixed colonies with the ordinary pink forms predominating, so that the rank of forma would seem the most appropriate. However, in 1903 Jordan (in *Ic. Fl. Eur.* 3:20) published a description of the pure white form under the name *C. albiflorum*, accompanied by an excellent coloured illustration. I therefore decided to take up Jordan's name, and the plant in question became forma *albiflorum* (Jordan) Grey-Wilson.

Cyclamen hederifolium is very closely related to *C. africanum* and the flowers, placed side by side, cannot easily be told apart, except that the flowers of the latter are almost invariably larger (excluding some cultivars of *C. hederifolium*), with a rather narrower and more extended 'snout'. Differences in the plants, especially in the tubers and the disposition of leaves and flowers, is quite marked on the other hand, as is hardiness. See p.12.

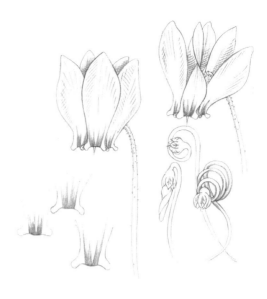

Cyclamen hederifolium.

DESCRIPTION *Tuber* depressed-globose, often rather flat above, up to 25cm (10in) diameter (occasionally more in cultivated specimens, to 36cm/15in), becoming corky and fissured with age, rooting mainly from the shoulders and sides, leaving the base bare. *Leaves* very variable, but the commonest shape encountered is cordate with 2–3 pairs of angled or short lobes in the lower half, giving the general shape that of the ivy leaf, but leaves on different plants may be lyre-shaped, oblong, lanceolate to broadly heart-shaped, with or without lobes or angles, the lamina 3–15cm (1.2–6in) long, 2.4–13cm (0.9–5.1in) wide, and the margin may be faintly to markedly toothed, with the basal sinus narrow but deep, the basal lobes diverging to somewhat overlapping; leaf colour is very variable but is commonly grey-green with a hastate pattern in a darker or paler shade, or in pewter, silver, or cream, sometimes the leaves with a double hastate pattern or with an overall cast of grey, silver or pewter above, while beneath they are usually green with a flush of red or purple, but rarely as deeply coloured beneath as in some other species; petioles 7.5–27cm (3–10.8in) long, usually elbowed in the lower half. *Pedicels* elbowed in the lower half, 8–20cm (3.1–8in) long, greenish to reddish-brown or purple, coiling from the top downwards as the young fruits begin to develop. *Flowers* appearing before or with the young leaves, occasionally earlier, sweetly scented or unscented; corolla pale to deep pink, pinkish-purple or reddish-purple, with a double V-shaped, purple-magenta mark at the base of each petal, rarely flowers pure white; corolla lobes oblong to elliptical, usually erect and twisted but not always so, 14–22mm

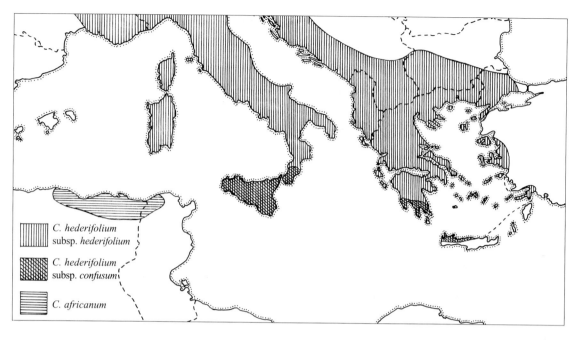

Map 8: Distribution of *C. hederifolium* and *C. africanum*.

(0.6–0.9in) long, strongly auricled at the base; style not or only very slightly protruding.

HABITAT Woodland (evergreen or deciduous) and scrub, often in maquis or garrigue, in ravines and gullies or occasionally on rocky river banks. It is sometimes abundant in olive groves or orchards, especially on the banks or beneath the walls separating terraces, sometimes growing in the crevices of walls or cliffs. Although generally found growing in dappled shade, *C. hederifolium* can occasionally be found in sunnier, more open situations, very occasionally in association with *C. graecum*; sea level to 800(–1300)m 2600(–4300)ft altitude.

In general *C. hederifolium* favours the leafier soils and dappled shade in a similar way to *C. repandum*. Indeed in the Greek Peloponnese *C. peloponnesiacum* subsp. *peloponnesiacum* (in the strict sense) and *C. hederifolium* can sometimes be found occupying the same site, as in the Langada Gorge to the west of Sparta, but they of course flower at very different times of the year. *Galanthus reginae-olgae* flowers at the same time as *C. hederifolium* and the two species sometimes occupy the same site; also in the Peloponnese.

DISTRIBUTION *Cyclamen hederifolium* is distributed in southern Europe from south and south-eastern France to southern Switzerland, the Yugoslavian States, Greece and Bulgaria, as well as extreme western Asiatic Turkey (Aegean region from Troy to Marmaris), including the

Mediterranean islands of Corsica, Sardinia, Sicily, north and north-west Crete and many of the smaller Greek islands; September to November, occasionally later. Map 8.

In recent years plants from the more southerly end of the species range have been studied more closely. Some populations are remarkable for the fleshiness and thickness of their leaves and the stouter more erect petioles and pedicels. In addition, the leaves are often more angled or even shallowly lobed, often being broadest at or close to the middle, and the leaf coloration is generally a brighter green, with a rather poorly defined hastate pattern. Furthermore, the leaves are noticeably shinier above and beneath. On the other hand, there are no noticeable differences in the flowers, either in the colour or the size, although some plants have a noticeably wider mouth with even more prominent auricles. The leaves can become very large and one specimen that I came across in the Mani peninsula, Greek Peloponnese, had the largest leaves I have seen (18 x 17.8cm/7.1 x 7in) and these leaves are now deposited in the Herbarium at the Royal Botanic Gardens, Kew, for future reference. In some instances the leaves are shallowly lobed in much the same manner as they are in *C. rohlfsianum*, especially plants from Cretan populations. To date plants of this type have been found in Sicily, the southern Peloponnese (Mani), several of the more southerly Greek islands and Crete (indeed all the Cretan plants appear to be of this type). Those measured so far have proved to be tetraploids (2n=68) rather than the normal diploid status for *C. hederifolium*. This factor, as well as the southerly distribution of these tetraploid populations, has led several authors to speculate that the plants are in fact analogous with *C. africanum*. However,

C. africanum can be distinguished readily by its tuber characteristics (see p.121) and leaf characters; the leaves are nearly always matt green or grey-green above and beneath, broadest in the lower half and with a more pronounced toothed margin, in addition to a more boldly defined hastate pattern above.

The 'tetraploid' *hederifolium*s were formally distinguished in the first edition of this work as var. *confusum*. Since then more research has been undertaken by me and others into this intriguing taxon. As a result I have now elevated it to subspecific rank (see p.207). The 'tetraploid' plants are to be found primarily at the southern extremities of the range of the species. Not all the plants designated subsp. *confusum* may in fact be tetraploids and this requires further investigation. An analagous situation occurs in *C. africanum* where diploid plants and teraploids are widespread, sometimes apparently co-existing in the same natural populations.

It would be wrong to claim to be the first to note these differences in *C. hederifolium*. Hildebrand certainly had observed some of the differences, even going so far as to suggest the name var. *crassifolium* in his epic account of the genus published in 1898, although the name was not validated at the time (see *Die Gattung Cyclamen* L., Jena; now translated by Erna Franck and published by The Cyclamen Society in 1999). Later, however, he formally described the taxon as a species in its own right: *C. crassifolium* Hildebr. in *Beih. Bot. Centralbl.* 22(2): 195, t.6 (1907). In the future if it is thought necessary to raise this plant to specific level, then Hildebrand's name would stand.

Subsp. *confusum* has a distinctive appearance. Foremost is the thickness and texture of the leaves which are very fleshy, glossy pale to deep green above and generally with a rather poorly defined hastate pattern. In some case the leaves are virtually pentagonal in outline and evenly lobed in the manner of those of *C. rohlfsianum*. Like the leaf lamina, both the petioles and pedicels are noticeably thicker than in subsp. *hederifolium*. On the whole the flowers are generally larger, sometimes twice the size of those of subsp. *hederifolium*. Furthermore, the auricles are even more pronounced, the mouth generally broader and the basal petal markings more extended, generally reaching further up the petal lobes from the base. Differences can also be observed in the sepals: in subsp. *hederifolium* they are slightly toothed and with three or five prominent veins (the mid vein and 1–2 pairs of laterals, that are particularly noticeable towards the sepal margin), while those of subsp. *confusum* are thicker, entire margined and with only the mid vein generally evident. Subsp. *confusum* is, in my experience, (both in the wild and in cultivation) highly scented, a far scarcer character in subsp. *hederifolium*. It also comes into flower rather later,

105 *Cyclamen hederifolium* subsp. *hederifolium* forma *albiflorum* in cultivation.

extending the flowering period in the garden almost up to Christmas. In Crete it has been observed still in flower as late as February (see *Cyclamen Society Journal* 25(1): 25, 2001). In the wild the flower colour ranges from pale pink to very deep pink, or almost magenta-pink, although no albinos have been found to date. More information is required on their exact distribution, whether or not they are to be found growing together with ordinary forms of *C. hederifolium* (this would appear not to be the case on present evidence) and, of course, whether or not the plants are consistently tetraploid. Interestingly, in the garden they have proved fully hardy, as normal *C. hederifolium*, but as stated they come into flower late, being often in full flower when the normal diploid forms have practically finished blooming. Observations in the wild and in cultivation also show them to be rather shy at setting fruit and the resultant seed capsules contain fewer seeds in my experience. They are also slow to develop compared to subsp. *hederifolium*, rarely flowering before three or four years from germination. The following distinguishes the two subspecies: it applies only to wild plants or plants of known wild origin:

- **Subsp. *hederifolium*.** *Leaves* generally rather deep green or grey-green with a well-marked hastate pattern, scarcely shiny above and beneath; lamina longer than wide, angled or shallowly lobed and finely toothed, generally hastate in outline, longer than broad; petioles mostly 1.5–2.5mm (0.06–0.1in) diameter. *Calyx lobes* thin, with three or five

distinct veins. *Corolla lobes* 14–24mm (0.6–1in) long. Throughout the range of the species apart from Crete, parts of Sicily, the southern Peloponnese and probably many of the Greek islands and SW Turkey. Map 8.

Forma *hederifolium*: flowers pale to deep pink to reddish-purple, with deep purple-magenta markings at the base of each corolla-lobe. Throughout the range of subsp. *hederifolium* (see below).

Forma *albiflorum* (Jordan) Grey-Wilson: flowers pure white sometimes with pale pink in the throat, petals unmarked. Found occasionally throughout the range of the species, especially in the east, but always rare and with forma *hederifolium*.

- **Subsp. *confusum*.** *Leaves* a bright green with a poorly-defined hastate pattern, thicker and fleshier, shiny, particularly beneath; lamina often as long as wide, sometimes wider than long and generally broadest at or close to the middle, shallowly 5 (–7) lobed with rather obscure, blunt marginal teeth or practically untoothed, pentagonal to heptagonal in outline, often as broad as long, sometimes broader; petioles 2.5–4mm (0.1–0.16in) diameter. *Calyx lobes* thick, obscurely veined. *Corolla lobes* 21–43mm (0.9–1.8in) long: Known from S Sicily, W Crete, the central and southern Mani and Monemvasia Peninsulas (Greek Peloponnese), and also reported from several Greek islands including Cephalonia, Corfu, Cos, Lefkada, Zakinthos (= Zante, south of Cephalonia), Poros and SW Turkey. Map 8.

Leaf measurements in subsp. *confusum* are mostly in the range 6.5–10.2cm (2.6–4in) long, 6.2–10.6cm (2.4–4.2in) wide. The largest measured (from a Cretan population) was 18cm (7.1in) long by 17.8cm (7in)wide but specimens from the Peloponnese (SW of Monemvasia) can reach almost the same dimensions. In addition, the flowers can be larger, but not consistently so; however, the mouth of the corolla is often broader and the auricles even more pronounced than in subsp. *hederifolium*, while the staining round the mouth may reach midway up the petal in subsp. *confusum*.

106 *Cyclamen hederifolium* subsp. *confusum*; leaves of different plants in a wild colony found SW of Monemvasia in the Greek Peloponnese. The coin is a British 50 pence piece showing how large the leaves can be in the Greek form of the subspecies.

107 *Cyclamen hederifolium* subsp. *confusum* in the wild SW of Monemvasia, Greece, Peloponnese.

108 *Cyclamen hederifolium* subsp. *confusum* in the northern Mani Peninsula, Peloponnese, Greece, where it is often found beneath trees in shaded gullies.

109 Above left: *Cyclamen hederifolium* subsp. *confusum*, a near white-flowered form photographed in the Mani Peninsula, Greece.

110 Centre left: *Cyclamen hederifolium* subsp. *confusum* from seed collected legally near Topolia by Cyclamen Society members; this dark-flowered form has been distributed by Ashwood Nursery.

111 Below left: *Cyclamen hederifolium* subsp. *confusum*; a particularly bold-marked leaf form in the author's garden from mainland Greek material.

112 Above right: *Cyclamen hederifolium* subsp. *confusum* ; the typical Cretan form, from plants collected legally by members of the Cyclamen Society.

113 Centre right: *Cyclamen hederifolium* subsp. *confusum* in a particularly dark-flowered form photographed SW of Monemvasia in the Peloponnese, Greece.

Subsp. *confusum* clearly requires further close analysis in the wild. If populations are shown to be both consistent and separate from those of subsp. *hederifolium*, then it could be raised to species level. I have observed this plant at various localities in southern Greece, especially in the easternmost peninsula south of Monemvasia, and in western Crete. Although extensive colonies can be observed in both places, the colonies themselves are scattered and by no means numerous. Small differences can be observed between the Cretan and Greek mainland populations, and indeed some of the island forms, but this requires further detailed investigation before any sort of judgement can be made. Interestingly, both *C. hederifolium* subsp. *confusum* and *C. graecum* subsp. *graecum* are only found in that region of western and north-western Crete closest to the Peloponnese.

Much has been said about the parallel evolution within the *C. hederifolium* complex and the *C. africanum* complex, some even suggesting that *C. hederifolium* subsp. *confusum* and *C. africanum* are one and the same thing. Clearly detailed studies of population in North Africa, particularly in Morocco, would help. However, apart from the rather nebulous character of hardiness (*C. africanum* is not frost hard in the garden, while *C. hederifolium* subsp. *confusum* is!), the easiest way to distinguish them is to examine the tubers: in *C. africanum* the tuber is generally deeper with a well-marked depression (concavity) on the upper surface, with roots appearing all over the shoulders, sides and base of the tuber; in *C. hederifolium* (including subsp. *confusum*) the tuber is thinner and without a depression above, while the roots are confined to the shoulders and sides. Differences can also be observed in the position of the flowers: in *C. africanum* they arise vertically from the tuber, while in *C. hederifolium* they arise to one side (as do the leaves) on pedicels that are decumbent at the base.

AWARDS
- *C. hederifolium* subsp. *hederifolium* forma *album*: A.M. 1937; F.C.C. 1959
- *C. hederifolium* subsp. *hederifolium* forma *hederifolium*: A.G.M. 1925; A.M. 1961 (as *C. neapolitanum*); F.C.C. 1967 (as *C. neapolitanum*), 1973

Cyclamen africanum Boiss. & Reut.

The North African counterpart of *C. hederifolium* is *C. africanum*, which can, in overall terms, be described as 'bigger and more robust looking'. It is a very handsome plant in its finest forms but few gardeners find it hardy in their gardens which is the prime reason for its neglect by all but the collector of cyclamen species, for plants need to be nurtured in a frost-free environment, or at the very

least an environment from which all but the mildest frosts are excluded. It used to be thought that *C. rohlfsianum* (also from North Africa) was one of the tenderer species but this at least has not been borne out by me nor by Kath Dryden. We have both found *C. rohlfsianum* will stand up to 2–3°C (36–37°F) of frost unaffected, while the leaves of *C. africanum* 'go down' under similar conditions and take some hours to recover once the temperature has lifted, while with heavier frost the plants of *C. africanum*, at least, will be killed or badly damaged.

Cyclamen africanum does in fact make an extremely good pot plant for the alpine house. It can, incidentally, be readily grown on a cool but sunny windowsill in the house, where the flowers can continue sometimes from the autumn almost until Christmas. Its chief requirements are a dry summer dormant season, with watering commencing in late summer and early autumn once the flower buds begin to appear, followed by ample water during the main growing period – November through to April, at the end of which the plants generally start to die down.

Early confusion between these two species stemmed mainly from their superficial similarity. As early as 1844 Duby (DC. *Prodromus* 8:57) had identified it as being the same as *C. hederifolium*. However, in 1852 Boissier and Reuter described the Algerian plant as a distinct species, giving it the appropriate name of *C. africanum*, by which we know it today. In 1898 Hildebrand reported a hybrid between *C. africanum* and *C. hederifolium*, confirming the close affinity between the two species. There is little reason to doubt Hildebrand's accuracy as he was a thorough worker and, in any case, the hybrid has been produced on several occasions in the intervening years. Some would argue that if two species interbreed and produce fertile offspring then they must surely be one and the same species. I in no way hold to this view, for there are countless examples of fertile hybrids in our gardens. Take, for example, hybrids freely produced between the true oxlip, *Primula elatior*, and the common primrose, or between many quite different-looking species of *Aquilegia*, in the garden. What keeps the species' identity distinct in the wild may be one of a number of factors such as habitat differences, distinct geographical locations or different pollinators which prevent them crossing in the wild. Brought together in the artificial environment of cultivation no such barriers exist and hybrids may occur. I say 'may' because there are also countless examples of closely related species in cultivation that never hybridize, however hard we try.

Having said this, though, *Cyclamen africanum* and *C. hederifolium* are without doubt very closely related both on morphological as well as cytological criteria; that cannot be disputed. What also is quite apparent is that typical wild source material of these two species can be separated quite readily by eye without resorting to microscopic or intricate chromosomal investigations and most cyclamen gardeners would concur with this. Botanists and gardeners get 'the feel' for a plant and can often tell without hesitation which species a particular plant belongs to, although it may often be difficult to say precisely what the difference or differences are. As a scientist this sounds far too imprecise and whimsical but it holds a certain validity; the 'feel' factor often reveals a combination of minor characters which in themselves may seem unimportant but which, taken in conjunction, may be significant.

I was once asked how I separated *C. africanum* from *C. hederifolium* and I said, somewhat tongue in cheek it has to be admitted, "Plant them in the garden and if they survive the winter they are *C. hederifolium*, if not they are, or were, *C. africanum*". Of course, hardiness is an inherited characteristic just as leaf shape or flower colour is. There may be nothing in the gross morphology of a species to reveal hardiness or lack of it but other characters may link in. Incidentally, *C. africanum* is one of the tenderest species whilst *C. hederifolium* is probably the hardiest!

To me typical *C. africanum* has several distinctive features (and I have examined quite a few known wild source plants, live and in the herbarium, although such investigations are hampered by the fact that there is a general muddle in cultivated material with some *C. africanum* being *C. hederifolium* or indeed putative hybrids between the two). First, there is the tuber which in *C. africanum* is more rounded, often hollowed in the centre above and rooting virtually all over its surface. In contrast, those of *C. hederifolium* are flatter and not hollowed above, rooting primarily on the top and the shoulders, leaving the base underneath free of roots. Second, the leaves, which can often be larger and brighter green (though not consistently so), have straight or curved stalks (petioles) which arise erect or ascending from the tuber; those of *C. hederifolium* arise to one side of the tuber on elbowed petioles. Third, the flowers appear very bunched, arising on erect stalks (pedicels) above the tuber; in contrast, in *C. hederifolium* both leaves and flowers arise to one side of the tuber on elbowed stalks and this is very noticeable in pot-grown plants where leaves and flowers always appear to be trying to escape from the side of their containers. In gross morphological terms *C. africanum* is generally a larger plant, especially as regards flower size.

Another less obvious difference can be seen by examining the stamens: in *C. africanum* the anthers are yellow, whereas in *C. hederifolium* they are reddish or purplish. The corolla shape is also slightly different: in *C. africanum* the corolla looks rather narrower, due to a somewhat extended 'snout'.

It is often written that *C. hederifolium* flowers before its leaves and *C. africanum* with the leaves partly developed at flowering time. However, this simply is not

114 *Cyclamen africanum*, showing the flowers arising on erect pedicels directly from the centre of the tuber.
115 *Cyclamen africanum*; the flowers are very similar to those of *C. hederifolium* but with a detectably longer 'snout'.
116 *Cyclamen africanum* in cultivation in the author's garden, where plants are kept in a frost-free environment.

117 A fine pot of *Cyclamen africanum*, a form with attractively patterned leaves.
118 *Cyclamen africanum*, showing the typical form with a long and rather narrow 'snout' to the flowers.

true. At the time of writing (early October) I have several plants of *C. africanum* in full flower without a leaf to be seen. I have found that this differs from season to season and is related to some extent to when water is first applied in the autumn; water applied early, before the flower buds appear, generally results in a plant with a lot of leaf development by the time the plants are in full flower.

Gardeners will, I hope, forgive me here for a digression into the realms of cytology, for no true appraisal of these two species can be made without resorting to mention of the C word – chromosomes. Over the years a number of cytological investigations have been carried out into this complex. Glasau in 1939 published a paper showing that *C. africanum* existed at two levels in the wild, diploids with 2n=34 chromosomes and tetraploids with 2n=68. The latter he considered to be the true *C. africanum* and the former, the diploid, he named *C. numidicum*, although the morphological features of separation were unclear or at least not clear-cut. Schwarz and Lepper (1964) as well as others disagreed with this analysis, insisting that the diploid plant was in fact *C. africanum* and the tetraploid was given a new name, *C. commutatum*. All very

confusing and unnecessary as the physical features of the plants could not be connected with any certainty to the number of chromosomes and today most botanists agree that these represent a single species whose correct name is *C. africanum*. The fact that species can exist with several ploidy levels is well known. Brian Mathew in his monograph of the genus *Crocus* ('The Crocus', 1982) comments on the fact that *C. chrysanthus* has chromosome numbers varying from 8 to 10, 12, 13, 14, 16, 18, 19 and 20 and that, although a variable species, no appreciable morphological differences can be accepted to divide the taxon, and in *C. nudiflorus* diploid and tetraploid individuals may be found growing side by side in the same wild population, with no observable morphological differences to separate them; many other similar examples are known in the plant world but the significance of different chromosome levels in the same species is not fully understood. But what does this mean to the plant; do extra chromosomes impart any advantage to the individual? Perhaps none in the short term but in the long term varying chromosome levels may impart evolutionary advantages which we can only guess at; for instance under increasingly severe climatic conditions, or isolation, polyploids may afford some selective advantage over diploids, although the physical appearance of the plants remains unaltered. In other words genetic diversity may be a great advantage to the species under certain conditions. In many ways this is borne out by the isolation of many cyclamen species in the wild with pronounced chromosomal variation from species to species or from subgenus to subgenus.

This is the simple picture but we have not yet taken into account the more widespread species *C. hederifolium*. For many years this was assumed to have a stable chromosome number with a diploid count of 2n=34. More recent investigations by Grimshaw and Bennett (1991), based partly on known wild origin material, has revealed that some plants, especially from the south of the range on the Greek islands, are in fact tetraploids, 2n=68, an analogous situation to that found in *C. africanum*. In passing, it is also worth mentioning that their studies revealed for the first time from the wild a triploid plant, 2n=51, from near San Marino in Italy. This plant is of little use in the overall argument as triploids are usually sterile (though not necessarily so; see Grimshaw and Bennett 1991) and present no evolutionary advantage to the individual; they are in fact in an evolutionary cul-de-sac. The triploid may in fact be a hybrid between a diploid and a tetraploid plant and this would show that tetraploids exist in this part of Italy as well as in southern Greece.

The tetraploid '*hederifolium*s' have certain, though far from consistent, features. They often have larger leaves of a brighter, often shiny green and appear to have more upright leaf- and flower-stalks and in cultivation, at least, they are somewhat later flowering and slower to flower from seed. However, this study is still in its infancy and the distribution of tetraploids of *C. hederifolium* in the wild is poorly understood, though I would strongly suspect that they will occur at the southern extremities of the range of the species, primarily I suspect because the climatic regime is more severe, certainly more arid in the south, and such extremes seem to promote the tetraploid status in some way which we yet do not understand. Certainly in the Mani Peninsula *C. hederifolium* is present in many places especially in the woodland in the north (west of Gythion) where the plants are typical of many found in garden with rather greyish leaves and spreading leaf- and flower-stalks. Further south, however, in more extreme habitats, plants can be found with far larger, bright green and shiny, more upright leaves and although these have not been investigated cytologically I would almost bet that they are tetraploids. They behave with the same distinctions in my garden and are fully hardy.

This brings me to the crux of the matter. Can these tetraploid '*hederifolium*s' in fact be equated with *C. africanum*? Grimshaw and Bennett (1991) have suggested that there may not be sufficient morphological differences between the two taxa to maintain them as separate species. I would disagree with this for there are as many differences between the typical plants (*C. africanum* and *C. hederifolium*) as there is say between *C. coum* and *C. alpinum* or *C. repandum* and *C. creticum*. Lumping may be a convenient way out but does it help our overall understanding of these complexes? I think not. One has to accept that 'species' are variable and that understanding the degree and range of variation is critical in evaluating the precise nature of a particular species or taxon. Maintaining the *status quo* shows that there are two species – one, *C. africanum*, confined to Algeria and Morocco, and the other, *C. hederifolium*, restricted to Europe and western Asia Minor, and that the two have probably been isolated from one another for some considerable time; certainly since the formation of the Mediterranean. They have clearly evolved from the same ancestral stock but increasing isolation to north and south have created divergence. In the north *C. hederifolium* is, in all probability, exhibiting gradual speciation with southern elements (in places like Sicily and the Greek Islands), becoming more *africanum*-like, but this is a secondary rather than a primary trend. My own impression is that these tetraploid *hederifolium*s resemble *C. africanum* rather than being *C. africanum*. Certainly lumping them all into *C. hederifolium* would solve nothing at this stage other than to blur specific boundaries; it certainly would not help, our overall understanding. More work clearly needs to be done in the wild, and gross morphological characters as well as

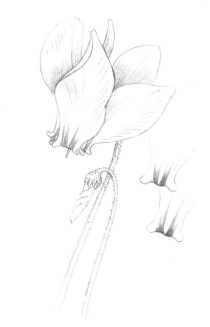

Cyclamen africanum.

cytological evidence needs to be looked at, hand in hand. This may not in the long run help, for species do not necessarily fit into neat compartments for our convenience. More work needs to be carried out in the field, observing wild populations with a scientifically based statistical analysis of the data as well as sampling the cytological diversity, either in the field or by the careful collecting of suitable plants (under licence) in the field for later examination in the laboratory. What is more important is that only wild-origin material should be studied and, although interesting, any plants of unknown origin, or those suspected of being hybrids should be excluded except for the purpose of comparison. The problem would make a very interesting postgraduate study for a budding young cytologist.

To sum up, as best one can: it would appear that *C. africanum* has been derived from *C. hederifolium* and has undergone various morphological changes. From the diploid plant has arisen, perhaps on more than one occasion, fertile polyploids which bear little if anything in the way of distinguishing morphological characters. There is absolutely no evidence that *C. hederifolium* is to be found in North Africa today nor, conversely, that *C. africanum* is to be found in Europe, despite the occurrence there of tetraploid forms of *C. hederifolium*.

Herbarium specimens collected in the vicinity of Djurdjura in Algeria reveal rather unusual leaf characteristics, the lamina being scarcely lobed or even unlobed and with rather indistinct marginal teeth. These require further investigation once the political problems in that country become more stable.

DESCRIPTION *Plant* generally rather robust with the leaves usually arising as the flowers fade in the autumn and dying down in the late spring. *Tubers* to 14cm (5.5in) diameter or more, depressed-globose, often hollowed above and in mature specimens becoming rough and corky and rather flaky on the surface, rooting more or less all over the surface, especially on the shoulders and over the base, sometimes rather unevenly so. *Leaves* broadly heart-shaped to oval, 5.3–18cm (2.1–7.1in) long, 4.6–18cm (1.8–7.1in) wide, often angled or shallowly lobed, with a finely to rather coarsely toothed margin, generally mid- to rather dark bright green, but sometimes greyish-green, with some paler or darker marbling above or with a more or less grey hastate pattern, green or sometimes flushed with pink or purple beneath; petioles curved to straight, not elbowed, arising more or less erect from the tuber. *Pedicels* 11–22cm (4.3–8.7in) long, erect to ascending, green or purplish-brown, coiling from the top downwards as the young fruits develop. *Flowers* generally appearing in advance of the leaves but, in cultivation at least, sometimes borne with the partly developed young leaves, occasionally fragrant; corolla variable in colour from pale pink to deep rose-pink, each petal with a basal purple or crimson-magenta, broad, V-shaped blotch; corolla-lobes 18–35mm (0.7–1.4in) long, twisted and distinctly and rather prominently auricled at the base.

HABITAT Growing in scrub or rocky gullies, often in partial shade, although sometimes in more exposed sunny places.

DISTRIBUTION North Africa, being confined to northern Algeria (mainly east of Algiers) and north-western Tunisia; September to November. Map 8.

AWARDS
• A.M. 1967

SERIES PURPURASCENS
(*Cyclamen purpurascens* Group)
C. purpurascens, *C. p.* forma *album*, *C. p.* forma *carmineolineatum*; *C. colchicum*

This and the previous series consist of summer- or autumn-flowering species with large and corky tubers. Although in their botanical classification all these species form a discreet subgenus within the genus (see p.47), they are best considered as two series both from a botanical as well as a gardener's point of view. In Series Purpurascens under consideration the tubers are often uneven, especially when mature, and root somewhat haphazardly from the sides and base. The leaves are unlobed, often with rather horny teeth along the margin. The corolla has poorly defined auricles which are sometimes apparently absent altogether. The sepals are 1-veined. This series contains two delightful and sweetly scented species, but they are not the easiest to please in the garden environment, although those with a more continental-type climate seem to fare far better.

119 *Cyclamen purpurascens*, the most northerly distributed species in the genus, with a centre of distribution in central Europe.
120 *Cyclamen purpurascens* is often found to be difficult to cultivate well; however, this photograph shows a very free-flowering form in the garden of Gerald Firak near Chicago, USA.

Cyclamen purpurascens Miller

Cyclamen purpurascens is a virtually evergreen species, with the previous season's leaves hanging on until the new ones appear in the summer. It and *C. colchicum* delight in being the only species that will produce blooms through the hot summer months.

Anyone walking in the woodlands of the Alps or neighbouring regions may well have seen the delightful summer-flowering *C. purpurascens*. I can remember small bunches of the sweetly-scented flowers being sold by street sellers in Geneva in the 1960s, presumably gathered on the mountain slopes of the Saléve close at hand where it is found in large numbers.

Reginald Farrer, that doyen of English rock gardening, thought that this species was by far the most exciting. In 'Among the Hills' (1911) he writes of *C. purpurascens* (then *C. europaeum*): "In all the garden there are no plants that more completely take my heart, they are so invariably, so indefatigably, beautiful. Their whole personality so winning and sweet. Exquisite they are when their pink blooms come fluttering up like butterflies."

Despite such remarks *C. purpurascens* seems to be the most tantalising of cyclamen in cultivation, promising a lot but rarely performing well, particularly in the open garden. Judging from its distribution (it is the most northerly species in the genus) it might be expected to be one of the easiest species to grow but the number of gardens in which it thrives are few and the number in which self-sown seedlings appear sadly seem even fewer. There is no question of the plant's hardiness. In my experience plants linger on like the proverbial tortoise and take an awfully long time dying, surviving for a number of years and throwing up the occasional flower or two during the summer months. In the wild it is often found growing in rocky woodland in deep leaf litter and those who have succeeded with it in the open garden have had greater success by planting the tubers in a deep leafy soil, especially one in which pine needles have been incorporated.

In contrast, I have had better luck in the alpine house, especially after Kath Dryden suggested I put them below the bench rather than above it. There my plants grow with the pots forever plunged in a moist sand bed where they remain more or less evergreen and flower intermittently from June through to October. Although I never recall one of my plants having more than half a dozen flowers at any one time I would not be without it for all the world, for it has one of the sweetest fragrances of any cyclamen, a perfume without the peppery undertone of so many cyclamen, and perhaps more reminiscent of sweet violets.

Others have greater success by removing their plants to the coolness of a shaded open frame in a quite corner

121 The flower of *Cyclamen purpurascens* showing a form with well-marked auricles.
122 *Cyclamen purpurascens*; a form with attractively patterned foliage.

of the garden for the summer months and I must get round to trying this one day. Certainly plants greatly resent heat and dryness and will repay such treatment by a rapid demise. One common factor in analysing success with this species in different gardens is that the tubers should be planted deep in the soil (15–20cm/6–8in being not too deep), and capped with a generous mulch of bark chippings or pine needles.

However, the above remarks should not put the reader off trying this little gem in the open garden, for I know several gardens in which it thrives, although rarely producing a great rash of bloom like its hardy cousins, *C. coum* and *C. hederifolium*. On the other hand there is no other species that will produce flowers from the early days of summer to the first frosts of the autumn.

It is perhaps significant that those gardening in areas with a more continental climate seem to fare better with this species. Gerald Firak writing in the *Journal of the Cyclamen Society* 24(1): 18 (2000) clearly enjoys great success with this speices in his Illinois garden, in a suburb of Chicago, USA, and his photographs of it in the same journal the following year [(25(1), 2001] certainly shows an impressive colony in full bloom. Firak comments that the species does extremely well when grown from seed, that pricking on seedlings is relatively easy, but moving older unpotted tubers is extremely hazardous. In fact he advocates moving or planting out only potted plants. Other points made in the article include the depth of planting ("there is no need to deep plant the tubers, rather they should be planted at the same depth they were in the pot") and that heavy soils are to be avoided (what the species really needs is a good highly organic soil, light, yet moist, and full of humus). Firak also records that his plants are extremely hardy, having withstood temperatures as low as –29°C (–21°F), with little snow cover at the time.

Cyclamen purpurascens is not always a reliable seed setter, especially when grown under glass; I have had more success with plants outdoors and can normally expect a modest amount of seed each year. Much depends on the weather during the summer, for if it is too hot the fruits fail to develop and often abort, even after fertilization. In some gardens it has been known to self-sow so the answer is probably to try it in as many parts of the garden as possible in the hope that the perfect niche can be found for it. A general reluctance to set a good quantity of fruit means that seed of *C. purpurascens* is generally rather scarce compared to that of other species such as *C. repandum* or *C. coum*.

Cyclamen purpurascens is rather variable in leaf size and markings as well as flower size and treatment over the years by various authors has ranged from the recognition of a single variable species, or a single species with a series of subspecies and varieties, to a complex of closely related species. None of these treatments has proved entirely satisfactory, primarily due to the lack of good and scientifically-based statistical data and by the fact that any attempt to divide the 'species' has been thwarted by the presence of intermediate forms which hamper clear subdivision.

Leaves vary greatly in size and shape from broad heart-shaped to kidney-shaped. Most have at least some markings on the upper surface, often in a paler cream, grey, pewter or even silver. In some instances a pewter or silvery wash may cover the entire leaf surface and these forms have been found in the Lake Garda region of Italy and in the vicinity of Bled in former Yugoslavia (now in Slovenia). Plain deep green-leaved forms without any hint of markings can be found throughout the range of the species, generally in mixed populations with marked-leaved forms; in the Fatra region of Slovakia the populations are entirely plain-leaved and this plant has been called *C. fatrense*.

Flower colour may also vary from pale wishy-washy pinks to deep rose-pink or carmine, or very rarely pure white, and this can vary between colonies or even within a single colony. In addition, the petals may be rather short and scarcely twisted or they may be longer and narrower with a more pronounced twist and these latter forms with their more elegant flowers are the most desirable in gardens.

The pure white-flowered plant *C. purpurascens* forma *album* (see p.128) is a rare plant in cultivation. It has been found a number of times over the years in the wild and such plants were known early on in the twentieth century. A Dr Alfred de Leitner, a member of the Alpine Garden Society, collected a fine white form in northern Croatia in August 1938. A plant from this gathering was shown by Doris Saunders in October 1944 when it received an Award of Merit under the name *C. europaeum* var. *album*. Doris Saunders comments: "According to Dr de Leitner, the *Cyclamen europaeum* from this locality (near Varazdin) never commence to flower before August, and this plant of white *C. europaeum* retains the August-flowering habit in cultivation. It is very floriferous, one year bearing one hundred sweetly scented flowers, and remains in flower over a long period, but so far has yielded no seed..." The article (*Bulletin Alpine Garden Society* 12:182, 1944) is accompanied by a good black and white photograph showing the plant which, strangely, appears to have set a number of fruits. Even today pure white *C. purpurascens* is rarely seen and it is not at present available; at least it is not listed in the current edition of *The RHS Plant Finder*.

The presence or absence of auricles in this species has long been argued and some botanists have firmly stated that the corolla is 'exauriculate'. The truth is that there is often a suggestion of auricles at the base of the corolla-lobes and there have been forms seen in the wild with unmistakable auricles. I have one plant in which the auricles are almost as pronounced as they are in *C. hederifolium*. Unfortunately, this feature is almost impossible to study in dried herbarium specimens of *C. purpurascens*. This may seem of little consequence but the presence of auricles, however small, helps to establish a close relationship to *C. hederifolium*, a view reinforced by the fact that the two species share the same chromosome number.

In its tuber *C. purpurascens* is rather unique. The young tuber is in no way exceptional but as plants age the tuber becomes gradually distorted and misshapen, often with several knobs, each with their own growing point or points, connecting by thinner 'necks'. In the wild the tubers often grow deep in the soil, generally among rocks, often developing long floral trunks 10cm (4in) or more in length.

This species was for many years known as *C. europaeum* and many still regret the passing of this name but it was abandoned as an ambiguous name (*nomen ambiguum*) for very good reason. In 1753 Linnaeus recognized only two taxa of *Cyclamen*, *C. indicum* (that need not concern us here, see p.204) and *C. europaeum*. Linnaeus had a broad view of his *C. europaeum* which included various elements which we recognize today as distinct species. The specimens upon which Linnaeus based his original diagnosis are to be found in the Burser and Clifford herbaria in London. Examination of these soon reveals that they include what we know today as *C. hederifolium*, *C. purpurascens* and *C. repandum*; there is also good reason to suppose that Linnaeus also included *C. coum* and *C. persicum* in this amalgam, although specimens of these latter two are not present in the herbaria indicated above. As Linnaeus's extremely brief diagnosis does not limit the application of the epithet *europaeum* to any one of these 'elements' it has been generally agreed that the name should be rejected as a *nomen confusum*. In fact the 'International Code of Botanical Nomenclature' (Seattle Congress, 1972) states quite clearly: "Linnaeus (Sp. Pl. 145, 1753) includes all the European and western Asiatic Cyclamen species then known under the name *C. europaeum*. the name was first restricted to one species by Miller ('Gard. Dict. ed. 8', 1768) and later to a different species by Jacquin ('Fl. Austr.' 5:1, t. 401, 1778) and Aiton (*Hort. Kew.* 1:196, 1789). Both interpretations have been followed, with a great preponderance in favour of the latter, incorrect application. The name *C. europaeum* has thus become a long-persistent source of error and is to be rejected."

Miller in fact applied the epithet *europaeum* to the plant we know today as *C. hederifolium* of Aiton and there is no doubt which species he is referring to. Miller also described another species giving it the name *C. purpurascens* and again this is clearly what we at present accept under that name. Both Jacquin and later Aiton, on the other hand, reverse this, applying the name *C. europaeum* to the species which we accept today as *C. purpurascens* Miller. As Linnaeus's epithet predates all the other proposed epithets then it must surely have precedence over them.

The reader can at this point be forgiven for pointing out that if the name *C. europaeum* of Linnaeus predates all the others then surely it can be used for one of the species which he originally encompassed within the name. The usual process would be what taxonomists call lecto-typification, that is choosing one of the elements (a dried specimen) and applying the name to it

(it becomes the lectotype): the specimens to which Linnaeus referred are quite adequate and there is no reason why one of them should not be chosen as the lectotype of the name *C. europaeum*. It can be argued that that is exactly what Miller did in 1768 by restricting the name to what we today call *C. hederifolium*. If this is so then *C. hederifolium* would automatically become *C. europaeum*, causing even more confusion. In fact the modification of Article 69 in the 1981 edition (Sydney) of the International Code no longer allows for the rejection of a name simply because it has caused confusion and an attempt to lectotypify it should be undertaken. However, in this example the plant has long been known under the name *C. hederifolium* and to suddenly have to call it *C. europaeum* would undoubtedly cause confusion and certainly, amongst the gardening and horticultural public at least, much annoyance and certainly ridicule. In such a controversy the interests of horticulture cannot be ignored, especially regarding the long usage of certain names and in such cases there is a strong and persuasive argument for preserving the latter synonym and abandoning the earlier name, in this instance *europaeum*. The fact that the name *C. europaeum* still lingers in some catalogues to this day shows how difficult it is to sometimes dislodge an old and familiar epithet, although the informed gardening public has readily accepted the name *C. purpurascens*.

DESCRIPTION *Tuber* rounded at first but in older plants becoming knobbly and characteristically distorted, to 6cm (2.3in) across, occasionally larger, rooting from all over the sides and base, occasionally dividing into several 'lumps' connected by 'necks'; the tubers sometimes break up into elongated 'fingers' that can detach themselves to become separate plants (this also happens occasionally in cultivated plants). *Leaves* almost evergreen, with the new leaves appearing in the mid- to late summer just as the old are fading, the lamina rounded to heart-shaped or even kidney-shaped, 3.2–7.8cm (1.3–3.1in) long, 2.8–7.5cm (1.1–3in) wide, generally being as wide as long, sometimes wider, with an untoothed or slightly toothed, unlobed margin, shiny deep green above and plain or with a marbled zone in paler green, cream or occasionally silver (forms in which the entire leaf surface is pewter-coloured have also been found in the wild, especially in northern Italy and Yugoslavia), the lower surface may be deep reddish-purple or green flushed with pink or purple; petiole 8–25cm (3–10in) long. *Pedicels*: 4–18cm (1.6–7.1in) long, usually purplish or purplish-brown, coiling from the top downwards as the young fruit develops. *Flowers* appearing from late June until September, or even as late as October, and varying in colour from pale rose-pink to purple or rosy-carmine,

Cyclamen purpurascens.

being generally somewhat darker around the mouth of the corolla; corolla-lobes, (14–)17–25mm/(0.6–)0.7–1in long, generally with rudimentary auricles, although small auricles can sometimes be clearly observed.

HABITAT The species inhabits woodland, deciduous or evergreen, but often of beech (*Fagus*) and hornbeam

Map 9: Distribution of *Cyclamen purpurascens.*

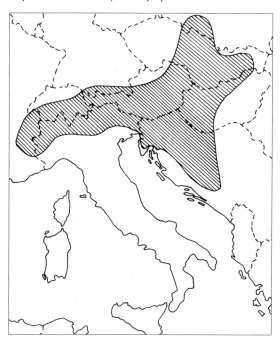

(*Carpinus*) or mixed beech and coniferous woodland. It relishes moist rocky slopes rich in leaf mould and growing in deep or dappled shade. Occasionally it is to be found in more exposed and sunnier situations on screes or in rock crevices, mostly in the altitude range of sea level to 1300m (4300ft).

DISTRIBUTION This species has the most northerly distribution of that of any cyclamen, being found from eastern France through Switzerland, southern Germany, northern Italy to Austria, Yugoslavia (including the coastal regions around Rijeka and several offshore islands such as Krk where it is sometimes found in association with *C. repandum*), the Czech Republic and Slovakia as far north as southern Poland and western Hungary; late June until September. In addition, the species is naturalized in mountainous parts of Rumania and western Russia. Map 9.

- Forma *purpurascens.* *Flowers* pale to deep pink, purplish or rosy-carmine. throughout the distribution of the species.
- Forma *album* Grey-Wilson (= *C. europaeum* forma *album* Hort.). *Flowers* pure white: occasionally found in the wild, especially in the east of its range; always rare and with forma *purpurascens*.
- Forma *carmineolineatum* Hendrikx. *Flowers* white with a narrow carmine zone around the mouth, extending upwards a little along the veins.

Forma *carmineolineatum* was described in 1989 from a photograph taken by Manfred Koenen in the Haute-Savoie between Geneva and Albertville on the French–Swiss border at about 1000m (3250ft). Here in 1983 Koenen had discovered a population of some 400 individuals growing within the area of ordinary forma *purpurascens*, which is locally abundant. The white flowers, with a narrow carmine rim to the mouth, are both attractive and unusual.

In my monograph 'The Genus Cyclamen' (1988:103) I was very dismissive of the related *C. fatrense* described in 1971 by Halda and Soják from the Fatra region of Slovakia. At that time I had not had the chance to observe either the dried type specimen nor, better still, any living material. However, I have since been able to observe live collections from several sources and I have now come to the conclusion that this plant cannot be distinguished on botanical grounds; its prime distinguishing feature is the plain unmarked leaves but such forms exist elsewhere in the species range. However, the plant in question behaves rather differently in cultivation and is, for that reason, best identified as the Fatra Form (see p.167).

The earlier confusion results mainly from the claim of the original authors that *C. fatrense* differed from *C. purpurascens* in having plain not marbled leaves. However, the Fatra Form is a far more uniform plant in the wild, all the individuals in the limited region in which it is found with plain leaves. The leaves are noticeably more matt rather than shiny green and with a more scalloped margin, and the flowers are often somewhat larger on average, though they fit within the overall dimensions of *C. purpurascens*. As these variants are in many ways rather minor ones, I am unable to accord the plant even varietal status.

The Fatra Form is a rather better garden plant than the more widespread forms of *C. purpurascens*, being both more prolific in flower and, in favoured sites, seeding around. In the eastern United States, where cyclamen grow rather poorly compared to many places in Britain, the great exception proves to be the Fatra Form which thrives in healthy colonies in several of the gardens that I visited in 1994. The only conclusion I could draw was that it favoured the acid soils of the region (pH 5.1–6.2 average), whereas most cyclamen appear to thrive best in neutral or somewhat alkaline soil conditions.

Cyclamen purpurascens is closely allied to *C. hederifolium* and *C. africanum*, sharing with them and the following species, *C. colchicum*, the same basic chromosome number of 2n=34; in fact no other species of cyclamen share this number. *C. purpurascens* is very unlikely to be confused with either *C. hederifolium* or *C. africanum*, differing in leaf shape and flower shape and colour (particularly the lack of coloured markings on the flower) and the usual absence of well-marked auricles. In addition, the tubers are very different.

Cyclamen purpurascens clearly shared the same ancestral stock as *C. hederifolium* but the two almost certainly split away at a very early stage in their evolution. Today it can be said that *C. purpurascens* occupies a rather isolated place within the genus, scarcely overlapping in distribution with any other species.

AWARDS
- *C. purpurascens* (as *C. europaeum*) forma *album*: A.M. 1944; F.C.C. 1946
- *C. purpurascens* forma *purpurascens*: A.G.M.

Cyclamen colchicum (Albov) Albov

The status of this plant has long confused the botanist and taxonomist and until relatively recently most gardeners have remained unaware of its existence because no live material was in cultivation, at least in Britain. However, now plants are in cultivation, particularly at the Royal Botanic Gardens, Kew, where they are thriving under alpine house conditions and where I have had a chance to observe them at first hand. There are also some fine collections of *C. colchicum* in several gardens in

123 *Cyclamen purpurascens* forma *album*, the white-flowered form which is uncommon in cultivation.

Denmark. In my monograph of 1988 I concluded with very little real evidence that this plant was best treated as a subspecies of *C. purpurascens* and it was therefore accorded the name subsp. *ponticum*.

However, in the first edition of this work I concluded, as did Albov just over 100 years ago, that this taxon was worthy of specific status.

But how does it differ? The most obvious feature is the leaves which are very thick and leathery, indeed they are thicker and more fleshy than those of any other cyclamen, with the veins distinctly sunk into the leaf surface (when the leaves are dried the veins become obscure, particularly beneath). In addition, the leaf shape is more markedly broad heart-shaped and has a shallower sinus with the basal lobes clearly diverging, and the margin is markedly yet finely toothed and thickened. Compare this with the leaves of *C. purpurascens* that are more rounded or kidney-shaped, are thin in texture with an untoothed or only slightly toothed margin, and have a deeper sinus with basal lobes that converge, often overlapping one another to some extent. In addition, the flowers of *C. colchicum* are rather on the small side, being no more than 15mm (0.6in) long, often smaller, and the fruits are decidedly smaller at maturity.

The leaves of *C. colchicum* can be more or less plain, though more often there is a rather faint, paler green pattern, but more well-defined marbling is found apparently on some plants in the wild.

Other minor differences can be found in the far smaller fruit capsules, the calyx lobes and apparently in the palisade cells of the leaves (the layer of cells immediately below the upper epidermis or skin) and this one might expect from the very thick and fleshy nature of the leaves.

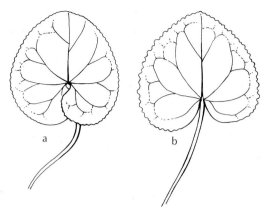

Cyclamen Series *Purpurascens* leaves: *C. purpurascens* (a);
C. colchicum (b).

Schwarz (*Cyclamen Society Journal* 5:18, 1981) states that
the flowers of *C. colchicum* are larger than those of
C. purpurascens. This is certainly not so in the live plants
at the Royal Botanic Gardens, Kew, nor in the few
herbarium specimens that I have been able to examine.

Cyclamen colchicum is well isolated from all the
known localities of *C. purpurascens*, being found some
1900km (1200 miles) further east in a limited region of
the Transcaucasus in what used to be called Adzhar.

DESCRIPTION *Tuber* globose to subglobose in young
plants, to 6.5cm (3in) eventually, smooth and pale brown,
often with some green patches, rooting primarily from the
sides and often producing floral trunks, 1–6cm (0.4–2.5in)
long, probably longer in the wild. *Leaves* often as wide as
long, the lamina broadly cordate, 2.8–7cm (1.1–2.8in) long,
3–8cm (1.2–3.1in) wide, very thick and fleshy with a finely
toothed yet horny margin giving a somewhat beaded effect,
with a narrow basal sinus with the lobes diverging, dark
green and marked with a narrow and uneven silvery pattern

Map 10: Distribution of *Cyclamen colchicum* in the western
Caucasus Mountains.

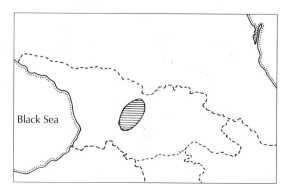

towards the margin above, green flushed with purple
beneath; petioles 8–14cm (3.1–5.5in) long, purplish-brown.
Pedicels purplish-brown, 4–14cm (1.6–5.5in) long, coiling
from the top downwards as the young fruits develop.
Flowers usually appearing a few at a time and borne with the
young or mature leaves at the same height or somewhat
above the foliage; corolla pale to mid carmine-pink,
somewhat darker around the mouth, fragrant (lilac-scented);
corolla-lobes elliptical, slightly twisted, erect, 8–16mm
(0.31–0.62in) long, with very slight auricles at the base.

HABITAT The species inhabits woodland on dolomitic
limestone, growing typically in rather dense shade among
tree roots or in rock crevices, even on cliffs; 300–800m
(1000–2600ft) altitude.

DISTRIBUTION Abkhazia (Caucasus): its classic locality
is in the Okum Gorge, to the south-west of Ossetia; the
prime flowering time in the wild is September and
October (in cultivation flowers can be expected any time
between July and October). Map 10.

CULTIVATION At the Royal Botanic Gardens, Kew
C. colchicum thrives in pots in similar conditions to those
of *C. purpurascens*, though it has not been tried in the
open. Plants are grown in houses or frames shaded during
the summer months but given little in the way of a summer
rest, the compost being kept moist throughout the year, but
watering is increased as plants come into renewed growth
at the end of summer. I have had no experience growing
this plant from seed but I can quote the late Prof. Otto
Schwarz (*Bull. Alp. Gard. Soc.* 42:192, 1974), a notable
grower of alpines, particularly cyclamen, who was a
distinguished botanist and superintendent of the Alpine
House at the botanic garden in Jena. "It is, in my
experience, the most slow-growing species in the whole
genus, never reaching flowering size before the fifth year
after germination: it is also the most shade-loving of
species, flourishing here in the completely sun-less
crevices of the tufa wall … We suspected them at first of
being sterile but discovered that they need cross-
pollination." Professor Schwarz goes on to say that plants
are crossed by hand and the fruit generally does not ripen
until August, taking a full year to mature.

Today young plants and seed are occasionally available
and this interesting and attractive little species is likely to
become more widespread in our gardens. On a visit to a
private garden in Denmark two years ago I was surprised,
yet delighted, to see this species flourishing in considerable
numbers in pots under the staging of a greenhouse.

In the *Flora U.R.S.S.* (18:285–89) Pobedimova states
that *C. colchicum* is fairly widespread throughout the
western Caucasus, even in alpine regions; however,
others have found this not to be the case and I suspect that

he confused it with *C. coum* subsp. *caucasicum*, which is indeed widespread in the region in various forms. Today it is probably more restricted than formerly: it is known that local people in the region in which it is found collect the flowers in bunches and also gather the tubers for medicinal purposes, two activities that can only reduce populations of this rather little-known and scarce species.

SERIES GRAECUM
C. graecum, C. g. subsp. *graecum, C. g.* subsp. *graecum* forma *album, C. g.* subsp. *candicum* and subsp. *anatolicum*

Cyclamen graecum Link
This interesting and charming autumn-flowering species forms a group of its own with several characters that are unique to the genus. *C. graecum* is grown for its autumn flowers as well as for its handsome and often striking foliage which comes in a great range of patterning and colouring. Indeed, the foliage is so appealing that some gardeners make a point of acquiring as many different leaf types as possible and their collections can be as interesting in leaf as they are in flower.

Cyclamen graecum is one of the floral highlights of southern Greece in the autumn. Scarcely have the scorching hot days of summer finished than the first flowers appear, spurred on not only by the cooler autumnal weather but by the first rainfalls (often in the guise of violent and unpredictable thunderstorms) since the spring. Within a short distance of the old international airport at Athens at Glyfada the first *C. graecum* can be spotted on the rocky roadside embankments, and in the rocky open woodlands to the north-west of Athens the species can be found in countless numbers in late September and October.

Cyclamen graecum is widespread in southern Greece, particularly in the southern Peloponnese and the Greek Islands (including Crete), as well as southern Turkey and north-western Cyprus. It is often to be found in extensive colonies and the sweet scent of the flowers can waft some distance from the colonies in fine weather, although, like *C. hederifolium*, not all plants (or indeed colonies) are scented.

Cyclamen graecum has a number of unique features that are worth commenting on at this stage. First, the corky, rounded tubers sport very thick roots that are widely referred to as 'contractile' roots as well as ordinary fibrous roots. Such roots, which delve down deep into the ground, are not found in any other cyclamen species and their purpose would seem to be to anchor the tuber firmly into the rocks. However, they are not contractile and it is far better to call them anchor roots to avoid ambiguity. In bulbs such as tulips and crocuses

124 *Cyclamen colchicum* cultivated at the Royal Botanic Gardens, Kew; similar in flower to *C. purpurascens*, but with a thicker, decidedly toothed leaf.

contractile roots actually pull the bulb down to the right level in the soil by simply contracting as the name suggests. In *C. graecum*, on the other hand, the purpose of the roots seems to be to hold the tuber close into the rocks and to hold it there firmly. Being thick and fleshy they may also serve some function as water storage organs. The tubers can often be seen quite clearly on the surface, not buried in the soil, and are often very firmly wedged into rock crevices.

Second, there is the leaf-margin which is generally unlobed but finely toothed, with a distinctly beaded feel when fingers are run along it; this alone, together with the leaf shape, clearly distinguishes this species from *C. hederifolium* with which it is sometimes confused. Thirdly, there are the fruit stalks (pedicels) which twist bizarrely in two directions from the centre as though they cannot make up their minds whether to twist from the top or the bottom as they do in most other species.

I have often been asked how to tell *C. graecum* and *C. hederifolium* apart in flower in the absence of leaves or tubers. This is not difficult despite the fact that both have similarly coloured flowers of more or less the same size and with prominent auricles. The difference really comes down to the markings at the base of the corolla which are consistently different: in *C. hederifolium* there are two broad, more or less V-shaped, marks at the base of each petal, whereas in *C. graecum* there are two similarly coloured, thin (pencil line) V-shaped marks with a single thin line between them. Occasionally in Greece (but far more often in some Turkish and Cretan populations), the coloured zone around the mouth of the corolla is more substantial with the colour suffusing the basal part of the

125 *Cyclamen graecum* subsp. *graecum*, showing leaf variation within a population at Gythio, Peloponnesse, Greece, in October.
126 As Pl **125** showing forms with a silvery centre to the leaf and one with uniformly pewtered leaves.
127 *Cyclamen graecum* subsp. *graecum*; south of Ariopoli, Mani Peninsula, Peloponnese.

petal, sometimes extending some distance up the petal at the same time.

I first recall seeing *C. graecum* some years ago at the northern end of the Mani Peninsula growing in rocky field surrounds, beneath and among the roots of venerable, gnarled olive trees in association with mauve *Crocus goulimyi* and its white cousin, *C. boryi*. But in another rocky field close by it vied for attention with the bright yellow stars of *Sternbergia lutea* in countless profusion. In yet another locality, it grew with myriad sweet-scented *Narcissus serotinus*. However, perhaps the most memorable colonies were on the sun-baked and seemingly barren slopes of the southern Mani close to the tower town of Vathia where the cyclamen appeared to occupy almost every available niche between the rocks. It struck me then, and does every time I see it in the wild, that this cyclamen inhabits one of the most hostile environments of any in the genus.

Unlike *C. hederifolium*, which also is found in similar regions, *C. graecum* is rarely found growing in the shade but prefers the full sun, especially where it can nestle into rock crevices: it is equally happy on a mountainside or close to the sea. In the wild, the flowers are generally borne before the leaves appear, but on occasions the leaves may be partly developed; certainly by the time the last flowers are fading, the leaves are often well advanced. A single mature plant can produce well in excess of 200 blooms. The flower colour is generally a rather uniform mid rosy-pink but pale forms and more striking ones of deep cerise-pink (especially in southern Turkey), sometimes with a hint of carmine, can be found in colonies of the normal form.

A pure white-flowered plant was found in the Greek Peloponnese in October 1980 between Gythion and Kastania by Ronald and Erna Frank, and plants were brought into cultivation by them, later described as forma *album*. Since then the odd white plant has been seen in the wild, although never to my knowledge outside the Peloponnese. In the autumn of 1992 I was in the company of Jack Elliott and others whilst leading a Field Studies Council expedition to the Peloponnese. The previous day we had been remarking that pure white 'graecums' seemed to be extremely scarce and that it must be 'pure luck' to come upon one. The following day on the outskirts of Gythion the first *C. graecum* that we came upon was pure white but we never saw another like it in the following ten days, search as we might. The plant is still where we left it to my knowledge, although it is in a site that could be easily developed in the future! *C. graecum* in general though is not under threat and many of its finest sites are unlikely to be developed; roadworks may often dissect colonies but the rocky embankments so created are often quickly colonized by young plants seeding down from above.

Cyclamen graecum was described as long ago as 1834 from plants collected close to Napflio (Naplion) in the Peloponnese by a German, Berger. Later botanists decided that plants outside mainland Greece deserved separate species status and so a series of names were proposed: *C. mindleri* was described by Heldreich in 1898 for the plant from the island of Aigina, south of Athens; both *C. maritimum* and *C. pseudomaritimum* were described in 1908 by Hildebrand for the Turkish mainland plants and in the same year (and also by Hildebrand), *C. aegineticum*, again from the Greek island of Aigina; *C. pseudograecum* was also described by Hildebrand in 1911 from Cretan plants; *C. cyprograecum* by E. & N. Mutch in 1955 for the Cyprus plant, although this name was never validly published.

J. H. Ietswaart wrote a paper in 1990 entitled 'Infraspecific delimitation of the *Cyclamen graecum* complex'. (*Journ. Cyclamen Soc.* 14,2:49). This more or less coincided with my own thoughts on what is in effect a rather variable species, though I do not go along with the author that "With *C. graecum* complex there is a greater variation of characteristics than in *C. repandum*"; indeed the reverse is almost certainly the case. However, in *C. graecum* the differences are, if anything, more clear cut. Previous investigations have been hampered by the lack of really good and reliable field data, a lack of good photographs of the species over its entire range and, more especially, by the fact that most of the cultivated material available at the time was of Greek origin. Ietswaart distinguishes three subspecies on the characters of the flowers (especially the size of the auricles and the type of blotching at the base of the corolla lobes). He also brings into play the actual colour of the corolla and whether or not the flowers are scented. As a result the Greek plant is recognized as subsp. *graecum*, the Turkish, Rhodes, Cyprus plant as subsp. *anatolicum* and part of the Cretan population as subsp. *candicum*. He chooses, as he is quite entitled, to adopt new names for the two new subspecies instead of taking on board one of the names already existing, because these now represent a new rank; the international rules of botanical nomenclature allow the choosing of a new name at a different rank (in this case subspecies rather than species). He could, for instance, have called the Turkish–Cypriot plant subsp. *maritimum* and the Cretan plant subsp. *pseudograecum*, and this would have saved bringing more epithets into the genus.

Of the characters selected by Ietswaart those of scent and flower colour are notoriously fickle in most cyclamen species and really cannot be relied on to any extent. The leaves of *C. graecum*, can be extremely variable in the wild; this variability is not so much in leaf shape but in patterning and overall coloration. The leaves often have a velvety sheen and can be more or less plain or with one or several bands or zones in greens, greys,

128 *Cyclamen graecum* subsp. *graecum* often occupies rock crevices in full sunshine, as here near Gythio, Peloponnese, Greece.
129 *Cyclamen graecum* subsp. *graecum* growing at Vathia, Mani Peninsula, Peloponnese.
130 *Cyclamen graecum* subsp. *graecum* will sometimes grow in sandy, grass-strewn places along the shoreline, as here at Gythio, Peloponnese, Greece.

131 A fine floriferous form of *Cyclamen graecum* subsp. *graecum* flowering near Stupa in the Peloponnese.
132 *Cyclamen graecum* subsp. *graecum* showing the characteristic vein markings on the flowers.
133 An exceptionally dark-flowered form of *Cyclamen graecum* subsp. *graecum* photographed south of Stupa in the Greek Peloponnese in late October.

pewter or silver. Some of the plants from southern Turkey have a central shield of cream, or silver in the finest forms, particularly from the areas close to Alanya, Fethiye and Mersin. Indeed the Turkish forms have the most attractive leaf markings of all the *C. graecum* I have seen. Particularly attractive leaf forms can be found around Gythio in the Peloponnese, including those with a silver shield in the centre of the leaf, as well as those with all pewter leaves.

Leaf patterning is extremely variable in *C. graecum* but some differences can be readily discerned in leaf characters in populations from the west and east of the range of the species. Plants from Greece and the Greek islands, including Crete, have smaller leaves on average without marginal lobing, whereas those from southern Turkey and Cyprus tend to have larger leaves (often twice as large), and with an irregular, generally somewhat lobed, margin; the lobing is usually uneven, sometimes affecting one side of the leaf more than the other. This character of the lobing of the leaf was strangely overlooked by Ietswaart, though it is fairly obvious in both dried as well as living material. The leaf characters have been both under-stressed and overlooked by Ietswaart.

In addition, the 'nose' markings on the corolla are often more pronounced, darker and more solid in the Turkish and Cypriot forms as well as some Cretan plants (subsp. *candicum*). As these features seem well marked I cannot but agree with Ietswaart and accept his subsp. *anatolicum*. The epithet is an unfortunate choice as the plant is distributed in Cyprus, Rhodes and southern Turkey – it is not to my knowledge found in Anatolia at all but that is, I fear, no grounds for rejecting the name. As indicated, plants from southern Turkey often have very attractively patterned and coloured leaves, though those from Cyprus are often duller and less attractively patterned (mostly in shades of green without silver or cream patterning); however, some plants do exhibit leaves with attractive silvered patterns. In Cyprus particularly large-leaved forms are sometimes observed and these are very similar to forms found on Rhodes. These differences in subsp. *anatolicum* populations require further investigation; the Cypriot plant, which is reported to have pale off-white to pale-pinkish flowers, may justify separation as a variety, but this requires further investigation. Another feature of subsp. *anatolicum* is in the reduced corolla auricles, which are far less pronounced, sometimes rather obscure.

But what of Crete and subsp. *candicum*? This clearly comes close to subsp. *graecum* according to Ietswaart, sharing the well-developed corolla auricles but having paler, often white (though not albino) flowers with more 'solid' markings at the base of the corolla-lobes. The pale flower character may distinguish the Cretan populations but very pale pink forms are also common in the Greek

Peloponnese. However, other differences are apparent. The flowers tend to be smaller, but they have a significantly broader mouth which gives them a dumpier appearance overall. In addition, the leaves tend to be held very close to the ground and are generally much darker, narrower and more pointed, with the undersurface a rich crimson or beetroot-red. In fact the leaves can be very dark, almost blackish-green, with handsome silvery zoning. When leaf and flower characters are studied in conjunction it will be seen that they correlate well with geographical distribution and upon such evidence it is possible and desirable to uphold the subspecific divisions of *C. graecum*. The reader should not think that all *C. graecum* plants on Crete belong to subsp. *candicum* for this is far from the truth. Subsp. *graecum* is the rarer of the two on the island, being restricted to its north-west, whereas in other localities scattered across much of the island, plants are referable to subsp. *candicum*. Ietswaart states that subsp. *candicum* is restricted to the Lefki Ori (White Mountains). This is simply not so for there are good population elsewhere, especially in the region of the Lasithi Plateau. The White Mountains represent an ancient island, once surrounded by sea which, in recent geological times, has become joined to other islands to become the Crete that we recognize today. On the former island *C. graecum* would have been isolated and may have been for a very long time, being today represented as a relict population having evolved its own particular features. These in themselves (on present evidence at least) do not warrant separating subsp. *candicum* out as a species in its own right. Interestingly, on Crete subsp. *graecum* inhabits that part of the island closest to the Peloponnese and is always found at low altitudes there.

DESCRIPTION Plants rather robust with the flowers normally appearing in advance of the leaves, occasionally with the young leaves. *Tubers* globose to subglobose, sometimes irregular, up to 30cm (12in) diameter, rough, corky and fissured when mature and often slightly flaky, especially on the upper surface, rooting from the centre of the base, often as a ring; roots of two kinds, fine and fibrous or thick, fleshy and thong-like, the latter rarely branching. *Leaves* broadly to narrowly cordate, the lamina 4–15cm (1.6–6in) long, 2.5–14.5cm (1–5.7in) wide, with a finely toothed, somewhat cartilaginous, beaded margin, the base with a deep and rather narrow sinus with the lobes more or less diverging, often with a velvety upper surface in various shades of pale to deep green, with or without a hastate pattern or banding in another shade of green, cream, pewter or silver, sometimes plain but with the veins picked out in another shade of green, or occasionally the entire leaf surface pewter, the lower surface green, sometimes flushed with pink or purple; petiole 5–17cm (2–6.7in) long, rarely elbowed, generally ascending from the tuber. Flowers appearing

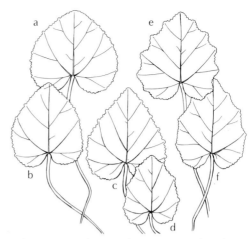

Cyclamen graecum leaves: subsp. *graecum* (a–b); subsp. *candicum* (c–d), subsp. *anatolicum* (e–f).

generally in advance of the flowers, scented or unscented; corolla very pale to deep pink or cerise-pink, rarely reddish-purple, with 3 magenta pencil-line streaks at the base of each petal, the outer streaks narrow V-shaped, the middle a single line, these sometimes extending upwards for half the length of the petal, or blotch more solid and not extending up the corolla-lobes, the flowers occasionally pure white; corolla-lobes oblong to elliptical, twisting, 1.5–3cm (0.6–1.3in) long (rarely to 3.5cm/1.4in), with distinct or poorly developed auricles at the base. *Pedicels* 6–16cm (2.3–6.3in) long, brownish or purplish, coiling from the centre in both directions as the young fruits begin to develop, sometimes commencing to coil from nearer the base.

SUBSPECIES OF *C. GRAECUM*

1. Corolla whitish or very pale pink, the mouth broad, 9–14mm (0.35–0.55in) diameter; flowers not sweetly scented; leaves generally narrowly ovate, pointed and with dark hues: **subsp. *candicum***
    or Corolla pink, sometimes deep reddish-pink, the mouth not so broad, 5–9(–10)mm/0.2–0.35(–0.4)in diameter; flowers scented or not; leaves usually broadly ovate and rather blunt, often paler and brighter green   **—to 2**
2. Leaves mostly less than 8.5cm (3.3in) long, with a beaded but not lobed margin; flowers unscented, sometimes sweetly scented, the corolla with well-developed auricles and with the basal blotch of each corolla-lobe extending along the veins and generally confined to the veins, the central vein strong:
    subsp. *graecum*
    or Leaves often more than 8.5cm (3.3in) long, with a beaded as well as a somewhat lobed margin;

flowers sweetly scented, the corolla usually with poorly developed auricles, with the basal blotch of each corolla-lobe more 'solid' and often not extending along the veins, the central vein poorly marked: **subsp. *anatolicum***

Subsp. *graecum* (syn. *C. graecum* subsp. *mindleri* (Heldr.) Davis & Govaerts, *C. mindleri* Heldr.; *C. persicum* Mill. subsp. *mindleri* (Heldr.) Knuth). *Leaves* are broadly ovate, rarely more than 8.5cm long (3.3in) and 7cm (2.8in) wide, and have a pronounced beaded margin but are unlobed, the upper surface dominated with green or grey-green tones, rarely with much silver, while the lower surface is often green but sometimes with a flush of pink or purple. *Flowers* borne on pedicels 10cm (4in) long or more (rarely less) and are mostly unscented, though scented forms do occur; corolla-lobes, which are often more than 20mm (0.8in) long, sometimes as long as 35mm (1.4in), are marked with a basal blotch that extends along the veins, sometimes for half the petal length, with a pair of well-marked auricles (1–2mm/0.04–0.08in) at the base of each petal; mouth of the corolla 6–9(–10)mm/0.23–0.35 (–0.4)in diameter.

HABITAT Its prime habitat is on terra rossa (red soils) where it grows on hill and mountain slopes in loamy rock pockets or rock crevices, sometimes along steam beds, but mostly in open, sunny situations, occasionally being found in oak scrub, open pine or cupressus woodland or in olive groves; sea level to 700m (2240ft) altitude.

DISTRIBUTION Subsp. *graecum* has the widest distribution of the three subspecies, being found in much of eastern and southern mainland Greece, especially the Peloponnese, Athos and many of the Aegean islands

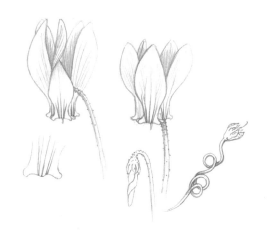

Cyclamen graecum subsp. *graecum*.

(especially the eastern ones) as well as NW Crete (Rhodopos and Geroskinos peninsulas) and Kasos; it is not found on Rhodes, where it is replaced by subsp. *anatolicum*, nor on Karpathos where it might well be expected to grow; September–November. Map 11.

• **Forma *graecum*.** *Flowers* pink to reddish-pink, the corolla-lobes with darker basal markings. Throughout the range of the subspecies.

• **Forma *album* R. & E. Frank.** *Flowers* pure white, unmarked. Rare in the wild; it has only been found in the Greek Peloponnese.

Subsp. *candicum* (Ietswaart) Grey-Wilson (syn. *C. pseudograecum* Hildebrand). *Leaves* usually narrowly ovate and rather pointed, rather small, the lamina rarely more than 6cm (2.3in) long and often held close to the ground, with dark tones dominating and often intricately marbled, deep reddish-purple or crimson beneath. *Corolla* white,

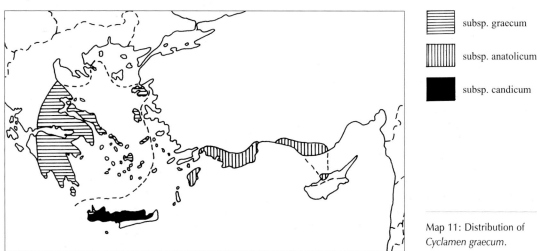

▤	subsp. graecum
▥	subsp. anatolicum
■	subsp. candicum

Map 11: Distribution of *Cyclamen graecum*.

134 *Cyclamen graecum* subsp. *graecum* forma *album* with dark, reasonably well-marked foliage.

135 A different clone of *Cyclamen graecum* subsp. *graecum* forma *album* cultivated by Rod and Jane Leeds.

136 *Cyclamen graecum* subsp. *candicum*: N of Tilissos in Crete.

137 *Cyclamen graecum* subsp. *candicum* showing the pale flowers with bold basal markings to the corolla, as well as the rather large and prominent auricles.

sometimes flushed with pale pink, rarely deeper pink, the corolla-lobes 18–30mm (0.7–1.2in) long, with the basal blotch more 'solid', blackish-purple and usually well-extended along the veins, with very well-marked auricles (1–2mm/0.04–0.08in) at the base of each corolla-lobe; mouth of corolla 9–15mm (0.35–0.6in) diameter.

HABITAT It is found in similar habitats to var. *anatolicum* but is most often found in garrigue, or sometimes beneath large oak trees or carobs, *Ceratonia siliqua*, at rather similar altitudes, though it is most common close to sea level; however, it has also been recorded as high as 1050m (3412ft) above the Omalos Plane in western Crete, where the plants are very squat, with dark leaves and few flowers.

DISTRIBUTION Subsp. *candicum* is restricted to Crete being centred on the Lefka Ori (White Mountains) region; however, it is found east as far as Fourfouras by Mt Idi, with outliers further east at Lasithi; September–November. Map 11.

The relationship of subsp. *candicum* to subsp. *graecum* on Crete is not properly understood, although they rarely appear to grow together on the island. The plants from the Lasithi region at the eastern end of the island with broader but similarly dark leaves and pale flowers with similar markings almost certainly belong to subsp. *candicum*, but this requires further investigation. If this is found to be the case then the hypothesis that the White Mountains acted as an island refugio before it was joined to the rest of modern-day Crete would seem to be less certain. Populations near Platanias in north-western Crete appear to be a mixture of subsp. *graecum* and subsp. *candicum*, but this also requires further investigation (see Melyvn Jope in *Cyclamen Society Journal* 24(1): 3 (2000). Having said this, typical subsp. *candicum* and subsp. *graecum* are very distinct and easily distinguished.

Cyclamen mindleri was thought to have come from Crete; however, it was in fact described by Heldriech in 1898 from the island of Aigina in the sea south of Athens. In the 'CITES Bulb Checklist' (130, 1999) Davis and Govaerts assumed that this taxon had been described from Crete, as did I in the first edition of this work, where it was cited as a synonym of *C. graecum* subsp. *candicum*. Finding that it

Cyclamen graecum: subsp. *candicum* (a); subsp. *anatolicum* (b).

had been transferred to *C. persicum* as a subsp. (*C. persicum* subsp. *mindleri* (Heldr.) Knuth) in 1905 Davis and Govaerts rightly made a new combination *C. graecum* subsp. *mindleri*, placing Ietswaart's subsp. *candicum* into synonymy. However, it is now known that *C. mindleri* is a synonym of subsp. *graecum* so that the epithet *candicum* must prevail for the endemic Cretan taxon in question.

Subsp. *anatolicum* Ietswaart (syn. *C. cypro-graecum* E. & M. Mutch; *C. maritimum* Hildebrand; *C. pseudomaritimum* Hildebrand). *Leaves* up to 15cm (6in) long and 14.5cm (5.7in) wide, with a beaded margin with moderately to well-marked angles or short lobes, basically green but often very attractively marked with a pale central zone above in paler green, pewter or silver. *Flowers* borne on rather short pedicels which are rarely more than 10cm (4in) long, sometimes as little as 3cm (1.2in), often sweetly scented. *Corolla* white to deep pink, with a pair of 'solid' dark diverging blotches at the base of each corolla-lobe but the colour not extending along

138 *Cyclamen graecum* subsp. *candicum* showing the characteristic flowers and dark, boldly marked, rather narrow, heart-shaped leaves.
139 *Cyclamen graecum* subsp. *candicum*; a form with rather narrow petals and beautifully marked leaves, cultivated by Bob and Rannveig Wallis.
140 *Cyclamen graecum* subsp. *anatolicum*; typical leaf variations in a population near Alanya in SW Turkey: note the slight lobing of the leaf margin which is characteristic of this subspecies.
141 *Cyclamen graecum* subsp. *anatolicum* photographed near Kalkan in SW Turkey.

the veins; auricles small (rarely more than 0.5mm/0.02in) and generally rather poorly developed, although always visible; mouth of corolla 5–9mm (0.2–0.35in) across.

HABITAT It grows most commonly in *Pinus brutia* or *Cupressus* woodland or scrub (garrigue) in sandy and rocky places, often on hills or mountainsides in terra fusca (brown soils), sandy or loamy clays with humus, often in gullies or along rocky stream beds, generally in full sun or light shade; sea level to 800m (2600ft).

DISTRIBUTION Subsp. *anatolicum* is found in southern Turkey (S Anatolia) from east of Milas in the west to near Anamur in the east, on the island of Rhodes and in northern Cyprus (Liveras area); September–November. Interestingly, the Cyprus location (where the subspecies is very local) is at that point on the island closest to the Turkish mainland localities. Map 11.

The distribution of subsp. *anatolicum*, or indeed subsp. *graecum*, in the islands of the Dodecanese such as Samos, Cos and Tilos is not understood and requires further investigation and may well throw further light on the relationship of these two subspecies.

Ietswaart refers to the mouth of the corolla in subsp. *anatolicum* as being 'furrowed' and uses it as a character of difference from the other two subspecies. I have examined fresh flowers of a number of plants of this subspecies and although several have a very slight furrow (running down the centre of the petal between the auricles), most have no sign of a furrow and this character must be viewed with some scepticism.

Some associated plants in the wild include *Biarum tenuifolium*, *Crocus boryi*, *C. goulimyi*, *C. hadriaticus*, *C. niveus*, *Cyclamen hederifolium* (rarely), *Fritillaria messanensis*, *Narcissus serotinus*, *Scilla autumnalis*, *Sternbergia lutea*, *S. sicula* and *Urginea maritima*.

CULTIVATION *Cyclamen graecum* is one of the most magnificent species in cultivation, in its pink-flowered as well as its white-flowered forms. In some of the former the flowers can be a very pretty blush-pink, whilst at the other extreme are forms (primarily from Turkey, subsp. *anatolicum*) with deep reddish-purple flowers that are equally appealing. One of the glories of this species in all its forms is the infinite variety of leaf colorations and markings, with scarcely any two plants the same. From plain greens or pewter, to those with the veins picked out in a different green, cream or silver, to those with hastate pattern (sometimes a double hastate pattern) in various shades of green, pewter or silver, or those in which an otherwise deep-green leaf has a central shield of silver. The leaves often have a silky look, especially when young. With so

142 *Cyclamen graecum* subsp. *anatolicum* showing the shallow leaf-lobing and small auricles characteristic of the subspecies.

143 A well-flowered pot of *Cyclamen graecum* subsp. *anatolicum*.

144 *Cyclamen graecum* subsp. *anatolicum* in the N Cyprus form, fomerly described as *C. cypro-graecum*; in cultivation.

many possibilities it is scarcely surprising that some growers have made a speciality of collecting as many leaf forms as possible.

In the past it used to be said that *C. graecum* was a difficult plant to flower with any regularity but this has since been disproved, although there are clearly some forms in cultivation that do not flower well. A few years ago it was generally stated that the species required a long summer baking in order to perform well, yet it has been found subsequently that plants thrive better and certainly produce more flowers if they are given at least some water during the dry summer months. For plants in pots the best way to ensure this is to sink them in a sand-plunge (even one below the greenhouse staging will suffice) and to keep the plunge moist, avoiding too much water getting into the pots.

Cyclamen graecum has long, delving roots that require extra-deep pots if the plants are to thrive unhindered. In shallow pots the long, fleshy roots will try to find an exit through the drainage holes and will be easily damaged when pots are moved around, as they inevitably will be.

Some growers succeed very well with this species in the open garden. A warm, secluded and sheltered site should be chosen. A place under a south-facing wall where *Sternbergia lutea* and *Iris unguicularis* are likely to flourish will suit it best. The tubers should be deep-planted (10–20cm/4–8in). Some growers advocate placing a flat stone or slate over the top of the tuber in the

belief that this will not only help to keep the top of the tuber reasonably dry but will help protect it from penetrating frosts.

A collection of different forms of *C. graecum* planted out permanently in a cold frame can be an attractive feature. The plants tend to be very long-lived and some more than 40 years old are known.

Plants often come into flower before the leaves appear but this is not a constant feature; certainly some flower consistently when the foliage is partly developed and some even flower when the foliage is more or less fully expanded.

The species is generally slow from seed and most young plants will not flower until they are at least four years old. I have had to wait six years on occasions; the wait is well worthwhile.

Of the three subspecies the various forms of subsp. *graecum* are by far the most common in cultivation; plants were brought into cultivation from mainland Greece and the Greek islands long before plant-hunters strayed into the remoter regions of southern Turkey and Crete. When buying from a nursery this is the subspecies most likely to be sold. Subsp. *anatolicum* has become increasingly common in cultivation in recent years, although most plants are in private hands rather than in nurseries and some of the leaf forms (especially those with a central shield of silver) are among the finest of all. In addition, the southern Turkish forms tend to be sweetly scented and floriferous. Subsp. *candicum* is least often seen in cultivation at the present time but if the true plant can be acquired it is well worth growing, if only for its strikingly handsome dark leaves with their paler patterning which is often outlined in grey or pale silver. Beware, though – many Cretan plants sold under the *C. graecum* blanket are ordinary subsp. *graecum*, not subsp. *candicum*. Unfortunately, the subspecies of *C. graecum* have not yet been assimilated by the Cyclamen Society and seed is often listed in their journal and in other seed lists as simply 'C. graecum', without qualification. In cultivation, the three subspecies are generally readily identified and as yet there does not seem to have been much hybridization between them: they are most readily told apart by their leaf characters: subsp. *graecum* by its broad, rather blunt leaves with a beaded but not lobed margin, subsp. *anatolicum* by its generally brighter leaves, often with some silver and with a mildly to pronounced lobed margin, and subsp. *candicum* by its rather dark small leaves which are narrower and more pointed, with a finely beaded, but not lobed, margin. All

145 *Cyclamen rohlfsianum* showing leaf variation within the species.

146 *Cyclamen rohlfsianum*; a particularly finely marked leaf form.

make splendid pot plants for the alpine house or cool conservatory, and fine leaf forms of all the subspecies, especially subsp. *candicum*, make especially fine specimens for autumn shows.

The beautiful white-flowered form, *C. graecum* subsp. *graecum* forma *album*, is an exquisite plant and as easy to grow as the normal pink ones. The leaves vary from plant to plant but are never as beautifully marked as they are in some plants of forma *graecum*, and are nearly always in various shades of green, without silver or pewter patterning. A good plant can produce in excess of 100 blooms and is a truly arresting sight in full flower. To my knowledge the seedlings of selfed white-flowered plants, or crosses between two white plants, come 100 per cent white-flowered.

AWARDS
- *C. graecum* subsp. *graecum* forma *graecum* A.M. 1954; F.C.C. 1973
- *C. graecum* subsp. *graecum* forma *album* A.M. 1988

SERIES ROHLFSIANUM
C. rohlfsianum

This very unusual species used to be considered both rare and difficult in cultivation but now it is present in most collections, although it is rarely a prolific bloomer. Two features distinguish this species from all the others in the genus: first and perhaps most obvious are the evenly lobed, broad leaves and second are the flowers with their characteristic protruding cone of stamens. As with *C. purpurascens* the tubers are often large and uneven, though the two species are not particularly closely related in most other respects. The coiling of the flower-stalks from the base upwards is a character possessed by only one other species and that is *C. graecum*.

Cyclamen rohlfsianum cannot be mistaken for any other species. Both leaves and flowers are highly distinctive. The protruding cone of stamens has led some authors to suggest a possible affinity between *Cyclamen* and the North American genus *Dodecatheon* whose flowers have similarly reflexed petals and protruding stamens; however, this similarity is purely superficial and the two genera are certainly not closely related, having far more differences in habit, leaf and inflorescence characters than similarities in flower characters. Although all genera in the Primulaceae must share a common ancestral stock the major morphological characteristics of *Cyclamen* show it to hold a unique position within the family. Any

Cyclamen rohlfsianum.

superficial similarities between it and *Dodecatheon* are probably the result of parallel evolution rather than a direct link (i.e. the reflexed corolla-lobes and protruding stamens have arisen quite independently in both genera).

The species is clearly a relict species being isolated from the rest of the genus and being confined to a fairly small area in the wild. *C. rohlfsianum* was discovered in 1879 by Rohlfs in Libya (then Cyrenaica) not far from Benghazi, but it was not described until almost 20 years later, in 1897. Although a local endemic it is fairly common in several of its chief domains. The plants are said to live to a considerable age in the wild: this is certainly true of plants in cultivation.

DESCRIPTION *Tuber* globose when young but becoming progressively more uneven and knobbly and distorted with age and often concave beneath, to 20cm (8in) diameter eventually, perhaps larger in the wild, the surface becoming deep brown and corky, rooting rather irregularly from the lower sides, occasionally also from the base. *Leaves* appearing from various points on the top

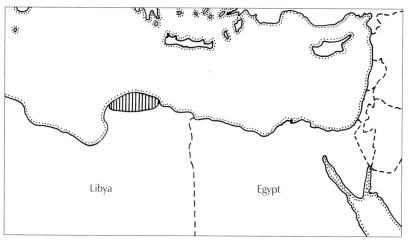

CULTIVATION *Cyclamen rohlfsianum* shows considerable variation in leaf patterning in cultivated plants. Some are quite frankly rather dull, with deep green, poorly marked foliage. However, others have a very attractive pattern in pewter or silver, and these are well worth seeking out. Flower colour is fairly uniform although some plants certainly sport rather deeper pink flowers than the norm. Recently a pure white-flowered plant has been reported. This had appeared by chance in a batch of seedlings (from long-cultivated stock) raised by Susan and Michael Ayling of Kingsley, Hampshire. The plant had pure white flowers and an attractively marked leaf. Although still a young plant, it is hoped that the eventual progeny will also bear white flowers, as is the case in both the albino forms of *C. cilicium* and *C. graecum*, as well as some clones of *C. hederifolium*.

of the tuber, the lamina usually wider than long, rounded to kidney-shaped in outline but generally with 5–9 broadly triangular lobes (generally only 3-lobed in young plants), 3.6–11.5cm (1.4–4.5in) long, 4.5–15.6cm (1.8–6.1in) wide, with a broad and rather shallow sinus at the base and a coarsely toothed margin, bright pale to deep green above with an uneven leaf-shaped pattern in paler grey-green, cream or silver, rarely plain, flushed with purple or carmine beneath, sometimes intensely so, occasionally plain green, matt or shiny; petioles 6–24cm (2.3–9.4in) long, usually brownish-purple or reddish. *Pedicels* erect to ascending, 4.5–10.5cm (1.8–4.1in) long, brownish-purple or reddish, coiling from close to the base upwards as the young fruits develop. *Flowers* appearing with the young or semi-mature leaves, occasionally one or two flowers are borne with the mature leaves, sweetly fragrant; corolla pale to mid-pink with a deeper carmine-magenta zone towards the base, with the stamen cone protruding by 1.5–2.5mm (0.06–0.1in) from the mouth of the corolla; corolla-lobes rather narrow and twisted, lanceolate to elliptical, 11–26mm (0.4–1in) long, with small but distinct auricles at the base and a pointed apex; style protruding beyond the stamen cone.

HABITAT Rocky habitats, especially gullies and cracks in limestone formations, but also in scrub (degraded maquis or garrigue), often on terra-rossa; sea-level to 450m (1500ft) altitude.

DISTRIBUTION: Northern Libya in a limited area of Cyrenaica, from Benghazi to Derna; September to November. Map 12.

Once thought to be a tricky species in cultivation and one that was difficult to flower well, *C. rohlfsianum* is today far more common and well represented in most cyclamen collections. The reasons for this are twofold. First, cultivation techniques have changed, or rather evolved, in recent years, and second, in the 1960s, fresh material was collected from the wild, particularly by Peter Davis and Jim Archibald: plants previously in cultivation were rather uniform and often reluctant to flower, whereas the more recent introductions have revealed the species to be far more variable in leaf size and patterning and certainly more floriferous. The species was brought into cultivation in 1929.

147 *Cyclamen rohlfsianum* often flowers in advance of, or with the immature, leaves.

One of the problems in the past with *C. rohlfsianum* has been in obtaining fresh seed. Plants seemed reluctant to set much seed and this can still be a problem today. With my own plants I find that plants set seed in some years but not in others. This seems to be due to a lack of pollination (or subsequent fertilization) at the critical period when most of the flowers are in bloom. Plants can be helped out by careful hand-pollination using a small camel-hair brush, preferably transferring pollen from one plant to another which seems to produce a better fruit set.

Seed can be sown in the usual way (see p.24). Young seedlings are very slow at becoming established and over-watering may cause damping-off. If they have not grown sufficiently by the onset of winter the young seedlings may not survive, but this problem can be alleviated by bringing them into warmer conditions so that they can be kept growing for as long as possible – a warm, sunny windowsill in the house is ideal! In any event they will not tolerate any frost in the seedling stage. After the first season patience is required as the young plants develop quite slowly and may only produce two or three leaves even in their third year.

Plants are generally grown in pots but they can be successfully planted out in a raised bed in a glasshouse, provided frost is excluded. The compost should, if anything, be rather grittier than that normally recommended for cyclamen but this is not too critical if plants are given a correct resting period.

Once they have reached flowering size (generally in five years in my experience, occasionally longer) then they should flower regularly each season. Plants will stand full sunshine provided they receive adequate ventilation and ample moisture during the growing season. After the initial years the tubers begin to expand quite rapidly, often unevenly so. They may even expand enough to crack the sides of clay pots and I have known friends who have given their old plants away because they have become too large.

In older plants leaves and flowers usually arise from several scattered points over the upper surface of the tuber. The flowers sometimes bear one or two spots or blemishes on the petals and these can sometimes spoil a good show of blooms. The reason for this is not clear but may perhaps be related to water splashes on the buds or newly opened flowers.

Cyclamen rohlfsianum requires a long summer dormancy when tubers and containers can be kept completely dry. The leaves tend to start dying down sooner than most other species. This often starts in early April when the leaves begin to yellow and this is a good indicator when to commence reducing the water. Watering should not suddenly cease at the first sign of yellowing but can be gradually withheld; the leaves rarely all yellow at the same moment and, in any case,

148 *Cyclamen rohlfsianum* flowering with semi-mature foliage.
149 *Cyclamen rohlfsianum* showing the typical protruding cone of stamens, a unique feature in the genus.

the semi-mature fruits still require some moisture at this stage, otherwise they may abort. By the time the last leaf begins to wither, all watering should have ceased and any water applied after this may well cause the tuber to rot.

Plants can be stimulated back into growth by giving them a good dousing of water, preferably in the latter half of August. No more needs to be given then until the young leaves and flower buds begin to appear above the compost. Too much water early on will lead to a rapid development of the foliage which may hide the flowers as they open. Ideally the flowers should open as the young leaves begin to unfurl. I have found that getting plants into growth rather earlier than for some of the other species allows *C. rohlfsianum* a longer growing season with the foliage maturing well in advance of the winter. This seems to help in flower production and I certainly get more flowers per plant since I adopted this procedure.

Incidentally, the best way to water plants initially is to place the pots (clay or plastic) in a basin of water for an hour or so, rather than to soak them from above, for this will keep the top of the tuber relatively dry and prevent botrytis infecting the foliage.

Despite this advice on growing the species in pots, I have had the greatest success by planting several semi-mature tubers directly into a well-gritted bed in a glasshouse from which only severe frost is excluded. The plants have grown more lushly and flower far better and more reliably than any other method that I have tried. They inhabit the bed with other tender species, *C. graecum*, *C. cyprium* and *C. africanum* in particular. Once the leaves start to yellow (generally in May) watering ceases and the fruits left to mature. At the end of August I clear off the old parched foliage, top-dress the border with fresh grit and some bone meal and give the whole area a thorough soaking. No further water is applied until the plants come into flower and the leaves start to grow.

As with *C. graecum*, plants seem to flower best after long, hot, sunny summers, least well after cool damp ones. The ideal temperature during the summer months for the dormant plants is 25°C (78°F), but many growers succeed with them well below this. Some growers advocate placing plastic bags over the plants to keep the temperature high and, at the same time, keeping some moisture around the developing flower buds but I have not found this to be necessary nor particularly desirable for there is always the danger of trapping too much moisture in the bag and setting off fungal infections and, worse still, rotting of the tuber.

Although not a particularly hardy species *C. rohlfsianum* can be grown in a cold glasshouse provided severe frosts are excluded. This means that in all but sub-zero conditions plants can be kept in a well-aerated and unheated house. Plants will in fact tolerate a few degree of frost on the foliage provided the frost is not prolonged and that it does not penetrate to the vulnerable tuber.

Cyclamen rohlfsianum can also be grown with considerable success on a sunny windowsill in the house, in much the same way as *C. persicum*, and will make both an attractive, as well as an unusual, house plant. During the dormant season the plants can be placed in the sunny part of a conservatory or frame and kept dry. Care must be taken when growing them in the house that the temperatures are not too high as this will lead to over-lush growth and may well inhibit flowering. They should not be kept in dense shade or the growth will be soft and spindly and the plant will probably go into early dormancy, wrecking the chance of a good crop of flowers the following autumn.

Recently an albino plant (with pure white flowers) has appeared by chance and this was reported in the *Journal of the Cyclamen Society* in December 2000, followed by a photograph of the single bloom so far produced in December 2001. The plant appeared in a batch of seedlings raised by Susan and Michael Ayling of Kingsley Nurseries, Hampshire. The flower was white with faintly greyish veins extending from the base to the apex of each petal. In addition, the flower had a pleasing fragrance. So far it is not known if any seedlings produced will also be white-flowered. If so, when enough material becomes available it would be worth formally recognising this interesting addition, preferably by describing it as a forma, e.g. forma *album*.

AWARDS
• A.M. 1951

Chapter Seven

Cyclamen Cultivars

Anyone keen on growing cyclamen, especially the hardier sorts, will want to collect the various forms and variants available as well as the hybrids. It is easy to be seduced by fancy names and glowing descriptions when checking through lists and catalogues and even more frustrating to find, having ordered a particular plant, that it is 'out of stock' or 'no longer available'. Of course the availability of a particular plant is dependent on the nurseryman's or grower's ability to produce sufficient quantities to meet demand; with slow-growing and difficult subjects that is not always possible.

Cultivar names have been applied to cyclamen in ever-increasing numbers in recent years. This reflects both a keen and growing interest in these little plants as well as the fact that new and exciting forms have been introduced, either from the wild, or by selection and hybridization of plants already in cultivation. It is only sensible that a good and distinct cultivated form should be given recognition by the application of a suitable cultivar name.

There are rules to follow in applying cultivar names but there is no law to prevent anyone from giving a plant a fancy name should they wish to do so. However, to apply cultivar names indiscriminately and without due consideration can only cause consternation and confusion.

It seems to me and others of like interest that certain conditions must be met before giving a plant a cultivar name:

First, and most important of all, the plant in question must be distinct; in other words it must have a feature or features that clearly separate it from its kin. This might be an obvious feature such as a particular leaf pattern or coloration, larger flowers or distinctly marked or coloured flowers, or it may be a less obvious, yet still unique, feature such as an earlier or later flowering habit. It is beholden on the person applying a name to a new cultivar to ensure that no such plant exists already and that the name has not been used before in that genus as a whole. Incidentally, the same conditions are applicable when a botanist describes a new species of plant.

Second, the cultivar must be reasonably uniform and its distinctive characters must be observable in every individual under that name. Of course, this is open to interpretation. Plants reproduced vegetatively, such as many trees and shrubs, and herbaceous perennials, can be expected to be uniform and one can be as certain as possible that plants found under a particular cultivar name will be as described. However, plants raised from seed, especially annuals, can often show a certain degree of variability. The amount of variability is important: for instance, if only one or two plants in every hundred vary then it is of little consequence; however, if 40 or 50 per cent vary then this to me is clearly not acceptable, without careful selection. In any batch of seedlings of a named cultivar, any misfits (rogues) need to be vigorously weeded out otherwise the percentage purity will gradually decline. In reality if only one seedling in a batch matches the criterion for a particular cultivar then it only should bear that cultivar's name. Efficient roguing might be essential to ensure that the cultivar is kept within tightly defined boundaries.

Third, the new cultivar must not exist as a single individual which might not be capable of being propagated. The originator should ensure that there is a stock of plants available and that it complies with the above criteria. There is nothing worse than a solitary plant with a cultivar name which subsequently proves difficult or impossible to reproduce. Even worse, when that individual dies leaving no 'offspring'; only a name remains to tantalize and frustrate us for evermore.

Fourth, any new cultivar must be adequately and accurately described, its salient features clearly delineated so that it can be readily recognized. Today there is no reason why all new cultivars should not be photographed or painted: a good illustration showing the salient features can be far more useful to future generations than a few lines of description or a dried specimen, however well prepared.

Of course, in a perfect world all cultivars would conform to these ideals and we would have no problem in recognizing them. But many cultivars are of long standing and the identity of some of these has become obscured by the passage of time and many have been lost altogether, or indeed, superseded by superior cultivars. One of the jobs confronting anyone researching a particular group of plants is to identify as accurately as possible old cultivars as well as new. When it can be shown quite clearly that a particular cultivar no longer exists or that plants present under that name do not conform with the cultivar as described or depicted, the time has come to abandon that particular name.

Cyclamen offered by nurserymen fall into several categories: species and selected forms of species, cultivars, groups and, occasionally, hybrids. Species are either offered in a straightforward way (*C. graecum*, *C. mirabile* and so on) or under their original collector's number (for instance, EKB 371, which is a selection of *C. coum* from plants originally collected in northern Turkey by E. K. Balls) or as a specified form (for instance *C. purpurascens*, Limone form, from plants orginally gathered close to Limone, near Lake Garda in northern Italy).

Named cultivars are presented, or at least should be presented, in single quotes and listed under the species to which they belong (for example *C. coum* subsp. *coum* 'Maurice Dryden' or *C. repandum* subsp. *peloponnesiacum* 'Pelops'). These cultivars may or may not conform to the criteria outlined above; if they do not then they should not have been given a cultivar name in the first instance but having been given the name we are stuck with it and those purchasing 'unstable cultivars' should do so with caution. A conscientious nurseryman will ensure that the customer receives what they ordered, even if this means discarding plants that do not conform to the norm for a particular cultivar.

Groups present another facet. They have generally been distinguished for use in cultivation by chance or by deliberate crossing. As a good example we can take the Pewter Group of *Cyclamen coum* that was distinguished from amongst the progeny of a deliberate crossing of *C. coum* EKB 371 with *C. coum* 'Nymans'; the result was a group of fine pewter-leaved plants varying somewhat in leaf size and coloration as well as in flower colour. Such crosses can be repeated to add to the Pewter Group pool. Exceptional individuals can be selected out and selfed and with luck they will come true, although clearly this may not happen; however, *C. coum* 'Maurice Dryden' is one such selection from within the Pewter Group. It is perhaps important to remember that the group name implies a certain degree of variability. Groups do not arise: they are distinguished by man for his own use. In other genera, groups can involve more than one species, but in cyclamen this is rare so far, although the Broadleigh Silver Group is of hybrid origin.

I now come to the rather vexed question of albinos and other colour variants within the species. These have been handled in various ways in the past. For instance the white form of *C. hederifolium* (or *C. neapolitanum* as it used to be called) is variously cited in literature as *C. hederifolium* 'Album', *album* or Album. A cultivar name as implicit in the name 'Album' can indicate a particular white form or it may refer more loosely to all white-flowered plants in a particular species. In the case of *C. hederifolium* there are quite a few different whites around and it is difficult to attach the name to any one in particular, indeed this seems to be undesirable.

However, many plants at present in cultivation under the name 'Album' are not pure white and often have varying amounts of pink in the throat or around the nose; these would, in my opinion, best be excluded from the cultivar. At the same time the use of *album* as a Latin epithet indicates some sort of rank in a formal sense but this has never been described in a valid way, to my knowledge. In recent years the trend has been formally to recognize albinos as formas (we have, for instance *C. cilicium* forma *album* and *C. graecum* forma *album*). Such formas encompass all the white forms of a particular species found in the wild and this seems to me to be the most sensible and least controversial solution to the problem, although it does imply creating some new names (see p.43). As a result the rank of forma applies only to plants of wild origin, whereas the ranks of cultivar and group apply only to selections of cultivated material. There is no reason why good white-flowered plants with particular characteristics such as silvered leaves should not subsequently be given distinct cultivar names. For instance *C. coum* subsp. *coum* forma *albissimum* applies to all pure white-flowered plants of subsp. *coum* found in the wild (some subsequently brought into cultivation), while the cultivar 'Tilebarn Fenella' is one particular manifestation of forma *albissimum* selected from cultivated plants. I am, as the reader will have surmised, rather loath to apply cultivar names to any plant other than those that are exceptional in one respect or another. In one or two instances I have had to create new cultivar names to clear up a confusion and, I hope, eliminate ambiguity.

It is surprising that more has not been done by growers to produce pure lines (by a programme of selective inbreeding) of some of these cyclamen (with the exception of *C. persicum*) by careful selection over several generations. Pure lines, provided that they were maintained, would remove the problem of variability and lead to the production of uniform cultivars. In the case of *C. persicum* this has been done very successfully for pot plant production by commercial breeders, where success is measured by standardization and uniformity and where markets apparently demand both excellence and a non-variable product, especially in countries like Holland and Germany where many fine cultivars of *C. persicum* exist today. It is interesting to note in passing that some forms of cyclamen that have been discovered in the wild do in fact breed more or less true (95 per cent with the occasional aberration), provided that they are selfed or crossed with a like individual; for instance *C. cilicium* forma *album*, *C. graecum* forma *album* and *C. graecum* 'Glyfada' – this shows clearly that pure lines can or should be fairly easy to produce in cultivation.

Another concern that faces many who have collections of cyclamen or who sell them through their nurseries is the use of collector's numbers. When plants are first introduced into cultivation, either as seed or living plants, they are often brought in under a collector's number. The collector may be a single individual (e.g. E. K. Balls), or there may be several collectors working together (e.g. Albury, Cheese and Watson) or they may collect under an expedition blanket (e.g. Southern Zagros Botanical Expedition). All these may or may not be abbreviated (e.g. EKB; AC & W; SZBE). The numbers should be unique to an individual, group or expedition so that each will only have one collection under a particular number and no number is repeated. Individuals who repeatedly make collecting trips carry on numbering at the point where the last trip finished so that in time the numbers may run into many thousands (Peter Davis's numbers run into in excess of 50,000 collections). Collections may represent herbarium gatherings (dried specimens) or live specimens (seed, plants, cuttings) or both. Herbarium specimens are a permanent record of a plant (or plants) seen in the field and are often accompanied by live material so that both share the same unique number. Collections are generally recorded in field notebooks or logs. These are notes written in the field and they normally include the plant's name (tentative or otherwise), the geographical location, altitude and the date, as well as a brief description of the plant in question together with habitat details. The amount of detail recorded varies enormously from collector to collector but to gardeners it is perhaps the description of the plant in the wild and its habitat that are of prime interest, for they can be extremely useful in ascertaining the needs of the plant in cultivation. When the dried specimens are eventually fixed onto herbarium sheets, full copies of the field data are attached and these are then filed in cupboards in a systematic order (just like books in a library) for future reference by anyone interested in research. The field note books or log books are either kept by individuals or placed in the care of institutes, universities or botanic gardens. They can be extremely useful years later for research purposes and should never be discarded.

I have gone into the collection and numbering in some detail because I am often asked about it and many want to know what the initials and numbers actually represent, especially when applied, as they often are, to living collections. As far as cyclamen are concerned this presents a bit of a dilemma as cyclamen are in essence transitory in cultivation and their continuation is through their progeny; they are for the most part copious seed bearers and it is easy to build up numbers; they are rarely reproduced vegetatively. Compare this example with, say, rhododendrons introduced as seed from Upper Burma or China early in the twentieth century by George Forrest or Frank Kingdon-Ward. When grown from seed, some of the plants took 20 years or more to reach flowering size, some even longer. From the moment they were sown, each batch

had its own collector's number and, as the plant was subsequently propagated by cuttings, the collector's number remained (in many cases) closely associated with that plant; it was in fact a true representation of the original introduction. This does not follow with cyclamen or indeed any other plant that is normally only reproduced from seed. It may be that the offspring are identical to the parents but this is rarely so for they present a range of variability. Over a few generations selection removes the poorer forms, weeds out the weakest and one begins to develop a strain of the original introduction which may begin to look very different from it, yet often the original collector's number remains attached to the plant. In addition the plant or plants may have hybridized with other collections which will naturally cause more variability to creep in. We often hear at shows or when discussing such plants: "That doesn't look anything like the original EKB 371 – I remember it when it first came into the country!" So be wary of collector's numbers: they may be meaningful or they may not. When raising seedlings from an original collection it is far wiser to write on the label 'ex EKB 371' to indicate to everyone concerned that the seedlings have been raised from, but are not, the original collection. In some lucky circumstances the offspring may so closely match the parent that this problem seems scarcely relevant. Occasionally a venerable plant with its original collector's number may survive in cultivation for many years (especially some forms of *C. hederifolium* and *C. graecum*) so that it remains a permanent live representation of that collection, dispelling any possible confusion of authenticity. A fairly full list of collectors and numbers was included in the first edition of this book.

All of these problems confront the cyclamen enthusiast when consulting catalogues and lists: what are the plants being offered and is cultivar A the same as, or different from, cultivar B and are they indeed what they purport to be? There is no better way of purchasing cyclamen than going to the nursery direct and selecting out the plants for oneself. It can be great fun choosing attractive leaf and flower forms when the plants are in full growth and at their best. Do not be surprised if the very best plants on display are 'not for sale', tantalising as this must be, for these are in all probability the choice plants that are being retained for future selection and breeding.

REGISTRATION AUTHORITY

The Cyclamen Society now acts as the registration authority (under licence from the Dutch) for all cyclamen cultivars with the exception of those of *C. persicum*. This was initiated in 1993 and set up the following year. It is to be hoped that the Society will act as a control to accept only distinct cultivars and to keep records of all the known cultivars previous to that date that are still in cultivation. A description and good colour photograph of each cultivar are badly needed for future reference, to save the muddle that has previously afflicted identification. This will take some time to achieve and I hope that in the meantime the list of cultivars and groups listed below, under various species headings, will make a useful starting point.

Cyclamen alpinum

This species shows a great deal of variation in stature, vigour and the subtle variations of leaf patterning and flower colour. Early introductions of the species were more uniform and smaller plants but today they are often larger and more variable. This may have resulted from unwitting selection in cultivation or apparent hybrid vigour of hybrids of the species from various sources. The named cultivars are all unstable and show considerable variation, and it is to be regretted that names have been applied to them at this stage; all are attractive plants but none deserve cultivar names.

"Album" This is put into quotation marks because under the present rules of horticultural nomenclature it is no longer acceptable to use Latinized names for cultivars, although those dating back before 1959 are still acceptable, due primarily to their long usage. If an authenticated albino *C. alpinum* were to turn up in the wild it would be quite acceptable to give it the rank of forma as with the albinos that have been discovered in other species in the wild. However, several albinos have turned up in cultivation, or at least they are near-albinos; those that I have seen have a discernible flush of pink, or at least open the palest pink, before fading to white. Undoubtedly, a pure white *C. alpinum* would be a great asset to collections for the species is delightful with its whirligig flowers and sweet primrose scent. All white manifestations of *C. alpinum* are referable to forma *leucanthum*, see p.86.

'Nettleton White' An unstable cultivar little distinguished from the above. It appeared in a batch of seedlings at the nursery of Potterton and Martin, being the better of two white-flowered plants. In leaf it is not distinct from most forms of the species. Awards: P.C. 1989.

AWARDS
• P.C. 1989.

'Pink Swirl' A selection with particularly large and elegant flowers in 'clear pink' made by Basil Smith in 1984.

'Red Devil' Another Basil Smith selection. The two-toned leaves set off numerous rather tall blooms of clear red.

'Speckles' A third Basil Smith selection, this one is rather smaller than the former two but the flowers are quite distinctive, pale pink with carmine speckling.

Cyclamen cilicium

'Album' This is best treated as *C. cilicium* forma *album*. This exciting pure white-flowered form of *C. cilicium* was discovered in the wild in Turkey in 1982. In general plants are as vigorous as, in some instances more vigorous than, the normal pink-flowered plant. See p.93.

'Bowles' Variety' Occasionally listed in catalogues, this presumably has its origin in plants grown at Myddleton House by E. A. Bowles, but the plants are scarcely distinguishable from many ordinary *C. cilicium* plants available at half the cost.

'Coquette' Misplaced by 'The Plant Finder', this cultivar belongs to *C. hederifolium*, see p.161.

'Elsie Thomas' The same applies as for 'Coquette' above, see p.161.

Cyclamen coum

These can be conveniently divided up into two major groupings based on the currently recognized subspecies of *C. coum* (named cultivars in quotation marks).

CULTIVAR CLASSIFICATION:
C. coum subsp. *coum*
• forma *coum* – 'Crimson King', 'Dusky Maid', 'Linnett Jewel', 'Linnett Rose', 'Macka', 'Magenta Surprise', 'Nymans', 'Roseum', 'Turkish Princess', 'Urfa'
  Pewter-leaved Group – 'Blush', 'Maurice Dryden', 'Tilebarn Elizabeth'
  Silver-leaved Group – 'Heavy Metal', 'Silver Star', 'Stirling Silver', 'Tilebarn Graham'
• forma *albissimum* – 'George Bisson', 'Golan Heights', 'Tilebarn Fenella'
• forma *pallidum* – 'Album', 'Marbled Moon'

C. coum subsp. *caucasicum* – 'Linnett Charm', 'Album'

It is worth mentioning in passing that the species is still sometimes listed in catalogues as *C. orbiculatum* and *C. hiemale*. Both of these latter names have long been accepted as being synonyms of *C. coum* and should no longer be used. The marbled-leaved forms of *C. coum* were formerly attributed to *C. orbiculatum* while the dark, plain-leaved forms were called *C. coum* or *C. orbiculatum* var. *coum*. At the same time, particularly early flowering plants with marbled leaves were accorded *C. hiemale* ('Hiemale'), these often starting to flower in late November. See also p.70.

Subsp. *coum* forma *coum*

'Album' White-flowered forms of *C. coum* have been known for many years under the name 'Album' to distinguish them from plants with various shades of pink, purple and magenta flowers. However, 'Album' does not have pure white flowers but flowers in which the petals are white but with the dark magenta blotches, typical of the species, retained at the base of each petal. More recently, pure white, unmarked, forms of *C. coum* have been found in the wild – see *C. coum* subsp. *coum* forma *albissimum*, p.74.

Formerly these 'white forms' of *C. coum* were listed under various names including *C. atkinsii* 'Album' or *C.* x *atkinsii* 'Album', *C. coum* 'Album' or *album*, *C. ibericum* 'Album' or *album*, *C. orbiculatum* 'Album' or *album*, or even *C. coum* 'Atkinsii Album' or *C. orbiculatum* var. *coum album*. This is enough to leave the most hardened botanist gasping. In the defence of the botanist one has to say that the majority of these combinations were dreamt up by gardeners; but whoever initiated them in the first place, the problem now is to try to sort them out. *C. atkinsii* 'Album', *C.* x *atkinsii* 'Album and *C. ibericum* 'Album' or *album* all refer to a complex of white-flowered members of *C. coum* subsp. *caucasicum* and, apart from their white flowers (with magenta basal markings), they conform to the subspecies with marbled heart-shaped rather than rounded leaves. I have no authenticated record of such 'white forms' being found in the wild but if they should then it would be appropriate to distinguish them botanically as a forma, but please not *album*, as there are enough of these around already. Having said this, however, I should point out that some plants sold under the above names are an ill-defined mixture of *coum* 'types' rendered unrecognizable over the generations and generally impossible to place within the recognized subspecies.

This leaves us with all the 'albums' masquerading under the *coum* and *orbiculatum* 'blanket'. These were long distinguished and were separated on leaf colours primarily, there being little or nothing to distinguish the flowers. *C. orbiculatum* 'Album' included plants with round or kidney-shaped, marbled leaves, whereas

150 *Cyclamen coum* subsp. *coum* forma *pallidum* 'Album': a cumbersome title for the white-flowered form widely seen in cultivation with plain, unmarked foliage.
151 *Cyclamen coum* subsp. *coum* forma *pallidum* 'Marbled Moon': essentially similar to 'Album' but with well-marked foliage.
152 A fine form of 'Marbled Moon' with well-marked foliage.

C. coum 'Album' encompassed plain-leaved forms with round or kidney-shaped leaves. *C. orbiculatum* has long been accepted as a synonym of *C. coum* and the name should not be used under any guise in catalogues, or indeed in horticultural literature in general. But one is still left with a problem: if they are the same species how are the 'white-flowered' variants separated? To begin with, all such white-flowered variants with magenta markings need to be formally recognized and I hereby accord to them the name forma *pallidum* (see p.75); they are found in the wild from time to time, generally mixed in populations of the more normal pink- or magenta-flowered forms. Plain-leaved variants of forma *pallidum* can then become 'Album' (equivalent of the old *C. coum* 'Album' or *album* or indeed *C. orbiculatum* var. *coum album*). In full then the plant is *C. coum* subsp. *coum* forma *pallidum* 'Album', a dreadful mouthful that is unavoidable. It can, however, be shortened to *C. coum* forma *pallidum* 'Album' without fear of ambiguity.

Cyclamen coum forma *pallidum* 'Album' is a splendid if somewhat variable group of plants probably (like *C. hederifolium* 'Album' of gardens) originating from several different sources. What you acquire depends on the source of plants, for different nurseries sell apparently different versions of it. True 'Album', as has been stated, has rounded (i.e. orbicular or kidney-shaped) deep green, shiny leaves without any markings and the characteristic dumpy white flowers with magenta markings at the base of each petal. The true plant will come more or less 100 per cent pure from seed provided that it is isolated from other forms of *C. coum*. Plain green-leaved forms that turn up in batches with leaves that are predominantly marbled often do not breed true and should not be regarded as 'Album' although they fit comfortably within forma *pallidum*. It is a most effective plant when placed in a group of its own where the flowers can be shown off against the dark, lustrous foliage. Unfortunately many plants sold under the name are far more variable. Thus plants can have small or large flowers, plain or attractively marked leaves that are orbicular or kidney-shaped.

The reader will notice that I have conveniently forgotten that other 'Album': I refer to *C. orbiculatum* 'Album'. Clearly it cannot have the same cultivar name and as no other exists for it, to my knowledge, then a new one needs to be applied. These plants with flowers like 'Album' but with handsomely marked leaves deserve a separate identity and I refer them to the new name, 'Marbled Moon'. It is important to remember that all these plants, whether *C. coum* forma *pallidum* 'Album' or 'Marbled Moon' or any other white-flowered variants of subsp. *coum* with dark marks at the base of the petals are referable to forma *pallidum*. They all make excellent garden plants and look particularly effective in mixed

drifts with the ordinary pink- or magenta-coloured forms. Once established, they will seed around freely in the garden, popping up here and there to delight the eye. A few nurseries list the variegated-leaved forms as 'Album' (patterned-leaved), although most do not distinguish their stock and it is rather pot-luck as to what one purchases; this is all the more reason to go and select plants for oneself!

Incidentally plain-leaved forms that occasionally arise from 'Marbled Moon' can be placed in 'Album'. In any cultivar, plants that do not conform to that cultivar need to be vigorously rogued out, otherwise the cultivar boundaries are bound to become blurred within just a few generations. In the same way pink-flowered plants that arise among seedlings of 'Maurice Dryden' can be referred to 'Blush'.

AWARDS
• F.C.C. (to *C. coum* forma *pallidum* 'Album') 1868.

'Atkinsii' This name should no longer be included in catalogues though its use persists despite evidence that the original plant is no longer in cultivation. The original plant is said to have been a hybrid (*C.* x *atkinsii*) between *C. coum* and *C. persicum*, a highly unlikely if not impossible liaison. With bold white flowers with magenta markings and elegant twisted petals (21mm/0.8in long), together with marbled and scalloped leaves, this must have been an attractive plant. The plant was first raised by James Atkins, head gardener to Lord Dickinson of Painswick House in Gloucestershire in the middle of the nineteenth century. It is reported that, at the time, Lord Dickinson was much pleased by *C. hederifolium* that had been planted by Atkins in the grounds of Painswick House and he wanted a similar display in the spring. Atkins then set about making as many crosses as possible including, it is believed, crosses in the *C. coum* group. At that time *C. coum* appeared primarily under the name *C. orbiculatum* and other plants today referred to *C. coum* subsp. *caucasicum* were found under other names, including *C. ibericum* and *C. vernum*.

Quoting from the *Journal of Horticulture and Cottage Gardener* (August 25: 150, 1861):

"After many attempts," writes Mr Atkins, "to produce a good cross between *Cyclamen coum* or *C. vernum*, and *C. persicum*, combining the neat habit of the two former with the colour and larger petals of the latter, having at the same time the foliage dark, yet relieved with a lighter band, or marbled, I at length succeeded in raising the hybrid now figured, from seeds produced by a variety of *C. coum* impregnated with *C. persicum*, and this, I have every reason to believe, I shall be able to perpetuate … Amongst the seedlings, it was found that every plant deviating in the markings of the foliage from the seed-bearing plant, produced white or blush flowers, whilst those retaining its plain dark leaf have invariably bloomed with different shades of the colour of that species…

"In *Cyclamen Atkinsi* the leaves are large (2 1/2 by 2 inches) ovate, obtuse, cordate at the base, with a deep sinus, the sides of which overlap, dark glossy green, with an irregular pale zone within the margin; the under surface is liver-coloured or dull purple. The flowers are elevated on longish verrucose stalks, and are of a French white, marked with a deep crimson blotch at the base of each segment; the calyx consists of five acute segments; the corolla has a short globose tube, and a limb of five broadly obovate segments nearly seven-eighths of an inch long; the mouth of the tube is nearly circular, the angles being indistinct … The flowers are scentless."

It is very probable that the purported hybrid at that time described as *C.* x *atkinsii* was in fact a hybrid between different forms of *C. coum*, as they are recognized today, and that the reference to a *C. coum* x *C. persicum* cross was wholly erroneous. In the Herbarium at the Royal Botanic Gardens, Kew, there is a single dried flower and leaf purporting to be *C.* x *atkinsii*. The flower seems to fit the original description of the plant and the leaf is heart-shaped with a somewhat scalloped margin, and the overall characteristics of these scraps are those of *C. coum* subsp. *caucasicum*. Indeed it is not unlikely that *C.* x *atkinsii* or 'Atkinsii' represents a variant of that subspecies and not a hybrid between species or subspecies at all.

Without very careful emasculation of the flowers at an early stage when undertaking crosses between species, it is not possible to be certain that seeds produced are hybrids. After artificial pollination, if the two species are incompatible then no fertilisation will take place. Yet there is still time for plants to self-pollinate or to cross within the batch of the same species. Seed will then be produced but it will not be the result of interspecific liaisons.

It is perhaps significant to note that in the same article Atkins goes on immediately to describe *C. ibericum* (now *C. coum* subsp. *caucasicum*), which he had in cultivation at the same time. The description closely matches that of *C.* 'Atkinsii' and he even goes on to say that "the flowers vary in colour; in some, they are pale rose or flesh-coloured, in other plants deep rose-colour; in some they are white; but in all cases they are marked with a broad ovate spot at the base of the segments, which spot is either purple or crimson …".

To back this claim there is Atkins's own description (above) and the pan of plants in flower depicted (as an engraving) with his article (above right). This matches *C. coum* subsp. *caucasicum* very well indeed. The colour of the flower as described above would fit with *C. coum* subsp. *caucasicum* 'Album' as we know it today.

That is as may be, but plants sold under the cultivar name 'Atkinsii' today bear little resemblance to either the

Cyclamen "Atkinsii", now known to be *C. coum* subsp. *caucasicum*.

few fragments to be found at Kew or to the early descriptions of this mystery plant. In general, most fit within that loose association of rather vigorous pink-flowered plants known as *C. coum* 'Roseum' and were at one time referred to as *C. atkinsii* 'Roseum'.

Interestingly, many plantings of cyclamen remain to this day in the grounds of Painswick House and in some of the cottage gardens in the village, and some may be descendants of those planted by James Atkins. However, most have in fact been planted in the last ten years or so, and cannot claim any such lineage. Even some of those *C. coum* growing today in Atkins's cottage are not 'original' and were purchased at the Royal Horticultural Society hall in London in recent years. It would be a brave person indeed who could pick any one individual out with certainty and claim it to be the long-lost *C.* x *atkinsii*.

In summary the name 'atkinsii' is referable to two entities: first to *C.* x *atkinsii*, an alleged hybrid between *C. coum* and *C. persicum*, now no longer in cultivation; second to *C. coum* 'Atkinsii' another plant of horticultural origin, probably of no connection to the original *C.* x *atkinsii* and represented today by white forms. The cultivar name 'Atkinsii', because of the earlier confusion and because the name has undoubtedly been transposed from a putative hybrid to a cultivar, should no longer be adopted. Plants under the cultivar name 'Atkinsii' fit well within the spectrum of *C. coum* subsp. *coum*.

AWARDS
- F.C.C. 1865.

'Barr Silver' See under 'Broadleigh Silver'.

'Blush' It is always nice to see a good pale-flowered form of *C. coum*, especially as many growers tend towards the

153 *Cyclamen coum* Pewter Group 'Maurice Dryden'.

brighter and deeper colours. However, this selection by Kath Dryden was derived from 'Maurice Dryden'. In every batch of seedlings of 'Maurice Dryden' there are a few plants with pale pink rather than white flowers and the best of these were selected and named 'Blush'. Plants have leaves edged and veined deep green and flowers of the clearest pale rose with a deep rose-magenta blotch at the base of each petal. They come more or less true from seed, provided that they are not contaminated with other *C. coum* types.

'Broadleigh Silver' This cultivar originates from plants purchased by Basil Smith at a Royal Horticultural Society Show from the Broadleigh Gardens stand. I have grown plants of similar origin for a number of years. Originally thought to have originated from the Pewter Group this is a very varied, but extremely attractive, group of plants, variable in leaf size and degree of pewter on the leaves (some are attractively silvered rather than pewtered) and the flowers range considerably in size and shape, as well as markings. Most are rather dainty plants producing many flowers and prolific seed. In many, but by no means all, the petal lobes spread outwards in the manner of *C. alpinum* and some are deliciously scented. In others, the petals spread up at a more oblique angle or are completely reflexed in the manner of true *C. coum*. In addition the nose markings range from a solid deep blotch to a paler and less distinct blotch or several diverging lines, sometimes a single central line only. These plants wholly or in part appear to represent a hybrid form between *C. coum* subsp. *coum* and *C. alpinum* and they would be better referred to the hybrid, *C.* x *drydenii*. The cultivar name 'Broadleigh Silver' is unacceptable because of the inherent variability of the plants and they are best referred to Broadleigh Silver Group. They are probably the same as 'Barr Silver'. Incidentally, the leaves of this group are decidedly more pewter than silver and the use of the word

silver can be very misleading, especially as there are some really good silver-leaved cyclamen about.

Broadleigh Silver Group See under 'Broadleigh Silver'. This group, probably of hybrid origin, should not be confused with *C. coum* Pewter Group, which are pewter-leaved selections of subsp. *coum*.
BS8927. A Basil Smith selection from a plant originally obtained from Kath Dryden. The foliage is dark green with a contrasting band of sage green, the dark centre being shaped like a tiny Christmas tree. The flowers are a good size and dark magenta. This, like the following, should not be confused with collector's numbers, they are simply Basil Smith's cataloging references.

BS8927P A hybrid cross derived from BS8927 with strongly patterned leaf markings and flowers in various shades of pink.

'Crimson King' A selection of *C. coum* subsp. *coum* with attractively marked leaves and flowers of a crimson hue, very similar to those of 'Meaden's Crimson'. It is sold only by De Jager & Sons of Marden, Kent.

'Dusky Maid' A rather unusual Basil Smith cultivar with rounded, pale green, rather scalloped leaves washed all over with metallic grey-green, with 'cat's whisker veins' and dusky purple (described as 'pinky-magenta') flowers with a deep basal blotch without the usual white 'eyes'. Quite vigorous and relatively free-flowering, with most progeny like the parents in leaf, but varying in the shade of flower, some being noticeably darker. It is reported to set seed rather poorly. The original plant was selected from a batch of young plants on a Cyclamen Society stand.

'Heavy Metal' A 1995 introduction by Basil Smith selected for its attractive, rounded, silver-washed leaves that almost look as though they were overlain by metallic paint. The flowers are pale pink with wide-spreading petals. Most seedlings come true to type but in some the leaves are bordered by a thin green margin and bear a thin green midrib; these are included within the cultivar. The source of the original plants is a mystery according to Basil Smith but they undoubtedly owe their origin to the Broadleigh Pewter Group which often 'throws' silver-leaved seedlings with pale flowers.

'Hiemale' This is a name formerly applied to particularly early-flowering forms of *C. coum* subsp. *coum* with marbled leaves and deep rose-magenta flowers. These would often come into flower before Christmas, sometimes as early as mid-November. They were probably the same as *C. hiemale* or even *C. hyemale* but these have all been sunk into subsp. *coum* and the cultivar has proved very difficult to define from all the infinite forms of subsp. *coum* in cultivation at the present time, many of which have been crossed with one another, either intentionally or by chance. In view of this it is best to abandon the cultivar name 'Hiemale'. The cultivar name is, in any case, derived from (co-extensive with) *C. hiemale*.

'Linnett Jewel' A plant selected by Basil Smith for colour and put out as a new cultivar in 1995. The leaves are unremarkable, though as with many *coum* types they are attractively patterned silver on a deep green background. The relatively large, well-rounded, flowers are a deep magenta-crimson with the centre of the petals somewhat paler. The flowers pale somewhat with age, as is the case with many forms of *C. coum* after the flowers have been out for ten days or so. The crosses which gave rise to these dark-flowered plants also produced impressive all-silver leaved seedlings which in turn became the basis for another cultivar, 'Sterling Silver'. Second-generation plants established the deep-coloured 'Linnett Jewel' characteristic. Seedlings mostly produce flowers in the dark magenta range.

'Linnett Rose' This cultivar is characterized by translucent blooms of warm rose-pink which deepens somewhat at the petal-margins. The leaves are deep green with a light-greyish pattern. A useful character of 'Linnett Rose' is its capacity to produce numerous blooms from a single tuber. The original plant which gave rise to the cultivar was selected for its profuse flowering habit, although the flowers had rather narrow petals of a wishy-washy pink; it was labelled 'Macka' (see below), although it clearly does not conform well to the usual description of that cultivar. Open-pollinated, this plant apparently set a large amount of seed; the flowers of resultant seedlings were either clear colour or diaphanous and 'Linnett Rose' was selected from the best of the latter which had well-formed flowers with rounded petals. Both 'Linnett Jewel' and 'Linnett Rose' make good and hardy plants for the open garden, where contrasting patches of different-coloured cultivars can be very effective when they come into flower during February. A Basil Smith introduction of 1994.

'Macka' This plant originated from a collection made at altitude in north-eastern Turkey in the 1960s by Albury, Cheese and Watson, growing in close proximity to *C. parviflorum*. Macka is in fact the name of a town in the region and the plants are characterized by rounded, silver-washed leaves with a small central deep green area. The flowers are deep rose-magenta. 'Macka' does not appear to be available today although plants originating from this source are undoubtedly still grown. Plants sold under the

name by Potterton and Martin bear deep green leaves with a light silvery or greyish pattern and rose-pink blooms, but they scarcely live up to the original description, although they may all represent variants of the original collection from Turkey.

'Maurice Dryden' A charming selection made by Kath Dryden and named in honour of her husband Maurice. The original plants were derived from the Pewter Group (see below) by crossing them with a white-flowered variant of EKB 371. Kath relates that "by selection it was only a matter of time before white forms appeared in the Pewter Group". Plants are relatively small with silvered leaves edged with green. The flowers are very similar to *C. coum* 'Album', being white with a deep magenta blotch at the base of each petal. 'Maurice Dryden' is perhaps one of the less vigorous cultivars of the *C. coum* complex, although it is certainly a stronger grower than many of the Pewter Group and does not come altogether true from seed, although rogue plants are easy to select out, the moment they come into flower. Kath Dryden in fact reckons a good selection to come 99 per cent true from seed! Flowers vary somewhat in size and the leaves also vary in the intensity of silver, some in fact being more pewter in general tone, rather than silver. None the less, this is a very nice plant and quick to flower from seed, which is produced in quantity. Because it is somewhat less vigorous than some of its cousins 'Maurice Dryden' is perhaps best grown in frames or pans. If planted in the general garden it deserves a site to itself, otherwise it can easily be swamped by more vigorous *C. coum* hybrids.

Some plants being sold under the name 'Maurice Dryden' are certainly more vigorous than the original selection and it may be that those growing them tend to select out the more vigorous seedlings or perhaps they feed them more heavily. Whatever the reason, do not expect this to be a uniform plant, however delightful. I have one plant in my collection which conforms to all the principal characteristics of 'Maurice Dryden' but is twice the size in both leaves and flowers.

Awards
* A.M. 1990.

'Meaden's Crimson' The original plants that gave rise to this cultivar came from Bob Meaden as three seedlings sent to Basil Smith and notable for their deep crimson blooms. The flowers vary somewhat in size and colour of their blooms and by plain deep green leaves. A stable deep crimson flower has proved difficult to establish in *C. coum* and 'Meadon's Crimson' is a step in that direction, although it has perhaps been named too

154 *Cyclamen coum* subsp. *coum* Nymans Group: variable plants sold as cv. 'Nymans' belong to this group but are unlike the original cultivar, as described.

155 *Cyclamen coum* subsp. *coum* Pewter Group: a typical pewter-leaved plant, here with attractive dark flowers.

time as the well-known EKB 371, which consisted of a number of plants originally) and sent to Nymans; it has been confirmed by the Countess of Rosse of Nymans in West Sussex that a consignment of *C. coum* was introduced to the gardens at Nymans in the 1930s (1933 or 1934), having been sent by Mr E. K. Balls under the number EKB 371 to the head gardener at that time, Mr Comber (see *The Cyclamen Society Journal* 8:24, 1984). The selected plant had typical rounded *coum* leaves but of a rather sickly, yet not unattractive, yellow-green offset by small and rather mediocre flowers of deep claret with the characteristic pale markings (in the form of a V) at the base of each petal. On Eliot Hodgkin's death in 1973, the lone tuber was passed on to his close friend Kath Dryden. Seedlings conforming more or less to 'Nymans' were passed onto various growers including Chris Brickell, but the plants proved weak and difficult to maintain for any length of time. However, 'Nymans' was crossed with the far more vigorous and better-known E. K. Balls collection of *C. coum* (EKB 371) and this resulted directly in the Pewter Group which has become so popular in recent years. The chief merit in 'Nymans' has been the part it has played in the Pewter Group.

Plants at Nymans garden today originating from EKB 371 (whose offspring are readily available elsewhere) are very variable in the richness of their bloom and in the amount of silver or pewter on the leaves, this being generally present as a broad, more or less circular, uneven band. None of them appear to match the original 'Nymans'. Plants sold under the name 'Nymans' today are rather variable (even, dare one say, from the same source). In general they have orbicular leaves with a greyish hastate pattern on a deep green base, generally but not consistently bordered with a broad band of dark, rather dull green. The flowers, which are often of a good size, are a deep magenta-purple with a darker blotch at the base of each petal. These plants owe more to EKB 371 than they do to the original 'Nymans', although of course they may have resulted from crosses involving 'Nymans' but, such details have been lost in the annals of history. This highlights the importance of recording details of origins and parentage of any plant that is subsequently given a group or cultivar name.

Incidentally, the original EKB 371 was a fine form of subsp. *coum* with reasonably large rounded leaves with a broad silvery hastate pattern and, in the centre, a characteristic deep green 'Christmas tree' pattern. The flowers were a deep rosy-purple. Kath Dryden has suggested that the offspring of EKB 371, which are a fine group of garden plants, should be recognized by formal cultivar names and has suggested that the pink-flowered form be called 'Edgar K. Balls'. The charming white-flowered variant from the same source she proposes could be called 'Quaker Pearl'.

prematurely and it would be better to see many of these hasty cultivars tested over a number of years; after all it is easy to see how earlier cultivars such as 'Apollo' and 'Nymans' have confused and perplexed cyclamen addicts.

'Nymans' Great confusion surrounds this plant mainly because a number of different plants are going around under that name at the present time, although the true 'Nymans' appears to be no longer in existence or at least to be very rare. The original plant (there was only one) was discovered by Eliot Hodgkin, a very distinguished and discerning plantsman, among a group of *C. coum* collected by E. K. Balls (at the same

Today 'Nymans' look-alikes' turn up from time to time. One such plant came from a batch of seedlings from Cyclamen Society seed, from plants originally collected in northern Turkey and grown by Kath Dryden. This plant is stronger than the original 'Nymans' and its seedlings often bear pewter-washed leaves. Such plants may look similar to the original Nymans in some respects but they cannot be considered to be the same cultivar.

The name 'Nymans' should not, in my opinion, be applied to any cyclamen plant doing the rounds at the present time; they are better referred simply to the Nymans Group, without qualification.

Nymans Group See above.

Pewter Group (sometimes referred to as the Pewter-leaved Group). This delightful group, which has become so popular, was produced by Kath Dryden by crossing the original rather weakly 'Nymans' with the bolder and far more vigorous *C. coum* EKB 371 (or at least plants purported to be the offspring from this collection). The leaves of the latter bore a green 'Christmas tree' pattern in the centre of the leaf, surrounded by a paler grey-green zone and margined with deep green. The purpose of the cross was to instil more vigour into 'Nymans' but the result was a race of pewter-leaved hybrids which had a uniform wash of pewter over the upper leaf-surface with the margin picked out in green (the midrib above is generally rather impressed and deep green). The cross was done both ways (using each as the female parent); with 'Nymans' as the seed parent a few seedlings were produced, these having small dark crimson flowers, while the other seed parent produced far more seedlings whose flowers were larger and pale to deep rose, often bicolored, sometimes almost white in the centre of the petals. After several generations the overall flower colour of the group ranges from pale pink to pale magenta, through to deep claret and pure magenta. In addition, the flowers may be subtly bicolored or picotee, especially those in the paler shades. From this important group have arisen some fine cultivars including 'Maurice Dryden' and 'Tilebarn Elizabeth'. The name of the group is said to have arisen when E. B. Anderson first saw Kath's plants, exclaiming "What a breakthrough, they look like jewels set in real old pewter!"

Further work on the Pewter Group in succeeding years eventually gave rise to *C. coum* 'Silver Leaf', identical to the Pewter Group but with silver rather than pewter-coloured leaves and there are a number of plants around at present of this persuasion, although they appear to have varied origins: see also 'Broadleigh Silver', 'Silver Star' and 'Sterling Silver'. The difference between pewter and silver is a subtle one in some ways and it is sometimes difficult to assign plants to one group or the

156 *Cyclamen coum* subsp. *coum* Pewter Group: a typical plant showing a picotee form common in the group, whose flowers are often scented. 'Tilebarn Elizabeth' is similar but with evenly silvered foliage.
157 *Cyclamen coum* subsp. *coum* Pewter Group.

other, especially as older leaves tend to lose their lustre. A good test, however, is to remember back to the good old days of the British florin (two-shilling piece, before 1947) which was an attractive silver; that is the colour that silver-leaved cyclamen should be, not grey.

Cyclamen coum Pewter Group as it is seen today is by no means uniform in leaf nor flower and it is just as well that a whole plethora of cultivars have not been selected from its midst. The group is united by having basically pewter-coloured leaves. Many have leaves with a thin marginal band of green as well as a midrib picked out in green, which contrasts well with the pewter ground cover of much of the upper leaf surface. In others the main veins are also picked out in green. The leaf size varies a great deal from 15mm (0.6in) diameter to 50mm (2in), sometimes more, the leaves mostly being orbicular or somewhat oblong. As has already been noted, flower colour also varies considerably within the group, with picotees and bicolors appearing in most batches of seedlings. Flower size is also very variable, although most plants bear intermediate-sized blooms for the *C. coum* group as a whole.

The prime difficulty with the Pewter Group lies not in the controlled manner in which the original group was engineered but what has happened to it in the intervening years. As a result different nurseries and growers have different strains and this has led to increased variability within the group. My attention was drawn to this interesting 'evolution' within the Pewter Group by Christine Skelmersdale who handed me a batch of plants at a Royal Horticultural early-spring show in London five or six years ago and asked me what they were. At first glance they looked like just another variable cluster within the Pewter Group. Admittedly the plants all bore pewtered or somewhat silvered leaves, yet a number of the plants had flowers with more pointed and spreading petals, several were bicolored, and several (certainly not all) had a sweet perfume. The blotch at the base of the petals was also quite variable, with those on some plants being very like the normal *C. coum* markings, whilst others consisted of a solid blotch to the very base of the petals, and others still had a series of lines rather than a solid blotch. Since then I have been able to study these plants closely and similar plants have turned up from several other sources. I have concluded rather hesitatingly that they represent hybrid plants between *C. coum* subsp. *coum* and *C. alpinum* (see Broadleigh Pewter Group). I say 'hesitatingly' because at this time I am not able to prove this without further experimentation and I am trying to reproduce the cross in my alpine house. The rather oblong leaf character of many of the putative hybrids also hints at *C. alpinum* in the plants' genes. As many of the plants available are in their third or fourth generation they almost certainly represent more than just simple hybrids between the parent species, and some at least may represent back crosses with one or other parent, or both; certainly it is difficult when searching among hundreds of plants to find two that are identical.

To keep the *C. coum* Pewter Group pure these hybrids need to be separated out and isolated, otherwise the group is likely to become a messy hybrid swarm. Incidentally, those growing Pewter Group for propagation purposes would be wise to isolate them from *C. alpinum* until more is known. See also p.189.

AWARDS
• A.G.M. 1993.

'Roseum' (also as *C. atkinsii rosea*, 'Atkinsii Roseum' or 'Roseum' or even *C. orbiculatum* var. *coum roseum*). This cultivar was quite common and widely available at one time, though today it is listed by just a few nurseries. The plant I remember had relatively large rose-pink flowers with the usual magenta markings and attractive, orbicular leaves handsomely patterned with silver; such plants are certainly still around. They fit comfortably within the range of variation of *C. coum* subsp. *coum* and such plants can be seen quite easily in the wild, especially at fairly low altitudes in northern Turkey. Unfortunately, some nurseries have lost sight of the true 'Roseum' and list plants that have 'deep pink' or 'rosy-carmine', or even red, blooms, indeed plants with almost any shade of pink flowers and all manner of leaf markings seem to be clustered under this cultivar; these should not be considered to be 'Roseum' in my opinion. 'Album' has a similar muddled history. Subsp. *coum* is also sold under various general colour groupings such as Reds, Magentas or Crimsons: these are not cultivar names but merely indicate the group colour of the flowers.

Silver Group Confusion reigns over silver-leaved forms of both *C. hederifolium* and *C. coum*, mainly because the tag has been applied to encompass any plant with silver leaves, whether part or wholly silver. To add to the confusion 'pewter' and 'silver' are used indiscriminately; for instance several nurseries sell so-called silver-leaved *coum*s which to my eye are decidedly pewter (see under Pewter Group), yet at the same time, good silver-leaved forms are available, though the best I have seen to date have been in private collections. From the gardener's point of view this may not seem a problem as most are excellent and good garden plants, indeed many are highly desirable in a collection of hardy cyclamen. The problem is mainly in catalogues where plants are variously distinguished as 'silver-leaved', 'silver strain', 'pewter-leaved' or 'silver leaf forms'. To these must be added further subdivisions such as 'silver-leaved red', 'silver-leaved bicolor', 'pewter-leaved red'. This is all a bit of a minefield for the catolgue-browser and is particularly annoying when, having purchased plants, they are found to be identical or almost so to plants purchased elsewhere under another descriptive epithet. Standardisation and uniformity in naming is just as important for cultivated plants as it is for wild species, otherwise confusion is bound to result.

Tilebarn Nursery sell 'silver-leaved forms' of *C. coum* which include 'silver or pewter leaf forms'. Most of these have nicely rounded leaves with a narrow or broad margin of deep green. In addition the main veins ('ribs') are also often green. The flower colour varies from mid- to deep pink or magenta-pink. The silvers have arisen from several sources; some at least have come directly from the Pewter Group, by chance.

In the garden these plants can be relied upon to make an attractive bed of leaves from the late autumn through to the spring with the first flowers usually opening early in the New Year.

'Silver Leaf' See under Silver-leaved Group.

Silver-leaved Bicolor Group Attractive group of plants of the typical *C. coum* subsp. *coum* type with relatively small orbicular, silvered leaves which generally have the main veins and margin picked out in green. The flowers are pale to mid rose-pink with a deep flush to the margin and with the usual dark pink or magenta mark at the base of each petal, although this may sometimes be less well-defined, with lines rather than a dense blotch. Many of these are indistinguishable from the Pewter Group and some are virtually identical to 'Tilebarn Elizabeth'. They possibly all have the same origin. Some closely match plants being sold by Broadleigh Gardens; see under Pewter Group.

Silver-leaved Red Group Very similar in leaf markings to Silver-leaved Bicolor Group but the flowers are a rich deep crimson-purple with an even deeper blotch at the base of each petal.

'Silver Star' This plant is perhaps best included in the Silver-leaved Group. It has striking orbicular leaves, with a slight point at the apex, which have an overall cast of bright silver; the veins are fairly obvious. The flowers are bicolored, pink and white, more or less shuttlecock-shaped. Unfortunately only about one-third of plants produce the desirable characteristic implied by the cultivar name so that seedlings need to be rigourously rogued out as soon as the leaf markings are shown to advantage. The plant is, in many ways, similar to 'Tilebarn Elizabeth', with similarly bicolored flowers of the shuttlecock shape. 'Silver Star' was developed from second-generation seedlings from a plant collected (under number S21 N397) in northern Turkey by the Cyclamen Society. The original plant had extremely handsome leaves with a bright silver cast contrasting with a central deep green Chrstmas tree pattern and bicolored flowers in white and rose. Several second-generation plants proved to have all-over silver leaves. The best two were crossed and the resultant seedlings backcrossed with the parents to produce a good proportion of silver-leaved plants – the basis for 'Silver Star'. As with 'Tilebarn Elizabeth' the seedlings are far from pure, throwing too high a proportion of green, patterned or dull pewter-leaved seedlings.

'Stirling Silver' This cultivar has a similar origin to 'Linnett Jewel', see p.153. The cultivar is notable for its very striking silvery-white, unmarked leaves that have an

158 *Cyclamen coum* subsp. *coum* forma *albissimum* 'Golan Heights'.
159 *Cyclamen coum* subsp. *coum* forma *albissimum*

almost luminous quality. It certainly has the best silver leaves of any *C. coum* form that I have seen. The flowers, of medium size, come in various shades of pale magenta, but are overpowered by the startling foliage. Plants flower poorly and set only a limited amount of seed. By no means do all seedlings show the highly desirable silvery foliage. It stands up well to weather in the open but this cultivar is still scarce (and expensive) and few are likely to plant them in the open garden before a stock of plants have been built up. In any event, it makes an extremely handsome pot plant for the alpine house.

'Tilebarn Elizabeth' Raised by Peter Moore, this is another delightful selection from the Pewter Group of subsp.

160 *Cyclamen graecum* subsp. *graecum* 'Glyfada'.
161 Close up of *Cyclamen graecum* subsp. *graecum* 'Glyfada'.

coum. The leaves are silvered overall, without the green veins of many in the group, while the bicolored flowers are very pale pink, almost white, with a flush of rose pink towards the margin of the petals and with the usual deep magenta-crimson blotch at the base of each petal. Plants breed true and generally flower in the third year from seed. It comes very close to some plants being sold under the heading Silver-leaved Bicolor.

AWARDS
• P.C. 1987.

'Tilebarn Fenella' This is a cultivar of *C. coum* subsp. *coum* forma *albissimum*. The name *albissimum* applies to all pure white variants of *C. coum*. Such forms have only recently been discovered in the wild: by Manfred Koenen in south-eastern Turkey and by the Cyclamen Society in northern Israel. Koenen's original plant has produced a race of plants with pure white flowers and attractively patterned leaves, and these have been given the cultivar name 'Tilebarn Fenella' at Tilebarn Nursery where Peter Moore has been able gradually to increase the stock. In contrast, the Israeli version of forma *albissimum* has plain, unmarked leaves.

'Tilebarn Graham' This is another of Peter Moore's selections from the silver-leaved variants of *C. coum* subsp. *coum*. The rounded leaves are silvered overall and the flowers are relatively small and pink with a deep magenta blotch at the base of each petal. The petals themselves are rather narrow and twisted, much in the manner of some of the elegant forms of *C. coum* subsp. *caucasicum*.

'Turkish Princess' This is a Basil Smith cultivar which probably arose from the same stock as 'Nymans' of gardens. The leaves are green overlain with silver, while the flowers are rose-pink and magenta bicolors; perhaps the richest bicolor available at the present time. Most of the offspring conform well to the parent cultivar.

'Urfa' Potterton and Martin are the only nursery (it is also listed by Roger Poulett) at present issuing this plant which gets its name from Urfa in south-eastern Turkey which is near to where the original plants were collected. It is rather a dwarf plant, the orbicular leaves with a slightly pointed apex and deep green with an attractive 'Christmas tree' pattern. The flowers are small and rather squat, deep magenta-pink with a deep basal blotch to each petal.

C. coum **BSBE 518** Plants are derived from the Bowles Scholarship Botanical Expedition of 1963 and were collected along the Black Sea Coast of Turkey. Plants may have leaves banded with silver (form 1) or deep green leaves with an attractive 'Christmas tree' pattern. Flowers range from mid- to deep pink with the characteristic magenta blotch at the base of each petal. A vigorous and free-flowering selection.

S3 N20 This unromantic tag conceals a little gem of a plant discovered by the Cyclamen Society Expedition to Turkey in 1988. The plants have attractively patterned leaves and white flowers with a pink flush at the base of the petals. It is to be hoped that this will be given a suitable cultivar name in due course. It is probably best included in *C. coum* subsp. *coum* forma *pallidum* as it cannot be comfortably placed elsewhere.

Subsp. *coum* forma *albissimum*

'George Bisson' A listed cultivar of forma *albissimum* but no further information at hand.

'**Golan Heights'** Plants with plain green leaves and pure white flowers without any markings whatsoever.

'**Tilebarn Fenella'** Like 'Golan Heights', but leaves with a paler hastate pattern.

Subsp. *caucasicum*

Under this name come a number of plants, primarily from the Caucasus Mountains, that were formerly accorded specific rank. These include *C. caucasicum* itself as well as *C. abchasicum, C. adzharicum, C. circassicum, C. ibericum* and *C. vernum*.

AWARDS
- A.M. (under the name *C. ibericum*) 1937.

Silver-leaved Group (often listed as "Silver Leaf Forms"). Just as subsp. *coum* has given rise to striking silver-leaved forms so has its counterpart subsp. *caucasicum*. The leaves may be overall silver or, in fact, pewter and are decidedly more heart-shaped than orbicular. The flowers are pink with longer, somewhat more twisted petals, with a deep magenta basal blotch with pink 'eyes' usually. No cultivars have been named from this group to date.

'**Album'** As with the subsp. *coum* the cultivar name is not applicable to pure white forms of subsp. *caucasicum* (no such plants have been found in the latter subspecies to date). Flowers are white with a magenta blotch at the base of each petal while the leaves are deep green with varying amounts of marbling above. *C. ibericum* var. *album* or 'Album' is almost certainly the same. The cultivar name 'Album' cannot be used in this instance as 'Album' is already employed for a long-established cultivar of subsp. *coum*, see above. As a result this particular plant requires a new cultivar name. See also under *C.* 'Atkinsii'.

'**Linnett Charm'** Selected by Basil Smith, this new cultivar was put out in 1995. The plant conforms well with various forms of subsp. *caucasicum* already in cultivation, with heart-shaped leaves of deep green, with a hastate pattern in various shades of rather dull pewter. The flowers have the characteristic strongly reflexed, pointed and twisted petals in mid-pink; the corolla rim is pink or lavender unlike the white more characteristic of subsp. *coum*. 'Linnett Charm' comes reasonably true from seed as might be expected from a plant that closely matches its wild progenitors; although the source material of this cultivar is uncertain, it is likely to be from plants that have been in cultivation for some years.

162 *Cyclamen hederifolium* subsp. *hederifolium* forma *albiflorum* 'Album'.

Cyclamen cyprium

C. cyprium '**E. S.'** Elizabeth Strangman (formerly Washfield Nursery in Sussex) passed on some beautifully marked leaf forms of *C. cyprium* to Peter Moore at Tilebarn Nursery. 'E. S.' stands for Elizabeth Strangman as might be expected, although it has been put about, quite wrongly, that it stands for 'Extra Silvery'. These plants have deep green leaves boldly marked with splashes of contrasting silver. These are now listed in catalogues as *C. cyprium* 'E. S.' The flowers are identical with the more normal leaf forms (many of which are also very attractive, some more subtly so) and equally deliciously scented. The original plants were selected by Hilda Davenport Jones in the 1960s and were passed by Ray Cobb to Elizabeth Strangman at Washfield Nursery. Elizabeth in turn passed the plants to Peter Moore at Tilebarn Nursery. Similar plants, formerly offered by Potterton and Martin, may share the same origin.

Cyclamen graecum

For the pure white form, forma *album*, see under the species on p.136.

C. graecum subsp. *graecum* '**Glyfada'** Glyfada is a small town to the east and on the outskirts of Athens, close to where the old Athens International Airport is situated. On a roadside embankment by Glyfada in March 1971 Brian Mathew came upon a specimen of *C. graecum* with

163 *Cyclamen hederifolium* subsp. *hederifolium* 'Ruby Glow'.

chance seedling amongst a drift in the open garden, first flowering in 1980. Only a small proportion of the seedlings come true to type. As the flowers age the pink coloration around the mouth of the corolla takes on a purplish hue. Rather later to come into flower than most *C. hederifolium* types.

AWARDS
* P.C. 1987.

'Elsie Thomas' A handsome plant with well-marked green leaves and pink flowers with broad petals richly stained with deep pink, from the basal nose markings well up the lobes, but leaving the petal-margins pale and almost (luminous) white. The plants are selected from batches of seedlings which vary in the richness of their

164 *Cyclamen hederifolium* subsp. *hederifolium* 'Silver Cloud' with outstanding silvery foliage; the flowers are pink.

blooms and leaf markings, some seedlings in fact having silvered leaves. Interesting, but do not expect seedlings to come true to type necessarily.

'Elsie Thomas' was named by Basil Smith in 1993, being selected from hybrid seedlings from a programme organized to breed red-flowered *C. hederifolium*.

It is a pity that this and the preceding plant have been given cultivar names before they have been more rigorously selected and refined to produce lines in which at least the majority of plants come true from seed.

'Fairy Rings' This is a cultivar put out by Basil Smith in 1990 with distinctive leaves which have a pale green centre surrounded by a dark then a pale band and margined by a further dark green band, set off by a profusion of mid-pink blooms. The foliage is bright and the contrasting pale and dark 'rings' quite distinctive but not unknown in ordinary batches of seedlings of *C. hederifolium*. Apparently, the full leaf pattern takes five years to reveal itself fully. Unfortunately Basil Smith admits that this "cultivar" although "most desirable" is "tantalisingly unstable with reversion from type in a considerable proportion of seedlings. Some of the reversions are quite striking and worth growing on in their own right". It is my opinion, and I am sure that of many horticulturists, that such unstable plants should never be given a cultivar name in the first instance. Repeated back-crossing between the original parent plant and the best seedlings may eventually stabilize the desirable characters, though this is by no means certain and may take quite a few generations. The establishment of formal registration of cyclamen species cultivars (excluding *C. persicum*) will not necessarily limit the over-zealous naming of cultivars in the future; unfortunately, in the real world, there is no law that prevents anyone applying a name, however fanciful, should they wish to do so, but it is to be hoped that those selecting new cultivars and proposing new names will do so with careful consideration and a good deal of restraint.

'Green Elf' Another Basil Smith introduction made in 1989 (formerly under the erroneous name minimus). 'Green Elf' was proposed as a name in 1994 and applies to plants with small green leaves less than 3cm (1.2in) long with a paler green hastate pattern and delicate flowers of pale pink borne on slender stalks. This small form of *C. hederifolium*, if it breeds true from seed, is an interesting novelty. The original plants were raised from seed of unidentified source and, according to Basil Smith, plants are reasonably robust and require dappled shade, though very deep shade inhibits both flowering and fruiting.

'Highfield' A form of ordinary pink-flowered *C. hederifolium* with distinctively glossy foliage, developed by Dave Hoskins.

'Joy's Choice' A pewter-leaved selection by Basil Smith (1995) with handsome 7-angled leaves in two-tone pewter (described as 'pewter on pewter'). The pink flowers are unexceptional, of the normal form and size of the species. The original plant came as seed from a plant selected by Joy Bishop which in turn had originated from Phil Cornish's 'Silver Cloud'. 'Silver Cloud' itself has very attractive silvered, rather than pewtered, leaves with usually 5-angled leaves and pink flowers and, in reality, 'Joy's Choice' is little different, except perhaps that the foliage is more pewter than silver.

'Joy's Choice' is hardy, like the species, and the foliage stands up well to harsh weather. Like 'Silver Cloud' plants throw occasional white-flowered seedlings, which perhaps should be called 'White Joy's Seedling' for the sake of clarity.

Minimus This is an illegitimate name as well as being an extremely awkward use of a Latin epithet for a cultivated plant which was put out by Basil Smith (listed as *C. hederifolium* minimus); as it stands the name cannot be adopted under the current rules of horticultural nomenclature. The same applies to the following name, hence they are not presented in 'quotes'. In 1994 the plant was renamed 'Green Elf', see previous page.

Monstrosum Another illigitimate name. Unusually large-flowered forms of *C. hederifolium* turn up from time to time and are alighted upon with unabashed glee by their finders. Some have arisen in cultivation but others have been discovered by chance in the wild. The average flowers of *C. hederifolium* are rather uniform, the corolla normally measuring 14–22mm (0.6–0.9in) long. Anything outside that must be considered very unusual. The plant in question was discovered in Greece in October 1972 by Herbert and Molly Crook and I can do no better than to quote what they had to say about in the *Bulletin Alpine Garden Society* 44:263 (1976):

"When it flowered in cultivation last autumn we were able to give it a more thorough examination. The flowers were the largest we had ever seen and very full-petalled, with lobes 28mm (1.1in) long from nose to tip and 25mm (1in) wide, carried on very thick stalks (around 4mm (0.2in) in diameter) looking almost as if they were fasciated. Opinions differed as to whether it was a thing of beauty or not (we have provisionally named it *C. hederifolium* 'Monstrosum', which may give a clue to our view!). We thought it might be a tetraploid form, but a chromosome count kindly provided by the Royal Botanic Gardens, Kew, proved it to be the normal diploid. It has apparently set seed and we hope for progeny."

I do not know if this plant is in existence today and if so how it differs from other large-flowered *C. hederifolium* at present in cultivation, particularly the cultivar 'Daley Thompson'. See also 'Discovery'.

'Nettleton Silver' This cultivar was developed at the nursery of Potterton and Martin in Lincolnshire over a number of years by Alan Martin. The selection, which is said to come 95 per cent true from seed has silver leaves which have a rounded, slightly toothed, but not lobed, margin and pure white flowers. It undoubtedly comes close to 'White Cloud' (and was developed from white-flowered, silver-leaved, plants from Phil Cornish in the first instance) but in that cultivar the leaf-margins are nearly always angled (not invariably so) and rather larger. In 'White Cloud' the silver cast covers the entire upper leaf surface evenly, while in 'Nettleton Silver' the marginal area tends to break up into pewter and silver veining. Both are exciting new cultivars to add to the attractive range previously found in *C. hederifolium*.

'Perlenteppich' This a is a German selection of white-flowered plants which seem to conform well with *C. hederifolium* 'Album' of gardens, although perhaps the flowers are a little more dainty. Many have pink in the throat of the corolla when examined closely. See also 'Rosenteppich'.

'Pink Pearls' Probably the same as 'Rosenteppich' and if so it is a later name that should be abandoned.

'Rosenteppich' Selection of red-flowered plants raised by Herr Richter of Dresden in eastern Germany. As grown in Germany for many years this name represents a group of rather variable plants with rather oval leaves, less lobed than most ordinary forms of *C. hederifolium*. The flower colour varies from pink to rich deep pink and even some reds. 'Ruby Glow' was selected from the deeper colours (see below). Many plants of 'Rosenteppich' have been produced, some finding their way into British garden centres and nurseries from the Continent. Some are highly desirable but they need careful selection as they are nearly always mixed with more ordinary-coloured forms. The German name translates to "Rose Carpet".

'Ruby Glow' (Ruby strain) Phil Cornish found dark-flowered plants of *C. hederifolium* among hundreds on sale at Abbotswood in Dorset. These had been imported as plugs from Germany (10,000 at a time) and almost certainly originated from 'Rosenteppich' which is widely

165 *Cyclamen hederifolium* subsp. *hederifolium* forma *albiflorum* 'White Cloud'.

sold on the Continent. About 1 per cent are good dark-flowered forms in which the dark colour extends throughout the petals. Although such plants are generally described as having red flowers, both this and the cultivar name are misleading. The colour is in fact a deep and rich magenta or magenta-purple, which is at its most intense around the mouth but which suffuses or feathers much of the length of the petals, though generally leaving a rather paler margin. The leaves are very deep green, rather sombre and almost as if they have a hint of black in them; they are not particularly well marked. Not generally available at the time of writing but a very fine selection that certainly extends the colour range within the species. Plants are slow to flower from seed.

'San Marino Silver' A selection made by Ray Johnstone presumably from plants or seeds originally collected near San Marino in Italy. No other information available.

Scented Some nurseries separate out scented forms of *C. hederifolium*. Scent is clearly an added bonus to an otherwise delightful and popular species. In the wild some colonies of *C. hederifolium* are scented, others not and, on occasions, only some plants in a colony may be scented. Scented forms isolated in the garden invariably, in my experience, give rise to scented offspring. Mixed with non-scented types the parents retain their scent year after year, yet few of the offspring seem to inherit this desirable characteristic.

'Silver Cloud' Silver-leaved forms of *C. hederifolium* have been known for some years yet most have marked leaves with green in the middle or on the margin. Phil Cornish, however, discovered forms in cultivation with unmarked leaves with an even and overall silver cast. These are splendid plants with pink flowers typical of the species. The leaf shape varies somewhat from lobed to heart-shaped and more or less unlobed, and the intensity of the silver (or pewter) is somewhat variable, but in the best the leaves have an iridescent quality which is very eye-catching in the evening light in the garden. Phil Cornish has given these plants the effective name 'Silver Cloud'. White-flowered plants with similar leaves are distinguished here as 'White Cloud'. It has been assumed by several growers that these silvers arose from 'Apollo', and this may be so although there is no evidence to confirm this and in any case silver-leaved forms periodically turn up today in batches of seedlings of ordinary *C. hederifolium*. All I can say from my own experience is that a high percentage of the green-leaved seedlings from a sowing from 'Silver Cloud' or 'White Cloud' bear the double shield pattern of the Bowles' Apollo Group.

'Silver Cloud' comes about 95 per cent true to type from seed, provided that the plants are isolated. In my experience 75 per cent would be a better average, but my plants grow in close proximity to other forms of *C. hederifolium* in the garden; the remaining 25 per cent are a mixed selection of plain green forms or forms with some silvering, especially in the centre of the leaf or with silvered leaves with some greening around the perimeter, especially along the veins. In some seedlings the silvering is more two-toned with the overall cast breaking up into a filigree of veins towards the leaf-margin. These are attractive plants but to maintain the purity of the cultivar they should really be weeded out and placed elsewhere.

I have grown 'Silver Cloud' in the open garden unprotected for about four years and have a small established colony. Plants are fully hardy as one might expect, but the leaves are more prone to damage in severe winter weather and this can result in botrytis attacking damaged parts of the foliage. Such leaves are best removed as soon as the disease is noticed.

'Silver Cloud' is quite the most splendid of all the silver- or pewter-leaved forms of *C. hederifolium* going around at the present time and it is becoming more readily available. It deserves a place in any collection.

Silver-leaved Group (sometimes called the Silver Leaf Form). This is an interesting group of silver-leaved *C. hederifolium* that pre-dates 'Silver Cloud'. The leaves are more pewter than silver in most instances and sport a distinguishing yet narrow band (often in the form of an arrowhead or an ellipse) in the centre or upper half of the leaf, as well as a green margin. The flowers are normally pale pink, but they may occasionally be white. This form probably arose in the first instance from the Bowles' Apollo Group and still arises from time to time in sowings of that group.

'Silver Shield' A pink-flowered *C. hederifolium* with 7-angled leaves of deep green with a shield pattern in the centre in sombre pewter or sage green. They were raised by Basil Smith from seedlings of a plant collected by Dave Hoskins near Epirus in Greece which were crossed with a similar-looking plant found at a small unnamed nursery.

'Stargazer' An American novelty with upward-facing pink flowers that loses much of the charm of the normal shy blooms of the species. However, it is different and growers will certainly seek to obtain it for their collections. At most though, it is no more than a curiosity.

Other upright-flowered forms of *C. hederifolium* have appeared and several are mentioned in the *Journal of the Cyclamen Society*, including another pink-flowered one raised by N. E. Dart which was apparently kept under glass with a mist watering system and he assumed that it never set seed because "the flowers filled with water". Another plant appeared by chance in the collection of Malcolm Birkett, in his Yorkshire garden, except that this was a white-flowered version. The plant in question has produced seedlings but it is not yet known whether the offspring have inherited this bizarre flowering habit.

'White Bowles' Apollo' A white-flowered version of Bowles' Apollo Group which was developed by Dave Hoskins. The combination of silvered leaves with their typical shield patterning and white flowers is very striking. The majority of seedlings bear white flowers also. This plant can be equated with 'Artemis', although the latter tends to have pewtered, rather than silvered, foliage.

'White Cloud' White-flowered forms of 'Silver Cloud'. See under 'Silver Cloud'.

'White Pearls' Probably the same as 'Perlenteppich' and if so this is a later name that should be abandoned.

Cyclamen intaminatum

'E. K.Balls' A name applied to the progeny of EKB 669a. They are scarcely distinguishable from other forms in cultivation and certainly do not warrant cultivar status.

In the wild *C. intaminatum* exists in both plain and patterned-leaved forms in simple or mixed colonies. Such plants are often offered for sale:
- Patterned-leaved form: leaves deep, rather matt green with a hastate pattern in paler green, grey or silver.

166 *Cyclamen mirabile* 'Tilebarn Nicholas'; the leaves are flushed with deep raspberry when young.
167 *Cyclamen mirabile* 'Tilebarn Nicholas'.
168 *Cyclamen mirabile* 'Tilebarn Anne'.

The flowers can be white or very pale pink, the veins less well defined than in the following group.

- Plain-leaved form: leaves plain, deep matt green, occasionally slightly shiny. The flowers are generally white with grey veins, occasionally somewhat green around the nose.

Cyclamen libanoticum

'**Album**' A pure white-flowered form of the species was reported in *Flora and Sylva* in 1903 and again in the *Bulletin Alpine Garden Society* (16:267, 1948), but I do not know of such a plant in cultivation today. In fact the original description reads "white shading through to deep pink" so a pure white probably never existed in the first place. With so many now being reared from seed they should appear from time to time. Plants do exist in cultivation with near-white flowers with faint blotching at the base of the petals, but the flowers usually blush pink as they age. Should such a plant be found in the wild then, for the sake of uniformity, it should be given the appropriate rank of forma.

Cyclamen mirabile

forma *niveum* The pure white-flowered form of the species found in the wild by Jill White (see p.99). The leaves are deep green with a narrow hastate mark in grey and the petals have a fairly serrated margin, especially towards the apex. Not available at the present time.

'**Tilebarn Nicholas**' This is one of the most beautiful forms of *C. mirabile* selected from one of his own seedlings by Peter Moore. The flowers are those of an average *C. mirabile* but the leaves have a dark green 'Christmas tree' centre surrounded by a broad, smooth band of silver. When young the entire upper leaf surface is suffused with glowing pink, this gradually fading away after some weeks as the leaf matures, to reveal the broad silver band. Many of the successive seedlings are equally fine but the plant does not come 100 per cent true from seed. Some plants come more like the wild plant while others closely resemble 'Tilebarn Ann'.

'**Tilebarn Ann**' This is very similar in flower to the previous, the prime difference being in the foliage which is evenly pewtered all over at maturity, with an attractive pink blush when young.

'**Tilebarn Jan**' This plant was named after Jan Ietswaart, Holland, who sent seed to Peter Moore at Tilebarn Nursery. The seed was taken from a hand-pollinated plant with almost-white flowers. The resultant seedlings were apparently very variable but were carefully selected over

169 *Cyclamen peloponnesiacum* subsp. *peloponnesiacum* 'Pelops'.

several generations for white petals. Even so the flowers are not consistently pure white, some seedlings having flowers with a pink 'nose'; all the petals have a finely serrated margin. The leaves are banded as in most *C. mirabile* and are attractively pink-flushed as they unfurl.

Peter Moore tells me that, once established, plants grow away strongly just like ordinary *C. mirabile* and plants are self-fertile with about 90 per cent of seedlings producing white or near-white flowers. The name is pronounced in the Dutch manner, Yan rather than Jan.

Cyclamen *peloponnesiacum* subsp. *peloponnesiacum* forma *peloponnesiacum*

'**Pelops**' This name was originally given to a very fine selection of the Peloponnese subspecies of *C. repandum* with somewhat shiny grey-green leaves generously speckled with pale olive-green, almost silvery, spots and dashes. The elegant flowers with their narrow twisted petals were pale reddish-purple with a rich maroon-red snout. The plant was originally collected by Herbert and Molly Crook in the Peloponnese in the mid-1960s and it received an Award of Merit under the name 'Pelops' when it was shown at the Royal Horticultural Society in April 1968.

In this work the Peloponnese/Rhodes plant is recognised as a distinct species *C. peloponnesiacum*, which contains three subspecies p.62. 'Pelops' fits comfortably into subsp. *peloponnesiacum*. Unfortunately, the cultivar name 'Pelops' has been applied rather willy-nilly to a whole range of plants originating directly or indirectly from the Greek Peloponnese. While some of these fairly closely match 'Pelops', not all do, and these latter should be excluded from the cultivar. Examine plants before purchasing them, to be certain; the finest have foliage delightfully and generously speckled with silver.

AWARDS
• A.M. (to 'Pelops') 1968.

'Pelops' (Red Form) Sometimes listed in catalogues, this plant has nothing to do with the cultivar 'Pelops' but is in fact the dark 'form' of *C. peloponnesiacum* subsp. *peloponnesiacum* subsp. *vividum*.

Silver Leaf Group. This name covers a group of subsp. *peloponnesiacum* with particularly well-silvered leaves. The leaves are speckled and dashed silver all over a contrasting deep green background.

Note. Pure white-flowered forms of subsp. *peloponnesiacum* are referable to forma *albiflorum* (see p.63).

Cyclamen persicum

Only cultivars of the wild type are dealt with here, otherwise refer to p.179–187.

'Album' A pure white-flowered form of this familiar species collected in the wild in 1990 in Israel by the Cyclamen Society. Pure white wild forms have been known in the past but have been lost during the intervening years until this re-introduction. This plant is best treated as a selection of *C. persicum* forma *album*.

'Tilebarn Karpathos' A fine wild-collected form of the familiar species with brilliant cerise flowers collected on the island of Karpathos. A charming addition to the wild forms available in cultivation. Stocked at Tilebarn Nursery. This cultivar is best treated as a selection of *C. persicum* forma *puniceum*.

Cyclamen pseudibericum

'Roseum' The same as *C. pseudibericum* forma *roseum* which is the correct name to use. Forma *roseum* covers all the pale and rose-pink manifestations of the species,

whereas forma *pseudibericum* covers the plant as originally described, with its deep magenta-purple blooms. 'Roseum' of cultivation is quite variable in the pinkness of its flowers. In some instances the corolla is very pale pink, or white flushed with pink, whereas the original cultivar bore attractive mid rose-pink flowers. As indicated, forma *roseum* encompasses all the pink shades of the species as they are found in the wild. Particularly good colour forms of forma *roseum*, or those with distinctive leaves, could, if they breed true to form, be given individual cultivar names.

Cyclamen pseudibericum was at one time primarily represented in cultivation by the deep coloured forma *pseudibericum* but increasingly today the pink shades seem to be more common. It may be that the pink shade is dominant over the magenta in this species; certainly batches of seedlings tend to produce a higher percentage of pinks in many instances.

The pink forms owe their origin to an Albury, Cheese and Watson collection under the number ACW 664.

Cyclamen purpurascens

'Album' This is referable to *C. purpurascens* forma *album*, see p.128.

Fatra Form Although the plain-leaved form of *C. purpurascens* has been distinguished as a separate species by some Continental botanists it is impossible to maintain the species as its overall characteristics fit comfortably into those of the widespread European *C. purpurascens*. However, from the gardener's point of view, the plant, which hails from the former Czechoslovakia, is distinctly easier and more floriferous, the deep pink flowers set off against a mass of plain green leaves which can be matt or somewhat shiny. It is variously listed in catalogues as *C. fatrense*, *C. purpurascens fatrense* or "Fatrense", or even *C. purpurascens* Plain-leaved form. Beware, however – not all plain-leaved plants are the Fatra form.

Silver Leaf Group A group name that encompasses any silver-leaved forms in cultivation.

Lake Bled Form Similar to Limone form except the original plants came from around Lake Bled in former Yugoslavia. The leaves are beautifully silvered but with the silver cast breaking up into a netted pattern on veins towards the margin of the leaf. Unfortunately, plants set seed poorly and then only a small proportion of the seedlings come true with the desirable characteristics of the parent plant or plants. This is certainly a weaker grower and less vigorous even than the Limone form.

The region around Lake Bled is noted for its outstanding populations of *C. purpurascens*, especially those with handsomely marked leaves in great variety, including the occasional well-silvered variants. These latter are said to represent about 5 per cent of the population.

Lake Garda See under Limone form. Listed by Fillan's Plants, Pound House Nursery, Buckland Monachorum, Devon, as a cultivar ('Lake Garda'), but this has not found acceptance elsewhere.

Limone form A delightful form of the species in which the upper leaf surface is almost entirely silvered, with the narrowest of green bands around the margin, and a faint hastate pattern (grey than silver) in the centre of the leaf which can be seen on close inspection. The flowers are the usual deep pink and scented.

The plant was originally selected from a wild population close to Lake Garda in northern Italy by Manfred Koenen and similar plants have been sold under various references including Limon, Limone form and Lake Garda form. All are fine plants but none have been given formal cultivar names, which is just as well as none appear to come true from seed. Indeed if 50 per cent of seedlings produced silvered leaves, that would be a good starting point, but they do not (even if the flowers are hand-pollinated) and rogues (those without silvered leaves) have to be vigorously weeded out. All of these plants, as well as similar ones from Lake Bled in Yugoslavia, are best treated under a general heading for the time being, Silver-leaved Group being appropriate, although some plants are to my eye at least more pewter than silver. All are very attractive and desirable in a collection, although in my experience they are slower growing than the more normal and widely grown green or marbled-leaved forms. Attractive partly silvered or pewtered leaf forms are also to be found in Austria, especially in woodland close to Vienna.

Chapter Eight

Cyclamen Persicum
Evolution in Cultivation

Cyclamen persicum has had a long history of cultivation and during the development of the modern strains of the florist's cyclamen numerous cultivars have been described. No other cyclamen species has been so pampered and developed in cultivation, indeed many find it difficult to equate the rather modest wild plant with its muted colours, sweet scent and delicately twisted petals with the mammoth florist's strains with their cabbagy foliage and over-endowed blooms in a whole range of different colours. Yet it is from the humble wild plant that all modern strains of *C. persicum* have been developed – no other species has been involved. This shows not only the great selective and breeding skills of the plant breeders but also the inherently 'plastic' nature of the species which has allowed such a development from the original wild plant to take place. In short, the plant breeders have exploited the genetic variability in *C. persicum* to create the large range of cultivars and forms that we see today. The prime areas in which this has been achieved have been in the production of forms with very much larger flowers, a greater diversity of flower forms and, perhaps most important of all, in an enormous increase in the range of colours.

The history and development of *C. persicum* and its subsequent cultivation as a commercial crop is a large and complex subject that would fill a whole book on its own and I only intend to give the bare outlines here. For those seeking a detailed study of the cultivation of *Cyclamen persicum* today I cannot do better than recommend 'La Coltivazione del Ciclamino' by Giorgio Rampinini. Unfortunately, this very interesting book is only in Italian at the time of writing but it is to be hoped that it will at some stage be produced in an English version, for it is of immense value to all who grow the modern types of *C. persicum*.

For the cultivation of the wild species please refer to p.11.

The florist's cyclamen has long been called the Persian Cyclamen. The reason for this is not at all clear for *C. persicum*, despite its name, has never been found in Persia (today Iran). As early as 1659 Sir Thomas Hanmer in his 'Garden Book' refers to 'The Cyclamen of Persia' which 'flowers most of the winter and is rare with us'. Sir Thomas also alludes to cyclamen from Antioch and the Lebanon. Today it is known that the wild form of *C. persicum* is common in the lands from southern and south-eastern Turkey, Cyprus and western Syria to the Lebanon and Israel. It is also known that many plants ('bulbs' in particular) were exported from western Asia via ports such as Constantinople (now Istanbul) and Smyrna (now Izmir) and one can be as sure as it is possible that the early forms of *C. persicum* reached western Europe from such origins. Certainly by the time Miller described the species as *Cyclamen persicum* in 1768 it was widely known as the Persian Cyclamen and one assumes that it was thought to have originated from Persia. In fact the only cyclamen native to that country is *C. coum* (in its subspecies *caucasicum* and *elegans*).

Yet another twist in the origin debate is in the flower colour. John Parkinson ('Paradisus Terrestris', 1629) states that 'The Sowebread of Antioch with double flowers, hath his leaves somewhat round like unto the leaves of the Summer Sowebread, but with less nobbles or corners and more full of white spots on them, which are very large, with ten or twelve apiece, of a faire peach colour, like unto the flowers of purple Sowebread of the spring and deeper at bottom ... There are of these Sowebreads of Antioch, that hath but single flowers, some appearing in the Spring and others in the Autumn.' There is little doubt that Parkinson's Antioch cyclamen (*C. Antiochenum*) is *C. persicum* as we know it today. What is of interest is the flower colour – peach. Perhaps the origin of the Latin epithet for the species lies not in its place of origin but in its flower colour which may have been likened to that of the Peach, *Prunus persicus*. It is perhaps of note that persinus in Latin means peach-flowered. Despite this I still feel that the name *persicum* originates from the mistaken belief that the plant came from Persia. Incidentally, although the name *C. Antiochenum* predates Miller's *C. persicum* it is not valid under the Rules of Botanical Nomenclature which has as its starting date the 'Species Plantarum' of Linnaeus of 1753; in effect no names used before that date are acceptable.

The Royal Horticultural Society's 'Dictionary of Gardening' gives 1731 as the date of introduction of *C. persicum* into cultivation in western Europe but it was almost certainly in cultivation before that date. 1731 was in fact the date of publication of the first edition of Miller's 'Gardener's Dictionary' which is often a first reference for many plants in cultivation and the species (a white-flowered form) was known to have been cultivated at Lille in France by that same year. There is, for instance, evidence that the species had long been cultivated in the eastern Mediterranean, particularly in monastery gardens.

Cyclamen has its origins far earlier in antiquity; it was certainly known to Theophrastus (371–287BC) and later to both Dioscorides and Pliny.

By 1651 Pierre Morin (Royal Gardens in Paris) clearly knew of the existence of *C. persicum*. In 1739 Van Kampen in Haarlem, Holland, listed three varieties of the species, varying in flower colour. By the time Miller published the eighth edition of his 'Gardener's Dictionary' in 1768 it was being cultivated at the Chelsea Physic Garden of which he was the Director. Miller's plants had come to England from Cyprus and had white, strongly-scented flowers.

However, it was not until almost a century later that the florist's strains of *C. persicum* began to be developed and that has led directly to the plants as we know them today. Up until the middle of the 19th century *C. persicum* was generally considered to be a half-hardy perennial taking three or four years to reach flowering size but all this was to change and by the latter part of the 19th century *C. persicum* had become a popular pot plant being grown from seed to flowering in 15 to 18 months. This was initially brought about from 1826 onwards when John Willot in England succeeded in eliminating the resting period by careful cultivation, cutting down the time from germination to flowering by half. Hybridization and selection of *C. persicum* took place in France round about 1853; the French growers were successful in selecting flowers in shades of pink, lilac and purple, although the flower size remained unaltered. However, major advances were made by Messrs Suttons of Reading from 1860 onwards and in Germany by growers such as Müller of Dresden and Kopsel of Koethen. What all the early breeders were trying to achieve was a greater range of flower colours and larger and more variable flowers. Scent and leaf variations were not important criteria in the breeding and selection programmes of the day! The results were larger flowers with broad petals without the marked twisting of the wild species.

Suttons used the wild type, the so-called 'crimson and white' (white flowers with a crimson nose, which is widespread in the wild) as a starting point. By careful selection and crossing they quickly began to introduce greater variability into their plants, especially in the size of the flowers. By the 1890s the flowers were up to three times the size of their wild counterpart, however with this increase in size the sweet scent of the blooms was lost. In 1868 the red-flowered diploid cultivar 'Firefly' appeared on the English market and this variety subsequently proved of great importance in the latter development of F1 hybrids.

By the 1860s and 1870s various forms of *C. persicum* were being displayed at competitions for potted plants in England.

A major breakthrough came in 1870 when Edmonds presented a very large-flowered plant with white flowers with a deep purple nose that was named appropriately 'Giganteum'. By 1884 Williams, using 'Giganteum' as a base, managed to produce eight further colours with giant flowers. These plants were a milestone in the development of the modern cyclamen and the influence of 'Giganteum' and its derivatives spread quickly to other breeders in Britain and Continental Europe. In 1873 Müller in Dresden presented the cultivar 'Splendens' while, also in Germany, Kopsel put forward another giant cultivar 'Universum'. Hybridizers in Europe used the giant cultivars that were becoming available towards the end of the 19th century as the basis of their own strains. The 'Giganteum' types were used for colour improvement, in the production of more compact plants with a greater range of leaf patternings.

During 1882–83 James Carter, Dunnett and Beale (seed growers) included several interesting cyclamen novelties in their list entitled 'Vegetable and Floral Novelties'. Reputed to be the finest and most up-to-date colours on the market, several were awarded First Class Certificates (of Merit) by the Royal Horticultural Society in London. They were 'Duke of Connaught', 'Giganteum Compactum Magnificum', 'Giganteum Roseum Compactum', 'White Swan', 'Picturatum' and 'Rosy Morn'. In 1894 Suttons of Reading introduced a very popular giant salmon-flowered cultivar named 'Salmon Queen' which proved very important in the development of the large-flowered cultivars.

During the late Victorian period there was a vogue for cyclamen with wide-spreading, non-reflexed, corolla-lobes. Such forms occur from time to time. One such described as '*C. persicum* var. *laciniatum*' was featured later in the *Botanical Register* in 1927 (t. 1095) and is remarkable for its spreading corolla-lobes with their fringed margins. The Victorians appreciated these wide-spreading blooms because of their rather orchid-like appearance. These were later known as 'Papilio' types and today are represented by the Rokoko series developed in Belgium.

Other novelties noted by the early breeders came with the spontaneous arrival of doubles in which the corolla in particular had more than the usual complement of five petals. Plants were selected with ten petals, twice the norm. Such doubling is often accompanied by doubling or partial doubling of both sepals and stamens. In some modern strains today, doubling often leads to partial or total sterility as the stamens are in fact replaced by petals or petal-like structures.

Particular attention was paid at the end of the 19th century to producing a greater range of flower colours. Breeders noted that, in forms with pink or white flowers with a purple or crimson basal ring, by careful selfing and selection, the colour ring could be extended up the petals, either as a band of colour or as a stripe along the centre of the petals. Such selection finally produced flowers that were uniformly pink or purple and such lines were crossed to produce an even greater range of colours. 'Vulcan' with deep crimson flowers was one early cultivar. Breeders were then able to concentrate even more on flower colour, separating out the colour progressively starting with the pinks and blue-mauves, then later the salmon-pinks and in more recent times the rich reds, scarlets and crimsons.

A number of the early cultivars proved to come true from seed, a fact that must have been a great help to the breeding and multiplication programmes. Many of the large-flowered types later proved to be tetraploids with a chromosome count of 2n=96 and this in itself has had a significant effect on modern cyclamen production (see p.172). But it was Stoldt in Germany who began to establish plants more suitable for pot plant production with the appearance of 'Rosa von Marienthal', a cultivar produced by back-crossing 'Splendens' with the wild type *C. persicum*. By this process Stoldt was able to produce, for the first time, flowers that were pure red, whereas previously the reds had been tainted with mauve or blue hues. Stoldt also produced the first pure salmon-flowered cyclamen, 'Ruhm von Wandsbek', although it was not a particularly large or robust cultivar. However, hybridizers then tried to transfer this colour into a more vigorous plant and the breakthrough came in the cultivar 'Salmoneum' produced by Froebel in Zurich. Using 'Salmoneum' as a base, Kiausch in Berlin in 1905 selected 'Rosa von Zehelendorf', a plant with all the characters of many modern large-flowered cyclamen and a cultivar that is still grown to this day. Kiausch also produced the deep salmon 'Perle von Zehelendorf'. Both these cultivars are still important as the basis for some modern strains of cyclamen and are still available in the horticultural trade.

Dlabka, also in Berlin, crossed 'Perle von Zehelendorf' with a red variant 'Dunkelrot' to produce (in 1921) 'Leuchtfeuer' (which under the name

'Vuurbaak' is the most important orange-red variety produced in Holland today). At the turn of the 20th century and right up until the late 1940s a good deal of the development of the florist's cyclamen was carried out in Holland as well as England. Maarse of Aalsmeer introduced 'Carmin-Salmoneum' (the reverse cross to 'Leuchtfeuer') in 1916, extending the range of reds still further, and in 1919 Braukmann introduced 'Flamingo' with its startling salmon-red blooms with paler margins to the petals.

Another fine and still-popular salmon cultivar, 'Rosa van Aalsmeer', produced by C. Spaargaren Dzn. in Holland, appeared in 1925.

One of the most popular varieties proved to be 'Apple Blossom' with its large yet delicate pink blooms, which appeared in England in 1948.

Unfortunately, much of the early development of the modern cyclamen by both gardeners and breeders was undertaken with very little data being recorded; plants were being developed not for scientific purposes but for their decorative potential and, as a result, only the end products of the various lines of development were properly recorded. One could have gained a great deal of interesting information in tracing the history of development, had good and detailed records been kept. Today, breeders in Holland, Belgium and Germany, and elsewhere, are far more scrupulous in their recording techniques, and breeding programmes are far more rigorously controlled, for mistakes waste time and cost a lot of money: developing new strains of cyclamen for commercial pot plant production is an extremely costly undertaking!

The Victorians were particularly keen on the more bizarre flower forms. These often arose as chance seedlings (as they do today) but can be fixed by repeated selfing provided that fertility and vigour are maintained at the same time. Of these the most notable types were: first, those in which the petals were frilled, toothed or lacerated along the margins, the so-called Butterfly or Papilio forms and, second, plants in which the petals had a distinctive beard or crest on the outer face (today these are called the Cristata series).

By the beginning of the twentieth century just a few decades of concerted cyclamen breeding had transformed the wild *C. persicum* into a far more substantial and variable plant.

In 1946 Professor Wellensiek set up a research project in Holland at Aalsmeer to try and expand the breeding potential of cyclamen by attempting to cross *C. persicum* cultivars with some of the other species with the aim to raise further new varieties. This did not prove successful and no such hybrids were produced with *C. persicum* as one of the parents. However, in 1962 Professor Wellensiek (then at Wageningen in Holland) published a paper describing the work on the International List of Cyclamen cultivars. It was

170 *Cyclamen persicum* pot plant production in Holland is big business, as it is in Germany, Italy and elsewhere: the old tetraploid varieties are being quickly replaced by F₁ hybrids.

found that not only were many of the large-flowered plants tetraploids (2n=96) but, furthermore, there was a good deal of overlap in the cultivars submitted by the various breeders (22 breeders in fact submitted material). This was to be expected from a group of plants that are reproduced primarily through seed via cross-pollination rather than by vegetative means. The list provided an important basis for the identification and correct naming of the cyclamen cultivars known at that time. Another interesting finding was that some of the Dutch and English cultivars submitted were either diploids or tetraploids (2n=48, 2n=96) and when these were found in the same cultivar no morphological differences could be detected. However, it was surmized that the appearance of tetraploids early on in the evolution of the florist's cyclamen was undoubtedly a major factor in their rapid development.

In Holland up until the 1960s the traditional method of growing cyclamen was based on a single season of production with plants in bloom in the November–December period in particular, often following on a crop of lilies or other flowers, thus obtaining maximum benefit from the glasshouses in which they were grown. But then attention was focused on producing varieties suitable for other seasons, particularly the spring period. Dirk Tas in Holland pioneered much of this work with the appearance of various Tas series in both rich colours and pastel shades. Today cyclamen production is based on two periods, winter and spring, made possible by the ready adaptation of the Type Tas varieties.

De Troyer in Belgium produced a number of series of which the open-pollinated De Troyer Series with large brightly-coloured flowers and silver-margined leaves has

played a very important part in the development of F₁ hybrids in Europe today, especially in Holland. In fact it could be said that de Troyer's work has revolutionized the modern production of commercial cyclamen.

The popular pastel types were primarily based on an old cultivar 'Flamme' produced by Braukmann in Germany in 1922. De Troyer in Belgium produced a pastel series but it was the Dutch hybridizers who primarily grasped the importance of the paler shades and many were introduced in the 1960s. The pastel or flamed series, named after famous composers, have pale flowers with the colour fanning out through the petals, which are generally paler at the margins. They are extremely popular today as house plants and among growers for their robust nature and disease resistance. The selection of pastel shades was further refined by Piet Tas to produce a precocious range called "Type Tas Pastel".

Today there is a vogue for the smaller types of *C. persicum* in a wide range of bright colours. As early as 1922 in Aalsmeer small plants were being produced and now their production is once more important and becoming increasingly significant. Breeders in Holland, France, Germany, Denmark and Switzerland, in particular, have produced various series of so-called Midi cyclamen (small plants suitable for growing in 8–10cm/3–4in pots), with breeders such as Clause, Gruendler, Jackson, Morel, Wellensiek and Scholten all producing different (although often overlapping) series of small plants in a wide range of colours, many being scented.

In the 1950s Wellensiek made a selection from crosses involving the diploid cultivar 'Sylphide' (with large pale lilac flowers) with wild forms of *C. persicum*. The resultant plants with compact habit and smaller flowers with attractively twisted petals helped pioneer the vogue for smaller cyclamen. Scholten, also in Holland, improved the 'Wellensiek' strain and marketed them for sale, primarily in Holland. In the 1960s Y.G. Gruendler in Weixdorf (formerly in East Germany) followed a similar breeding programme involving the wild species and produced an attractive Midi series 'Kleine Dresdnerin' which is still marketed to this day.

Work on these Midi series is at present very active and recently Royal Sluis in Holland have produced a fine F₁ Intermediate series.

Even smaller plants suitable for production in 5–6cm (2–2.5in) pots have been introduced by Schlatter in Switzerland under the series 'Piccolino'. These smaller or Super Mini plants are easier to grow in the more northerly countries of Europe but in Italy it has been found that they dry out too quickly in the hot, dry atmosphere and are generally more difficult to maintain than the larger types.

Modern cyclamen cultivars have a great range in plant size and flower colours with the flowers anything from 4–10cm (1.6–4in) long according to their class. One of the biggest steps in development in the past few years has been the production of F₁ hybrid cyclamen which was the result, in the first instance, of a change in hybridization technology. The production of F₁ hybrids by crossing two pure lines is an expensive and time-consuming business but it allows for a greater range of varieties by exploiting the genetic diversity in the species, speeds up production and allows for greater uniformity. From their very nature F₁ hybrids have to be continuously recreated to keep them in cultivation. Their success is evident today for the F₁ hybrid series (such as the 'Concerto' and 'Firmament' series) have seized an important and profitable slice of the cylamen market in Europe.

Today, especially in Holland, Germany and Italy there has been a huge development in pot grown cyclamen for homes and offices. The trend has been towards uniformity and this has been achieved in two ways mainly: first, by the establishment of pure lines and second, by the production of F₁ hybrids.

I do not want to get involved in the complex business of genetics and plant breeding but a little explanation is required here. Pure lines are produced by careful selection of plants with the desired character(s) initially and then by selfing the plants repeatedly to fix the characters (for outbreeders such as cyclamen selected lines have to be selfed and then crossed with one another). Having obtained these pure lines, which may take a few to many generations of plants, two of these pure-bred lines are crossed to produce an F₁ hybrid. For these the female parent has to be emasculated; this is done while the flowers are in bud by holding the base of the bud firmly in one hand and twisting off the corolla with the fingers of the other – the stamens are attached to the corolla and come away with it. Unfortunately, it is often difficult to maintain pure lines and in cyclamen at least several generations of selfing often leads to severe weakening of the line, so to increase vigour plants have to be outcrossed from time to time in a controlled manner. Pure lines have therefore to be remade occasionally if they are to be maintained. Outbreeding involves allowing selected plants to cross at will; no emasculation is necessary.

F₁ hybrids can be repeatedly produced by crossing the same two pure-bred lines and many of the large-flowered cyclamen (in a great variety of colours) which are sold today are the products of such crosses. Yet the production of pure lines is in itself an arduous undertaking. Pure lines are groups of genetically similar individuals, but with outbreeders such as cyclamen they are often tricky to maintain because after a few generations they begin to lose vigour, malformations in leaves and flowers may become evident, plants become less floriferous and seed production is subsequently affected. So to maintain pure lines they have to be occasionally outcrossed with a similar pure line in order to maintain vigour and stability. The pure

171 Mini *Cyclamen persicum* have become very popular in recent years; here an experimental block in Holland shows the wide range of colours that are available.

lines are of course essential and fundamental in the production of the F₁ hybrids. The uniformity of F₁ hybrids (each batch will be the same colour, the same height, and will mature at the same time) makes them highly attractive to commercial growers.

But in recent years there has also been a trend towards smaller plants, the so-called Mini and Super Mini cyclamen, with their more refined blooms and scent. Many of the Midi series are maintained by open-pollination techniques (allowing plants to cross freely within the limits of the series), although F₁ hybrid Midi types are now also becoming important. There has also been a greater move in Continental Europe towards cyclamen for the cut-flower market with special types being bred for the purpose.

It should not be assumed that all the large-flowered cultivars on the market are tetraploids for this is far from the truth and some of the largest and brightest colours are in fact diploid plants that have been developed by careful breeding. Diploid plants have certain advantages over their tetraploid brethren. Seeds of diploid types geminate more quickly and more evenly and the plants are generally more disease resistant and, most important of all, they mature much quicker, allowing for a speedier rotation of crops. In addition, the diploids are easier to select in a breeding programme, the flowers are often fragrant (or at least it is relatively easy to breed in fragrance) and they are generally more readily adapted to short-day regimes. In general, diploids produce smaller more floriferous races and smaller seedlings, although today there are several diploid races with flowers as large as any tetraploid. In contrast, tetraploid races are slow and erratic in germination, the plants more prone to

172 Much of the cyclamen production in Europe today is geared to the production of pure lines and F₁ hybrids.

disease and in a breeding programme are generally more difficult to select and sustain; furthermore they have lost their fragrance. On the positive side is their adaptability to resist higher temperatures and long-day regimes, as well as the greater possibility of producing from them unusual combinations of flower colours and shapes. Many tetraploids are large leafy plants with larger seeds and seedlings. The importance of the tetraploid races in the evolution of the modern cyclamen should not be underestimated for it has played a vital role in its history and development.

Incidentally, tetraploid and diploid plants can generally be distinguished by eye in the vegetative state, the former having large matt leaves, while those of the latter are generally smaller and shinier.

The modern trend toward diploids and F₁ hybrids has led to a sudden and rapid decline in the older tetraploid varieties. These have been of great historical significance and despite their drawbacks (slowness to mature and low disease resistance) it is vitally important that they are preserved for the future, when trends may change once more. Most of the big growers have already ceased production of the tetraploids and few are now available commercially. Fortunately, Kees Sahin in Holland has managed to gather up seed of many of these and they are stored in his extensive seed bank at Alphen aan den Rijn.

The importance of the old open-pollinated cultivars in the development of the florist's cyclamen should in no way be underestimated. Of those of prime historical importance perhaps the following should be singled out:

- 'Barbarossa': a diploid cultivar with rose-pink flowers shading to lilac and with a contrasting white crest in the centre of the petals.
- 'Carmin Salmoneum': an old and very important tetraploid with large flowers nearest to orange.
- 'Firefly': the diploid origin of many of the finest de Troyer cultivars.
- 'Flamme': as above.
- 'Kätchen Stoldt': the only large-flowered white tetraploid.
- 'Lichtkönigin': a large-flowered tetraploid with petals of Bengal purple with a scarlet glow.
- 'Magic Melody': a diploid with totally silver leaves and large scarlet flowers with pale pink margins to the petals.
- 'Victoria': an irregular tetraploid with large white flowers with a frilled red edge to the petals.
- 'Vuurbaak': with brilliant scarlet blooms is still, after many years, the most popular of all tetraploid large-flowered varieties.
- 'White Giant': another cultivar that proved to be the origin of many of the de Troyer cultivars.
- 'Winter Sun': a new variety with the yellowest flowers of any cultivar ever produced; diploid.

Today cyclamen production on the Continent is big business with many millions of pots being sold in flower annually. In the large nurseries the production is highly automated and computerized and the temperatures and light carefully controlled to maximize production with the aim of producing a uniform and good crop in the shortest time possible. Plants are grown on from sowing to maturity in an even regime which allows for no checks in growth, something the amateur grower and gardener finds almost impossible to replicate in most instances.

Walk around any large production nursery in Holland today and you will see a fine range of different *Cyclamen persicum* forms being grown from small plants to giant ones and those with plain petals, striped, ruffled or frilled, fringed and crested, to double-flowered forms and picotees (petals with pale edges). Apart from the bright, often gaudy colours, there is a trend towards attractive pastel shades and those with subtle feathering (technically called flaming) in the petal colours.

In the old days florist's cyclamen used to take a full 15 months from sowing to full bloom. This meant that seed had to be sown in August or September for flowering at Christmas in their second year and the process involved a series of 'pottings on' (sometimes as many as 4–5) until the plant reached flowering size. These large-flowered plants were very often tetraploids, notoriously slow to produce a saleable 'crop'. Today many of the large-flowered diploid types take precedence. Being sown early in the year they can be flowered easily in eight to nine months to produce plants of equal size and floriferousness to some of the older and slower cultivars. But this all requires carefully controlled cultivation.

The key to success in commercial cyclamen production is in controlled and even development of the plants from the moment they germinate. Faults in the temperature regime or in lighting or feeding will certainly cause a check in development which will lead to a delay in flowering time, even a severe reduction in bloom, and less profit for the grower.

Commercially, seed is sown in large trays or, increasingly today, in plugs or cellular trays with one seed per cell. A thousand seeds weigh between 11–14g (0.5oz) in most of the medium and large-flowered types, with the seed

173 Seed production of *Cyclamen persicum*, a very important crop in Europe.
174 In Japan very highly priced plants of exceptional quality are produced for a connoisseur market, as this plant produced by Sakata shows.
175 F₁ hybrid cyclamen are produced in five main sizes: Magnum (centre back), Maxi or Normal (left), Midi or Medium (right), Mini or Miniature (front right) and Micro or Super Mini (front left).

of white varieties tending to weigh less, 7–8g (0.25oz) per 1,000. Seed germinates best at between 15–20°C (59–68°F), with 17–18°C (63–64°F) being the optimum for quick germination, and this is maintained as steadily as possible in the dark until germination occurs, which generally takes about 24–28 days, 2–3 days quicker for white and ruffled-flowered types (as in all cyclamen light inhibits germination, but once the roots emerge from the seed, light can be applied without ill effect).

The trays are then moved into the light and the temperature maintained at 17–18°C (63–64°F) for the following 4–5 weeks when plants are transferred to larger trays and then after a further 5–6 weeks they are placed in pots for the final growing-on phase to flowering, which as previously stated is a cycle of 8–9 months for many modern cultivars and series. Alternatively, the intermediate stage is missed out and seedlings are pricked out after 10–12 weeks into their final pot. The tubers are barely covered with compost and come half-proud of the surface as they mature.

For the final phase (from final potting on to flowering) an average temperature of about 14–15°C (57–59°F) is maintained with shade being applied whenever the weather becomes too bright and sunny. Ample ventilation and light are essential and shading is only applied when the sun becomes too intense (above 30,000 lux). In any event shading must not exceed 50 per cent as the light intensity affects bud formation, which is severely reduced in over-shaded conditions. Bud initiation takes place after the seventh leaf has developed, about 120 days after sowing.

The compost is critical for it must be open and well-drained. Too fine a compost or one that impedes drainage in any way will delay flowering for up to four weeks and may well invite fungus infections of the roots and the tuber. Many commercial growers today use a compost composed of coarse fibrous peat with added bark chippings, rice husks or coconut fibres. A general fertilizer is applied at a rate no higher than 1kg/m^3.

Much of modern cyclamen production is highly automated and, walking round a large modern nursery, one is struck by how few people seem to be maintaining the large areas of benches covered in potted plants. The mixing of composts, sowing of seeds, potting on, watering and so on is all highly automated and follows a strict schedule. A large nursery will be producing well in excess of one million flowering pots per year. In addition some nurseries also produce very large numbers of small plug plants for other nurseries to grow on to maturity.

The light to shade factor is important in pot-plant production. Cyclamen are neutral day plants, that is flowering is not promoted by the onset of either shorter or longer day lengths. However, a greater light intensity leads to a greater flower to leaf ratio and better leaf markings, whereas low light intensity leads to few flowers and over-sized leaves. A balance has to be struck in allowing plants enough light, but shading them sufficiently to keep down temperatures which will otherwise cause wilting and general loss of quality.

This reflects the natural growing condition of the wild species which put on all their growth during the cooler part of the Mediterranean year.

Whereas pot-plant production works on maximum automation and minimum labour, the production of seed, which is a fundamental part of the large cyclamen market, is far more labour-intensive. The production of pure lines and F$_1$ hybrids relies on hand emasculation of the flowers and the careful transfer of pollen by hand. The average mother plants will produce something in the order of 1000 seeds. Mother plants used to be kept for three years but most nowadays are discarded after a single crop of seeds, except for special or rare series or cultivars. Botrytis and fusarium in particular are major hazards in the commercial production of cyclamen seed and the parent plants have to be rigorously protected by an active spraying regime.

Seed is cleaned and washed by machine and then carefully dried before being stored at 16–18°C (61–64°F). Seed can be stored for up to five years at lower temperatures: 4–5°C (39–41°F) but eventually begins to lose viability. But where are the breeders heading in the next few years? Their basic concern is to produce quality plants that appeal to the public. Novelties are always important as they can bring in a lot of money, particularly if they become popular. As with most breeding programmes the aims are to produce not only quality but also uniformity and cultivars with good disease resistance. In addition a long shelf life and quick maturation will always prove important. In recent years the importance of foliage has reasserted itself. Many of the old tetraploid cultivars and strains had rather gross and uninteresting (even boring) matt leaves. This is a pity because the wild plant can often have exciting and appealing foliage marked or splashed with pewter or silvery patterns and breeders have bred in these more interesting leaf characters in quite a few modern cultivars. Scent is another character that has been lost during development, especially in the large-flowered cultivars, although it does not appear to be a priority in breeding programmes today. However, many of the smaller cultivars (especially the miniatures) have had scent bred back into the strains and they are all the more delightful for it.

Another trend is in the development of the larger-flowered types for cut-flower rather than for pot-plant production. Various cultivars have been used for the cut-flower trade in the past, especially in Germany and the Baltic States (Estonia, Latvia and Lithuania). Such plants need to be floriferous and to have long stout stems for picking, and several different colours are on the market at the present time and will no doubt prove popular. The German cultivar 'Rheingaufeuer Schnitt' has bright red flowers and stout stems fully 40cm (16in) in length that are ideal for cutting. The market for cut-flower cyclamen is still really in its infancy and may become far more important in the future, especially if flowers of the right substance and quality can be produced.

Cerny in the Czech Republic has produced an interersting series of double-bloomed cultivars in four colours. Like the crested types they have a passing appeal but are very unlikely to enter mainstream cyclamen production.

Cultivars are also required at different times of the year and some will perform best in the autumn, others in the winter or spring. Whereas the market used to cater largely for the Christmas and New Year period it is now expected to supply plants from August to May, or even all the year round. The quality of production in Denmark, Holland, Belgium, Germany, Switzerland and Italy is quite outstanding and is carefully controlled. In both Holland and Germany schemes exist to monitor the production of seeds and to maintain quality control on plants.

Naturally, the market dictates to the breeder. Fashions for plant size and flower colour vary from year to year and breeders have to be aware of such trends, annoying as they might be. Yet despite this, some of the traditional cultivars, long proven and tested over the years, still have a good market and will continue to be grown (see list of cultivars following). Some breeding firms carry out market research and get feed-back information from their customers so they are able to predict market trends more accurately and in this way breeders are able to keep ahead of the market and even dictate to it to some extent.

As far as the market is concerned breeders recognize five distinct groups of florist's cyclamen:
1. Magnum (Gigantic): primarily old cultivars from France, the so-called Paris and Tours races, but little seen today; they were primarily tetraploid races.
2. Normal (Maxi): the most common type seen today which have been developed primarily from the older cultivars of the latter half of the 19th century and the first half of the 20th. They include most of the F1 hybrid series and cultivars as well

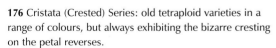

176 Cristata (Crested) Series: old tetraploid varieties in a range of colours, but always exhibiting the bizarre cresting on the petal reverses.
177 Another Crested Series type.
178 Magnum White (Giant White): a recent breakthrough in cyclamen breeding has resulted in this large-flowered white diploid; the flowers are larger than the tetraploid cultivars, which are slower growing.

179 Experimental F₁ diploid hybrid form Sahin in Holland developed from an old cv. 'Apple Blossom', with subtle pastel flowers.
180 A fine double-flowered tetraploid variety: these have limited appeal in the commercial market.

characteristics. Leaf size and patterning is very variable but the following can be distinguished:
- Argentata: leaves that are primarily silver or pewter with a green centre.
- Decora: leaves with a well-defined silver or pewter hastate pattern bordered by a green zone and with green in the centre of the leaf.
- Rex: forms in which the leaves are green but with silver or pewter dominating the periphery of the leaf-blade and often also running along the veins to the centre of the leaf.
- Variabile: green leaves with some silver or grey patterning, often in the form of blotches away from the leaf-margin, often with the colour running along the veins.

Petals are classified as follows:
- Flat: the majority of cyclamen series and cultivars have broad, flat petals often with a slight twist to them.
- Fringed: petals with a clear fringe. Three subclasses can be recognized here:
- Normal Fringed – petals flat with a fringed margin.
- Ruffled – petals undulating and with a fringed margin.
- Fringed Bicolors – petals flat or ruffled but the fringed margin a contrasting colour to the rest of the petal.
- Picotees – petals with a contrasting pale or dark margin.
- Undulate: petals that are undulate (ruffled) but without a fringed margin.
- Crested (Cristata): petals with a distinct crest (beard) of raised cells in the centre.

Cyclamen production in Japan is also important but Japanese production, although geared in part to similar mass production as that in Europe, is also focused on many customers who demand very high quality but are willing to pay for it. In Japan very high quality plants are produced by intensive labour. Plants are often large and heavily manicured with each leaf and petal carefully manipulated into the desired position. The result is a highly individual and symmetrical-looking plant which is very expensive, even in Japan. One of the chief breeders in Japan is Sakata who produced several interesting double-flowered forms a few years ago (such as 'Kimona'), though such plants are of little interest to the rather blinkered European market.

The Japanese produce a large number of open-pollinated types that are not generally available in the west. Firms such as Dai-ichi, Miyoski and Sakata are foremost in cyclamen production in Japan, but there are many other growers. Some Japanese series such as Lip and Shimano are also little known outside Japan.

In Europe today the trend is towards the production of diploid F₁ hybrid plants in many different series. This

as the Pastel Series. Mainly grown in 12–16cm (5–6in) pots.
3. Midi (Medium): some old varieties suitable for cut-flower production and series of French F₁ hybrids of fairly recent origin. Mainly grown in 8–10cm (3–4in) pots.
4. Miniature (Mini): small plants suitable for growing in 6–8cm (2.5–3in) pots and developed in the past 30 years by back-crossing the large-flowered cultivars with the wild species to produce smaller and more refined races. Many of the series are of very recent origin.
5. Super Mini (Micro): the smallest plants which can be readily grown to maturity in 5–6cm (2–2.5in) pots.

Besides the size classification of *C. persicum* series and cultivars, they are also classified by their leaf and flower has meant a sad decline in the use of open-pollinated varieties and many good cultivars have vanished or been withdrawn in the past 20 years. However, open-pollinated seed is still being produced by a number of firms: France (Eyraud, Gaboriau); Germany (Chrestensen, Weigelt); Holland (Mann, Royal Eveleens, Scholten, Tas, Visser, Vollebregt); Japan (Dai-ichi, Miyoski, Nomura, Sakata); Switzerland (Haller, Mauser, Roggli, Schlatter); USA (Davernheim).

As far as commercial production goes, the uniformity of the F₁ hybrids, the fact that the entire batch will be ready at the same time with little or no wastage, that they are more economic of space and show increased resistance to diseases, are all persuasive reasons for many growers to opt for them at the expense of older cultivars and series. The cost of producing pure lines and F₁ hybrids is high but it is more than offset by the cheaper cost of production of mature flowering plants.

Tissue culture (micropropagtion) might perhaps be employed to stabilize and produce some of the finest open-pollinated cultivars but growers generally find that this technique is rather unreliable (sometimes producing plants that are less free-flowering and slow to come to maturity) and, perhaps more important, expensive.

In recent years, in Holland, Sahin of Alphen aan den Rijn has bred some interesting novelties that may stir future markets that are always on the look-out for something different. They include a pale yellow-flowered cyclamen (a large-flowered diploid recently named 'Winter Sun'), a series of frilled-edged plants in which the frill contrasts sharply in colour with the rest of the petals (these have been developed primarily from the old tetraploid cultivar 'Victoria' but they are in fact diploids and so quicker maturing) and, finally, bizarre yet striking plants in which the sepals are expanded to half the length of the petals and generally of a contrasting colour – the petals splay out horizontally so that the whole flower looks like a child's whirligig.

In the future perhaps cut-flowered cyclamen may become more important. Cutting varieties have been known and used (especially in Holland and Germany) for many years but have never become an important part of cyclamen production although the potential is there for someone to exploit.

The use of cyclamen for bedding displays in the open garden, especially in Mediterranean-type climates may well become increasingly important as more resilient and quicker-maturing varieties are produced, especially those which are capable of flowering during the summer rather than the winter months. With their rich range of colours and mass of flowers it is easy to imagine the effect of large areas in parks and public displays, bedded out with cyclamen in the same way as pelargoniums, petunias and impatiens are used already.

181 Diploid Victoria Series developed by Sahin in Holland from the old tetraploid 'Victoria' and now available in a range of colours.

CYCLAMEN PERSICUM SERIES AND CULTIVARS

SERIES

The series are groups of similar cultivars, generally differing in flower colour, and produced by separate seed houses. Some seed houses produce several series. Unfortunately the series are not necessarily distinct in their own right and there is a good deal of overlap between some of them; they in fact often share the same origins. The cultivars listed after the series, on the other hand, are distinct from one another and must differ in at least one recognizable character from one another, besides reaching the criteria expected by a good cultivar in this group, such as colour, ease of cultivation, floriferousness, disease resistance and so on. The series group is indicated in brackets after the cultivar name as follows (series without named cultivars have no code) and readers should refer from the series to the cultivars and vice versa:

Anglia Series See Wye College Series.

Apollo Series A diploid series developed by C. Stoldt in Germany distinguished by their pure colour, floriferousness and disease resistance. The different colours are prefixed by the word Apollo; e.g. Apollo deep lilac, Apollo soft salmon, etc. The firm of Stoldt has recently closed.

Belle Hélène Series A miniature series in six main colours bred by Haller in Switzerland; plants bear numerous scented flowers.

Belles Provinces Series (B) A vigorous large-flowered series from Gaboriau in France. They are named, as the

182 New Wave Series 'Snow White'.

series indicates, mostly after French Provinces.

Bornthaler Dufty Series See under Scentsation Series.

Brilliant Series An F₁ diploid Midi series from Walz with flowers in various pinks and reds as well as scarlet and violet.

Butterfly Series An F₁ hybrid series from Royal Sluis-Olanda, Holland, (now Pan American Seeds) with large frilled and fringed (frangiati) petals, without named cultivars. Colour range from pale to rose pink and salmon.

Cheops Series An F₁ tetraploid series developed by Ch. Morel in France. No named cultivars but the colour range is from rosy-scarlet to salmon, violet and pure white.

Coccinella Series A diploid Mini series issued by Mohr (a broker not a breeder) in Switzerland. Colour range from pure white to lilac, salmon, pale to deep rose and red.

Concerto Series (C) An F₁ diploid series from Zaadunie. Primarily named after operatic or Shakespearean characters such as Aida, Fidelio and Romeo.

Dauernheim Series A superb giant strain ideally suited to today's large plant production with rather wavy foliage and flowers primarily in shades of pink, or white, often with a pink nose. From Dauernheim in the USA.

De Troyer Series A Belgian series characterized by large brightly-coloured flowers and silver-margined leaves. This diploid, open-pollinated series developed by De Troyer has revolutionized cyclamen production in Europe and is the main basis of the development of F₁ hybrids in recent years.

Decora Series A diploid series with silver-edged leaves, often with a dark centre and flowers in a range of colours from pink, to rose, salmon and mauve-lilac. From De Troyer in Belgium.

Diploid Victoria Series Diploids developed by Sahin in Holland from the old and popular tetraploid cultivar 'Victoria'. The flowers are mostly in shades of pink, mauve, purple or red with a fringed margin in a deeper colour.

Dressy Series From Sakata in Japan, a miniature series suitable for 7–10cm (3–4in) pot culture. A uniform and floriferous series with seven colours to date, prefixed Dressy, e.g. Dressy White, Dressy Purple, etc.

Early Minex Series (E) Very early-flowering, medium-sized plants from Wyss in Switzerland, with large flowers borne on sturdy stems; foliage deep green with paler veining. 'Jim, 'Jack' and 'Jonny' belong here.

Edelstein Series A diploid Mini series from Moll in Switzerland. Colour range primarily in the pinks, salmons and rose reds.

Esprit Series A quick and early-maturing series of Mini cyclamen with medium-sized flowers (some scented) and well-marked foliage, from Clause (Flora Nova) in France. The eight colours are all prefixed Esprit, e.g. Esprit Lilac Bicolor, Esprit Salmon, etc.

Favole Series An F₁ diploid series from De Ruiter in Holland with cultivars named after fairy-tale characters such as Aladdin, Cinderella and Snow White.

Fimbriata (Fringed) Series A series in a wide range of colour but characterized by having petals with attractively fringed margins. They are tetraploids and have arisen as spontaneous mutants from various sources over the years.

Fragrance Series A mixture of open-pollinated plants in a range of colours, but all pleasantly scented. Introduced by J. T. Fisher, near Erfurt, Germany.

Firmament Series (F) A large-flowered F₁ diploid series with uniform clear colours from Royal Sluis, Holland; most are now obsolete. They have various names such as 'Dorado', 'Phoenix' and 'Tucana'.

Friesen (= Frisian) Series (FR) A small F₁ diploid series from C. Stoldt, Germany. The cultivars are all prefixed Friesen, but are little seen today.

Germanica Series (G) An F₁ tetraploid series developed in Germany at Erfurt, Weixdorf. The cultivars are named after towns in former East Germany such as Eisenach and Weimar.

183 Pastel Series 'Chopin'.

184 Pastel Series 'Lizst'.

Gold Medal Series (GM) A Dutch series from Aalsmeer in a wide range of colours. Cultivars include 'Bonfire', 'Cattleya' and 'Rosa von Aalsmeer'.

Gradation Series From Sakata in Japan comes an interesting F₁ hybrid series with unusual bicolored blooms. The flowers in purple, soft pink, rose or salmon-red grade to paler tones at the petal margins.

Halios Series An F₁ diploid series from Ch. Morel, France without named cultivars. Colours range from pure white to lilac, violet, rose-pink, salmon, scarlet and deep red.

Insel (= Island) Series (I) A diploid Mini series from Wyss in Switzerland. Colours range from white to lilac, pink, purple, rose, salmon, carmine, scarlet and red. The cultivars are named after islands such as 'Bali', 'Java' and 'Samoa'.

Intermezzo Series An F₁ diploid Midi series from de Ruiter in Holland in a wide range of colours.

Junior Series An F₁ diploid Midi series from Clause (Flora Nova), France, without named cultivars. Colours range from white to rose, salmon and scarlet. They are prefixed Junior, e.g. Junior Magenta, Junior Rose, etc.

Kleine Dresdnerin Series A diploid, open-pollinated, Mini series from Weixdorf, Germany. Colour range white, white with a pink nose, lilac. rose, salmon and red. They have been given girls' names: 'Anneli', 'Betti', 'Brigitte', 'Gabi', 'Kati', 'Heidi', 'Rosemarie' and 'Steffi'.

Laser Series An F₁ diploid Midi series from Goldsmith, Holland, without named cultivars. Colours range from pure white to lilac, purple, salmon, rose-red and scarlet.

Latinia Series An F₁ diploid Midi series from Ch. Morel, France, without named cultivars. Colours range from pure white to lilac, violet, purple, salmon, deep red and scarlet.

Luckenwalder Gefranst Schnitt Series (L) A group of long-stemmed and large-flowered varieties suitable for cut flowers, with cultivar names such as 'Lucie', 'Luise', 'Luna' and 'Lulu'. From Chrestensen in Erfurt, Germany.

Marvel F₁ Series An F₁ diploid Mini series from Royal Sluis, Holland, without named cultivars. Colours range from pure white to white with a pink nose, violet, pink and salmon. Earliest to flower of all the Mini types. They are prefixed Marvel, e.g. Marvel Pink Shades, Marvel Dark Fuchsia, etc.

Micro Mini Series Developed by Mauser in Switzerland these very small and rather delightful plants, in a wide range of colours, were developed from the Schöne Helena Series but are even smaller. These have subsequently been taken on by Goldsmith and regrown under the name Cinderella.

Minimate Series An F₁ diploid series of miniature cyclamen from de Ruiter in Holland in a full range of colours.

Monarch Series (M) A large-flowered tetraploid series developed by Hurst in England, including some of the better-known older cultivars such as 'Apple Blossom', 'Mauve Beauty' and 'Scarlet King'. Although presented as distinct cultivars these were never truly distinct; they were not bred by Hurst and their origin is now only of historical interest as they appear to be extinct.

New Ruffled Fringed Giants Series From Wyss in Switzerland (Solothurn) comes this large-flowered series with strongly waved and ruffled petals in various colours but particularly pinks, reds, white and white with a pink nose.

New Wave Series An F₁ diploid series with large waved (frilled or frangiati) petals, without named cultivars from Sahin in Holland. Colour range pure white to pale pink with a white nose, white edged with rose, lilac, salmon, deep rose-red and violet. They are the modern counterpart of the old 'Undulata' types.

North Sea Waves Series Developed from the diploid Apollo Series come these interesting compact plants with well-marked leaves and flowers in a wide range of colours, including bicolors. From C. Stoldt in Germany.

Novello Series This is one of the finest F₁ hybrid Intermediate series bred by Royal Sluis (now Pan American Seeds) in Holland. The series has a full colour range and plain unruffled petals.

Olympia Series A German series with large fringed blooms grown for pot-plant as well as cut-flower production.

Papilio Series See under Rokoko Series.

Pastel Series (P) An attractive diploid, open-pollinated, series with pale flowers with faint and delicate feathering or flaming. Many cultivars that are named after composers such as Beethoven, Ravel and Strauss. Popular and very much in vogue today. This series was developed from some older pastel De Troyer types by reselection in Holland by Vollebregt. The Type Tas Pastel series is a further improvement made possible by reselection.

Pastel Fringed Series Pale shades with fringed petal-margins, developed by Vollebregt in Holland.

Petite Wonder Series A diploid Mini series from Daehnfeldt in Denmark. Colour range white, pale to deep rose. series now extinct.

Piccolino Series A diploid, open-pollinated, Super Mini series from Schlatter in Switzerland, without named cultivars. Colours range mostly from white to rose and salmon.

185 Whirlygig Series produced by Sahin in Holland in which the calyx becomes expanded and petal-like; here a bicolored form.

Piccolo Series A diploid, open-pollinated, Mini series from Schlatter in Switzerland. Colours range from pure white to lilac-rose, rose, pink, salmon and red, sometimes with a deeper-coloured nose. The colours are generally prefixed Piccolo, e.g. Piccolo Burgundy Red, Piccolo White, etc.

Puck Series A series of Mini cyclamen developed in France with a wide colour range from pure white to lavender, pink and red as well as bicolors.

Puppet Series A group of Mini cyclamen from Suttons Seeds in England. They are generally plants with bright flowers in a wide range of colours, most strongly scented and some with beautifully silver-patterned leaves.

Rasse Weixdorf Series A large-flowered series from Weixdorf, Germany with a good range of colours. The cultivars have men's names such as 'Dick', 'Sven' and 'Tom'.

Rex Series An old tetraploid series with large silver-edged foliage.

Rochford Series A series of Mini cyclamen marketed as 'Alpine Violets'. Flowers in a wide range of colours from white to lilac, lavender, purple, pink and red. Derived from the Wye College Series.

Rokoko Series A Belgian tetraploid series noted for its large frilled and ruffled petals which is often grown as a cut flower. Originally bred under the name 'Papilio' this was an uneven and unstable series and it scarcely exists at all today. Only a small percentage come true to type but those that do can be very fine plants indeed.

Romi Series A diploid Mini series from Roggli in Switzerland. Colours range from white to lilac, salmon, rose and red.

Scentsation Series A group of open-pollinated, semi-large-flowered, tetraploid plants introduced by Hurst of England in 1977 with scented blooms, mostly in shades of pink, rose, salmon and crimson. Renamed Bornthaler

Dufty Series when it was further developed by N. L. Chrestensen, Erfurt in Germany.

Schöne Helena Series A diploid Mini series from Haller in Switzerland. Colours range from pure white to lilac, salmon, rose and scarlet.

Senior Series From Clause (Flora Nova) in France, an F_1 hybrid series with large, well-formed flowers and marbled foliage. The series comes in ten colours all prefixed with Senior, e.g. Senior White, Senior Violet, etc.

Sierra Series An F_1 hybrid diploid series developed in Holland by Goldsmith. No named cultivars but with varieties in a wide range of colours from white to lilac, pale purple, pink, salmon, rose, fuchsia and deep red.

Silver Cloud Series A diploid series put out by Hurst Seeds in England with silver-margined leaves and large blooms in a variety of colours, but derived unaltered from De Troyer's Decora Series.

Silver Lustre Series (S) This diploid series was raised by J. T. Fisher with a number of cultivars with silver leaves and self colours which come true from seed and named 'Dawn', 'Rose', 'Salmon' and 'Scarlet'; derived from the De Troyer Decora series.

Sinfonia Series A diploid Mini series from Naegeli in Switzerland. Colours range from white to white with a pink nose, lilac, pale to deep rose, salmon and red.

Stäedte (Stoldties) Series (ST) A diploid Super Mini series from C. Stoldt in Germany with more than 12 named cultivars in a wide range of colours and named after Swiss towns and cities such as Basel, Bern and Zurich.

Symphony Series An F_1 series of large-flowered F_1 hybrids raised in Holland in a wide range of colours from pink to salmon, purple and scarlet. From Sluis and Groot in Holland.

Triumph Series (T) An old series from Messrs Suttons in England. The large flowers come in bold colours, self-evident from the names such as 'Scarlet', 'Firebrand' and 'Mauve Queen'.

Type Tas Series An important modern diploid series of fast-growing cultivars for early and late production developed in Holland from De Troyer mixtures. The cultivars are unnamed but are marketed as Pure White, Rose, and so on.

Valiant Series (V) An English strain of open-pollinated plants with large flowers in a range of self colours. 'Huntsman', 'Pink Waves' and 'Sunrise' belong here. A J.T. Fisher series of reselections.

Weigelt's Ideal Series A diploid Mini series from Erfurter Samenzucht, Germany. Colours range from pure white, white with a pink nose to lilac, salmon, rose and red.

Whirlygig Series This interesting series of diploid plants from Sahin in Holland are wholly unique in their unusual blooms in which the sepals are coloured and petal-like, often half the length of the petals and, like the petals, spread out horizontally. The sepals may be the same colour as the petals or a contrasting colour (pink or mauve with white sepals, red petals with pink sepals and so on). The flowers look like a child's whirlygig. The series is still being developed and improved.

Wye College Series (W) A diploid Mini series developed at Wye College, England, in the 1960s by back-crossing some of the smaller cultivars with wild *C. persicum*. The plants are neat with often attractively-patterned leaves and scented flowers, and include 'Wye Admiral', 'Wye Brimstone', 'Wye Downland', 'Wye Fritillary', 'Wye Orchid', 'Wye Peacock' and 'Wye Ringlet'. On the Continent these strains have been absorbed and refined into the Anglia Series.

Zodiac Series An F_1 diploid series from Royal Sluis, Holland. No named cultivars but the varieties range in the following colours: white, lilac, purple, pink, salmon, rose, red and scarlet. They are prefixed Zodiac, e.g. Zodiac Salmon with Eye, Zodiac Cherry Red, etc.

Zwerg Miniature Series (Z) A diploid, open-pollinated, Super Mini series from Erfurter Samenzucht, Germany, with seven named cultivars in white, lilac, salmon and rose-pink shades.

CULTIVARS

Letters in (brackets) indicate the series to which many of the cultivars belong – see above. In some literature the coloured centre of the flower is referred to as the 'eye'; however, I prefer to call it the 'nose', as the snout of the flower looks more like a nose than an eye. Unless otherwise stated, F_1 hybrids are diploids, not tetraploids.

'Admiral' (W): red flowers; *withdrawn*.

'Aida' (C): pale salmon-rose flowers with a darker nose; F_1 hybrid.

'Aladdin' (F): F_1 hybrid with vivid red flowers; withdawn.

'Alouette' (C): F_1 hybrid with vivid rose-pink flowers; *withdrawn*.

'Alsace' (B): flowers orchid pink with green foliage.

'Anjou' (B): flowers pure salmon with green foliage.

'Apple Blossom' (M): this popular cultivar was introduced as long ago as 1948 and is noted for its large delicate pink flowers.

'Aquila' (F): flowers salmon-pink.

'Arnstad' (G): flowers pale salmon-pink.

'Artois' (B): flowers salmon-red, the foliage green.

'Baardse's Wonder' (GM): red flowers with a salmon edge to the petals. An old cultivar from Aalsmeer in Holland; except for the leaves it is very similar to 'Flamingo'.

'Baby Charm': raised by Z. K.Tvrtkovic-Sahin (Kees Sahin) in Holland. A.M. 1979. No longer available; nor are two more in the same group, 'Baby Dream' and 'Baby Face'.

'Bach' (P): flowers lilac with a deeper nose.

'Bali' (I): flowers salmon with a deeper nose.

'Bambi': a Mini cyclamen with small leaves and white flowers with a dark pink nose.

'Barbarossa': raised by C. Stoldt in Germany this is a Cristata type with rose-pink shading to lilac flowers with the characteristic crested petals.

'Basel' (ST): flowers dark salmon-pink.

'Béarn' (B): flowers deep salmon; foliage green with some silvering.

'Beethoven' (= 'van Beethoven') (P): flowers violet-purple.

'Bengali': a recently introduced floriferous F_1 hybrid with very vivid shiny scarlet blooms; *probably already withdrawn*.

'Bermuda' (I): flowers salmon with a flush of carmine.

'Bern' (ST): flowers white with a pink nose.

'Bianco': a diploid or tetraploid with pure white flowers.

'Biel' (ST): flowers dark lilac.

'Bluebeard' (F): colour of 'Sylphide'; *withdrawn*.

'Boheme' (C): a strong F_1 hybrid with flowers of fuchsia-red.

'Bolero' (C): F_1 hybrid with pale lilac flowers with a deeper nose.

'Bonfire' (GM) = 'Vuurbaak'.

'Borneo' (I): flowers white with a rose nose.

'Bourgogne' (B): foliage deep green.

'Brahms' (P): flowers lilac with a deeper nose.

'Bretagne' (B): flowers deep salmon; foliage deep green with silver marbling.

'Brienz' (ST): flowers pale rose-pink.

'Cardinal': an old cultivar of medium size, producing flowers of cerise-scarlet.

'Carmen'. a strong-growing and floriferous F_1 hybrid with scarlet flowers and somewhat marbled foliage.

'Carmin Salmoneum': an old tetraploid cultivar with near-orange flowers.

'Cattleya' (GM): flowers lilac.

'Charm' (V): *withdrawn*.

'Chopin' (P): flowers pale pink.

'Cinderella' (F): flowers pale salmon-pink with a deeper red nose.

'Columba' (F): a strong-growing and large-flowered cultivar with pale pink flowers with a deep red nose.

'Corona' (F): flowers deep rose.

'Corsica' (I): flowers lilac, the petals with a paler margin.

'Cristata Bush Hill Pioneer': an old Cristata cultivar with crested petals.

186 'Harlequin', an old tetraploid cultivar with striped blooms, still grown commercially today on the Continent.

'Davos' (ST): flowers pure white.

'Dawn' (S): pale pink flowers; *withdrawn*.

'Debussy': flowers lilac with a darker nose.

'Dorado' (F): F₁ hybrid with salmon-pink flowers.

'Dunkellachs' (Z): flowers dark salmon.

'Eisenach' (G): F₁ tetraploid hybrid with white flowers with a pink nose.

'Erfurt' (G): F₁ tetraploid with bright red flowers.

'Esmeralda' (C): F₁ hybrid with pale rose-pink flowers with a deeper nose.

'Excelsior' (M): *withdrawn*.

'Fidelio' (C): F₁ hybrid with pale violet-rose flowers.

'Fiji' (I): flowers bright lilac-purple.

'Finlandia' (C): F₁ hybrid with pure white flowers.

'Firebrand' (T): tetraploid; flowers orange-scarlet; *withdrawn*.

'Firefly': a diploid cultivar with deep red flowers.

'Flamingo': a Braukmann introduction, tetraploid; flowers salmon-red with a paler margin; the foliage is a reversed silver leaf, silver in the centre, green towards the margins.

'Flamme': an old diploid cultivar with flame-red flowers.

'Fornax' (F): flowers bright satiny-red.

'Friesenglut' ('Frisian Glow') (FR): flowers bright orange-red with a hint of paler orange; foliage attractively marked.

'Friesenraum' ('Frisian Dream') (FR): flowers pure white; foliage deep green with paler veins.

'Friesenstar' ('Frisian Star') (FR): flowers bright salmon-pink with a silvery sheen, the petals slightly ruffled; foliage attractively marked.

'Fritillary' (W): *withdrawn*.

'Genf' (ST): flowers cherry-red.

Giselle' (C): F₁ hybrid with bright salmon-rose flowers with a deeper nose.

'Gotha' (G): F₁ tetraploid hybrid with pale rosy-pink flowers with a deeper nose.

'Grandia': a cultivar with markedly ruffled and spreading petals in white with rose.

'Grandiflorum Fimbriatum': an old cultivar that was introduced in 1897, with fringed petals.

'Handel' (P): flowers dark lilac-rose.

'Hallo': introduced by Messrs Ernst Benary in Germany, this cultivar has glowing red flowers.

'Hallo Rex': a variegated-leaved form of the previous cultivar; *withdrawn*.

'Harlequin' ('Striata'). an old tetraploid cultivar in which the petals are striped with a different or usually deeper colour such as red, purple or lilac stripes on white, or purple on lilac and so on. The stripes are generally markedly uneven and random and do not affect all petals similarly. Still fairly popular today, especially in Holland, but not widely sold. They are reminiscent of the 'broken' tulips whose striping is caused by a virus, but in this instance the cause is a chimera. They are open-pollinated and rather unstable, and mutations and reversions are common in a batch of plants.

'Hawaii' (I): flowers dark lilac.

'Haydn' (P): flowers phlox-pink with a deeper nose.

'Heidi' (F): flowers creamy-white.

'Huntsman' (V): an old tetraploid; *withdrawn*.

'Hydrangea-pink' (T): an old tetraploid; *withdrawn*.

'Iceland' (I): flowers pure white.

'Jack' (E): flowers deep salmon-pink.

'Jena' (G): F₁ tetraploid hybrid with satiny-violet flowers.

'Jim' (E); flowers luminous scarlet.

'Jonny' (E): flowers pale pink with a deeper nose.

'Kätchen Stoldt': the only large-flowered white tetraploid cultivar.

'Kimono': tetraploid raised in Japan in the 1960s by T. Sakata, this cultivar is noted for its double flowers and comes in several colours; probably best considered as a series rather than a cultivar.

'Kirschrot' (Z): flowers cherry-red.

'Korfu': a German cultivar raised by R. Mayer with neat foliage and small, scented, salmon-pink flowers.

'Lachs Miniatur Silbersaum' (Z): flowers smoky-salmon.

'Lehar' (P): flowers lilac, the petals margined with white.

'Leuchtenburg' (G): flowers bright satiny-scarlet.

'Lichtkönigin': a large-flowered tetraploid with Bengal purple flowers with a scarlet glow.

'Liszt' (P): flowers white with a purple nose.

'Lorraine' (B): flowers deep salmon; leaves with a broad silver margin.

'Lucie' (L): flowers long-stalked, silvery salmon.

'Luise' (L): flowers long-stalked, dark salmon.

'Luna' (L): flowers long-stalked, bright salmon.

'Lulu' (L): flowers long-stalked, salmon, prolific.

'Luzern' (ST): flowers lilac-rose.

'Lugano' (ST): flowers pale rose-pink with a deeper nose.

'Maarse's Purple'; a tetraploid with deep purple flowers.

'Magic Melody': a fine diploid with all-silver leaves and large scarlet flowers with pale pink margins to the petals.

'Magnificum' (GM): a classic tetraploid with white flowers with a red nose.

'Mallorca' (I): flowers bright rose with a deeper nose.

'Malta' (I): flowers cherry-salmon.

'Manon' (C): F₁ hybrid with bright, pale salmon flowers with a reddish nose.

'Mauritius' (I): flowers dark salmon.

'Mauve Beauty' (M): a large-flowered tetraploid; *withdrawn.*

'Mauve Queen' (T): an old tetraploid; *withdrawn.*

'Merry Widow': raised by Messrs Sluis & Groot, this F₁ hybrid has white, scented flowers which are on the small side; *withdrawn.*

'Mozart' (P): flowers red, the petals margined with rose.

'Nabucco' (C): a large-flowered F₁ hybrid with pale salmon flowers with a darker nose.

'Neulachs Gefranst': a large-flowered tetraploid variety with pink and red flowers with frilled petals; unreliable.

'Norma' (C): F₁ hybrid cultivar with pure white flowers with a rose-red nose.

'Normandie' (B): flowers bright salmon-rose, large.

'Oberon' (C): a recent introduction, an F₁ hybrid with numerous pale lilac flowers; 'Tosca' is a deep-flowered version.

'Ophelia' (C): F₁ hybrid with pale rose flowers with deeper nose.

'Orpheus' (C): F₁ hybrid with scarlet-red flowers.

'Orion' (F): a strong-growing pink-flowered F₁ hybrid.

'Pastourelle' (CL): an F₁ hybrid with deep green foliage and rather ungainly white flowers feathered with blue; raised by Clause in France; *withdrawn.*

'Pavo' (F): rich salmon-pink flowers with a deep purple nose.

'Peacock' (W): *withdrawn.*

'Pegasus' (F): flowers bright cherry-red.

'Perle von Zehlendorf' (GM): a large-flowered tetraploid with salmon-scarlet flowers, still widely grown.

'Phoenix' (F): an F₁ hybrid with bright rose-pink flowers; from Royal-Sluis in Holland. A.M. 1979; *withdrawn.*

'Picardie' (B): flowers bright salmon; foliage with a silver margin.

'Pink Pearl' (M): an old tetraploid; *withdrawn.*

'Pink Ruffles': a German cultivar with handsomely marked leaves and full ruffled flowers in carmine-rose. One of the finest ruffled cultivars.

'Pink Waves' (V): an old tetraploid with large flowers; *withdrawn.*

'Polka' (CL): a French F₁ hybrid with somewhat marbled foliage and pale mauve flowers; tends to be autumn-flowering; *withdrawn.*

'Provence' (B): flowers violet; foliage green.

'Quebec' (B): flowers violet; foliage deep green with a silver margin.

'Ravel' (P): flowers dark salmon.

'Reinweiss' (Z): flowers pure white.

'Reinweiss Miniatur Auge' (Z): flowers pure white with a purple nose.

'Rheingaufeuer': an outstanding tetraploid cultivar with bright red flowers of great substance.

'Rheingaufeuer Schnitt': developed from the preceding cultivar for the cut-flower trade; the bright red flowers are borne on tall strong stalks to 40cm (16in) in length.

'Robin Hood' (F): F₅ hybrid with intense dark red flowers with a deeper nose; *withdrawn.*

'Rococo': a large-flowered, long-stemmed cultivar with salmon-pink flowers, suitable for cutting.

'Romeo' (C): F₁ hybrid with deep rose-scarlet flowers; *withdrawn.*

'Rondo': a French F₁ hybrid with medium-sized rose-pink flowers, often early in the season; *withdrawn.*

'Rosa von Aalsmeer' ('Rose of Aalsmeer') (GM): a tetraploid cultivar with rose-pink flowers.

'Rosa von Marienthal' ('Rose of Marienthal') (GM): an old tetraploid cultivar from the nineteenth century.

'Rosa von Zehlendorf': a vigorous tetraploid cultivar with large flowers in salmon-pink with a deeper nose. One of the most popular and widely grown cultivars, especially in Holland.

'Rosamunda' (C): F₁ hybrid with violet-rose flowers; *withdrawn.*

'Rosamunde': F₁ hybrid once widely grown in Holland with bright fuchsia-pink flowers borne on tall, thin stems. One of the first F₁ hybrids to be introduced, maturing in 7–8 months from sowing; *long withdrawn.*

'Rosemarie': flowers deep rose-pink with a deeper nose; this cultivar was bred by Professor Wellensiek in Holland.

'Rossini' (P): flowers purple, flamed.

'Royal Rose' (M): an old tetraploid with large deep rose flowers; *withdrawn.*

'Salmon-pink' (T): a fine old tetraploid with large flowers; *withdrawn.*

'Salmon Scarlet' (M): a fine old English tetraploid; *withdawn.*

'Samoa' (I): flowers red, the petals with a silvery margin.

187 'Winter Sun', the first experimental yellow cyclamen, from Sahin in Holland; the flowers are yellow in bud and gradually fade as they mature.

'Santa' (F): flowers pale satiny-red.

'Sara': a cultivar with bright rose-pink flowers, bred by Professor Wellensiek in Holland.

'Scarlet King' (M): another old English tetraploid; *withdrawn.*

'Schubert' (P): flowers rose-red with a deeper nose.

'Scorpion' (F): flowers bright scarlet.

'Shell-pink' (T): an old tetraploid cultivar from Suttons Seeds, England; *withdrawn.*

'Silberstrahl' ('Silver Ray'): a fine German cultivar with medium-sized flowers of deep crimson, each petal with a thin silver margin.

'Sirius': a miniature F_1 hybrid cyclamen with rose-red flowers.

'Snow White' (F): flowers pure white.

'Solothurn' (ST): flowers pale lilac.

'Sonja': another of Professor Wellensiek's introductions; the flowers are white with a deep pink nose.

'St Galen' (ST): flowers dark red.

'Strauss' (P): flowers vivid red.

'Sunrise' (V): an old large-flowered cultivar from England; *withdrawn.*

'Swan Lake': an old F_1 hybrid with attractive foliage and medium-sized pure white flowers borne on strong stems; raised by Sluis & Groot in Holland; *withdrawn.*

'Sylphe Cattleya': a lavender-flowered cultivar with rather elegant flowers with somewhat twisted petals.

'Sylphide' : flowers large, lilac.

'Sylvia' (C): F_1 hybrid with flowers of violet-purple; *withdrawn.*

'Taures': flowers salmon-scarlet.

'Tinkerbell' (F): flowers pale rose with a deeper nose.

'Thun' (ST): flowers rose-pink with a deeper nose.

'Timor' (I): flowers pastel pink.

'Tip Top': a De Troyer scarlet-flowered cultivar.

'Tonga' (I): flowers luminous red.

'Tosca' (C): F_1 hybrid with deep rich lilac flowers with a deep purple nose.

'Tucana' (F): F_1 hybrid with intense violet flowers; *withdrawn.*

'Tzigane': a floriferous F_1 hybrid with tall, strong stalks and flowers of rich cherry-red.

'Ursa' (F): flowers rose-pink.

'Vela' (F): flowers rose-pink with a red nose.

'Vendée' (B): flowers pale orchid pink.

'Verdi' (P): flowers lilac-rose, the petals with white margins.

'Victoria': an old and very popular cultivar, much grown in Holland and Germany; the flowers, of medium size, are white with a frilled margin that are crimson at the tips; an unstable tetraploid but in recent years the desirable characters of this impressive cultivar have been transferred to a more stable diploid.

'Violett' (Z): flowers lilac.

'Virgo' (F): a large-flowered F_1 hybrid cultivar with rather plain green leaves and pure white flowers; *withdrawn.*

'Vivaldi' (P): flowers salmon-pink, the petals with paler margins.

'Vuurbaak' (= 'Leuchtfeuer'): tetraploid; Gigantic cultivar which has long proved to be one of the most popular on the Continent. The flowers are a deep glowing scarlet-red. The seed production of this one cultivar far exceeds that of any other in Holland.

'Weimar' (G): flowers pure white.

'Wendy' (F): flowers pale rose-pink.

'White Giant': a large-flowered diploid with pure white petals.

'White Triumph' (T): an old English tetraploid with very large white flowers; *withdrawn.*

'Winter Sun': from Sahin in Holland, this unique diploid cultivar has flowers that are pale yellow when they open but gradually become white as they age; further development from this cultivar may eventually lead to a deeper yellow cyclamen.

'Wye Downland' (W): a miniature variety from Wye College, England; *withdrawn, as are the others [refoxed 'Wye'.*

'Zatrosa Miniature' (Z): flowers pale rose with a deeper nose.

'Zug' (ST): flowers pale salmon-pink.

'Zurich' (ST): flowers vivid satiny red.

Awards to *C. persicum* cultivars and groups before 1955 (mostly extinct or no longer available)
'Albatross', A.M. 1940
'Albert Victor', F.C.C. 1885
'Baroness Burdett Coutts', F.C.C. 1879
'Brilliant', F.C.C. 1870
'Burgundy', A.M. 1954
'Carmine', F.C.C. 1870
'Charming Bride', F.C.C. 1881
'Cherry Ripe', A.M. 1917
'Compactum Magnificum', F.C.C. 1877
'Crimson Beauty' F.C.C. 1884
'Crimson Gem', F.C.C. 1882
'Crimson King' F.C.C. 1879
'Crimson St. George' A.M. 1917
'Fimbriatum' A.M. 1907
'Fimbriatum Giganteum', A.M. 1907
'Firefly', A.M. 1923
'Giant Shell Pink', A.M. 1925
'Giant Wonder', A.M. 1924
'Giganteum', F.C.C. 1870
'Giganteum Album', F.C.C. 1885
'Giganteum Compactum', F.C.C. 1882
'Giganteum Dame Blanche', F.C.C. 1884
'Giganteum Delicatulum', F.C.C. 1884
'Giganteum roseum Compactum', F.C.C. 1882
'Giganteum St. George', A.M. 1913
'Giganteum Superbum', F.C.C. 1873
'Grandiflorum Album', A.M. 1897

'Highdown', A.M. 1963
'Kermesinum', F.C.C. 1870
'L.M. Graves', A.M. 1914
'Miss Lilian Cox', F.C.C. 1881
'Mont Blanc', F.C.C. 1878
Mrs Buckston Strain, A.M. 1911
Papilio Strain, A.M. 1897
'Picturatum', F.C.C. 1879
'Prince of Orange', A.M. 1889
'Princess Ida', F.C.C. 1884
'Purple Gem', F.C.C. 1879
'Purplish Rose', F.C.C. 1870
'Purpureum', F.C.C. 1870
'Queen of the Belgians', F.C.C. 1879
'Queen of the Crimsons', F.C.C. 1871
'Reading Gem', F.C.C. 1879
'Rose Queen', F.C.C. 1874
'Roseum Grandiflorum', F.C.C. 1978
'Rosy Morn', F.C.C. 1878
'Royal Purple' F.C.C. 1874
'Ruby', F.C.C. 1877
'Ruby Gem', F.C.C. 1881
Salmon King Strain, A.M. 1908
'Snowflake', F.C.C. 1871
'Vivid', A.M. 1896
'White Beauty', F.C.C. 1878
'White Gem', F.C.C. 1882
'White Perfection', F.C.C.

Chapter Nine

Cyclamen Hybrids

Cyclamen species do not hybridize in the wild. As a scientist, I know that making rash statements of this kind or sweeping generalizations on the distribution or variation within species is inviting trouble, even criticism. Yet not a single authenticated hybrid has ever been recorded in the wild in the genus and there are very good reasons for this. Firstly, most species grow in isolation from one another, or occupy different habitats, so that the chances of them even receiving pollen from another species is fairly unlikely. Secondly, where two species do occupy the same region (even occasionally the same habitat) they have different flowering times (one can think of *C. repandum* sensu lato and *C. hederifolium* in the Greek Peloponnese) so hybridization is again precluded. Thirdly, should they grow close together and flower at the same time then hybridization may well be excluded by species incompatibility; this may be a physical or chemical barrier that prevents the pollen of one species germinating on another or they may be genetically incompatible by bearing different chromosome numbers (as in the case of *C. graecum* and *C. hederifolium* that occasionally occupy the same habitat in the Greek Peloponnese or in south-western Turkey). Other factors may also be involved such as specific pollinators, although very little is known about these at the present time.

Incompatibility barriers clearly are important if closely related species are to grow in close proximity and keep their own identity, otherwise hybridization would be rife and the species would be swamped by hybrid offspring and this would lead to loss of identity. Conversely, evolution may not have equipped closely related species that have evolved in isolation from one another with any incompatibility mechanism, so that when they are brought together in cultivation crosses will occur, either by chance or by design.

It is always said that cyclamen are very difficult to hybridize, an assumption based primarily on the diverse cytological variation found among the different species. One would not normally expect species with 20 chromosomes to cross with those with 30, 48, 84 or any other number. Much of this assumption was based on work with *C. persicum*. When I was at Wye College in the 1960s as an undergraduate I was fascinated by the work being carried out to increase the diversity in

C. persicum as a pot-plant. A great deal was achieved at the College but attempts to cross *C. persicum* with any other species proved a failure and the situation has remained the same to this day with all who have tried similar pollen to stigma crosses. Incidentally, Professor Wellensiek in Holland tried similar interspecific crosses with *C. persicum* as one of the parents at about the same time but with equal lack of success. In recent years the Japanese have succeeded in transferring some genes of several other species into *C. persicum* by complicated laboratory procedures aimed at overriding the natural incompatibility. The results of this work are still continuing and its effects in the long term difficult to assess at the present time.

Most of the known hybrids have been produced within the same chromosome grouping; for instance *C. cyprium* x *C. libanoticum* and *C. libanoticum* x *C. pseudibericum* all have 2n=30 chromosomes, *C. creticum* x *C. repandum* have 2n=20 or 22, while *C. africanum* x *C. hederifolium* have 2n=34 chromosomes (also 2n=64 in the same species). The fact that these 'groups' (based on chromosome number) do not hybridize with members of another 'group' shows a pronounced incompatibility as might be expected. Even within the same group hybrids are on the whole rather rare; for instance *C. coum* and *C. libanoticum* both share a chromosome number of 2n=30, but attempts to cross them have failed, which perhaps indicates another incompatibility mechanism at play. Incidentally, the fact that no hybrids between *C. coum* and *C. cilicium* or *C. mirabile* exist is due to the fact that the latter two species are autumn-, not spring-flowering, rather than any known incompatibility (other similar crosses can be envisaged between species with similar chromosome numbers but different flowering seasons).

It is unfortunate that the majority of inter-species hybrids that are known today are unsubstantiated. Apart from the well-documented *C.* x *wellensiekii* most have arisen by chance and their parentage has had to be worked out by logic and putative parents suggested. This is so with many hybrids that occur spontaneously in gardens! What is needed is a more scientific approach with crosses carefully recorded and results analysed as it has been done in the case of genera such as Pleione or Gerbera. There is no reason, for instance, why pollen of autumn-flowering species should not be collected and stored in readiness to cross with the spring-flowering species when they come into bloom.

Most of the hybrids examined to date are fertile and some are prolific seeders. The purist in me shies away from hybrids for they can often swamp species in cultivation (look what has happened to poor Pleione in recent years!) This has happened to a greater or lesser extent in collections of *C. repandum* which freely hybridizes in cultivation with both *C. balearicum* and *C. creticum*. As a result the true species may become adulterated, rarer or less grown by gardeners; this is unlikely to happen in cyclamen to any great extent fortunately, as there are many growers who maintain as many species in cultivation as possible and most of these are freely available, indeed one of the specific aims of The Cyclamen Society is to promote species to a wider gardening public. For the average gardener who just wants a patch or two of cyclamen to enjoy through the year then it matters little whether the plants are pure species or hybrids. On the other hand interspecific hybrids can tell us a good deal about species affinities and their morphology and may, in the long term, bring a better understanding of the evolution of the species and their origins.

Why are species hybrids important? Hybrids increase the range of diversity available to gardeners. They may increase hardiness, extend the flowering season or simply be easier to grow, or more vigorous. More important, they may be simply very beautiful and desirable. From a nurseryman's point of view interesting new hybrids extend the list of plants available, createsinterest and, more important, lead to more sales; after all if you collect cyclamen, or indeed any other group of plants, then you will want to own all the different types that are available. New hybrids and cultivars and other novelties, especially if they are in short supply, will elicit high prices.

Except in the case of *C. x wellensiekii* it is not known which species was the female parent or which way the cross has occurred, so in the following account the species are presented in alphabetical order, and only those hybrids whose parentage is certain and unequivocal are given formal scientific names. The others must wait until more detailed information is available.

ESTABLISHED HYBRIDS

C. x *drydeniae* (*C. coum* x *C. alpinum*)
C. x *hildebrandii* (*C. africanum* x *C. hederifolium*)
C. x *meiklei* (*C. creticum* x *C. repandum*)
C. x *saundersiae* (*C. balearicum* x *C. repandum*)
C. x *schwarzii* (*C. libanoticum* x *C. pseudibericum*)
C. x *wellensiekii* (*C. cyprium* x libanoticum)
C. x *whiteae* (*C. graecum* x *C. hederifolium*)

188 *Cyclamen* x *drydeniae* (*C. alpinum* x *C. coum* subsp. *coum*); the flowers are almost intermediate between the parent species.
189 Another form of *Cyclamen* x *drydeniae*.

Cyclamen x atkinsii T. Moore

A 19th-century hybrid reputed to be a cross between *C. coum* and *C. persicum* but few would accepts its validity today. See p.151.

Cyclamen x drydeniae Grey-Wilson

C. coum subsp. *coum* x *C. alpinum*
This interesting hybrid has been discussed in part under *C. coum* Pewter Group, see p.155. Putative hybrids between *C. coum* and *C. alpinum* that I have seen to date all seem to have arisen through the Pewter Group and do not seem to involve other forms of cultivars of the *C. coum* complex. The reasons for this are unclear.

190 *Cyclamen* x *hildebrandii* (*C. africanum* x *C. hederifolium*).

Hybrids tend to inherit the rather oval leaf shape and scalloped margin from *C. alpinum* as well as the propeller-like arrangement of the corolla-lobes and occasionally the pleasing fragrance. The pewtered leaves are clearly inherited from *C. coum* Pewter Group. Whereas some flowers have a solid basal blotch at the base of each petal, others have ones more typical of *C. coum*, or even a blotch composed of lines, occasionally with a single central line running from the mouth well up each corolla-lobe.

The parent species are closely related but are isolated geographically in the wild. In cultivation they come into flower at more or less the same time.

DESCRIPTION *Leaves* orbicular to oval, 3–4.5cm long (1.2–1.77in), 3.1–4.6cm (1.22–1.8in) long, generally with a slightly to markedly scalloped margin, usually an even pewter colour above, often with a deep green midrib and sometimes margined with deep green, suffused with deep crimson-magenta beneath; petiole to 12.5cm (5in) long. *Pedicels* ascending to erect, 9–14.5cm (3.5–5.7in) long, coiling from the top downwards as the fruits develop. Flowers appearing with the mature leaves (February–April), pale pink to deep rose-pink or magenta-pink, with a pale magenta to deep magenta or pink blotch, or single to several similarly coloured lines at the base of each petal, the blotch solid or with 'eyes', often primrose-scented but not consistently so; corolla-lobes spreading out horizontally to ascending (then often making a shuttlecock-shaped corolla), 13–16mm (0.5–0.6in) long, the margin usually somewhat toothed, sometimes markedly so, especially towards the apex.

Cyclamen x *drydeniae* is very fertile and sets copious seed. In the garden it has proved to be fully hardy and is an attractive addition to the range of hardy late winter-flowering cyclamen for the garden. It also makes an attractive pan plant for the alpine house; the best forms need to be selected for this purpose.

Most of my original plants of this hybrid were given to me by Christine Skelmersdale who grows many similar plants on her nursery, Broadleigh Gardens, near Taunton, Somerset.

I have named this hybrid in honour of a good friend, Kath Dryden, who has over the years done much to promote hardy cyclamen, especially the Pewter Group, and who has inspired so many young growers in the art of growing alpine plants and bulbs.

Cyclamen x *hildebrandii* Schwarz

C. africanum x *C. hederifolium*

Cyclamen x *hildebrandii* was the first cyclamen hybrid to be formally recognized, being described by Otto Schwarz in 1955. This hybrid is not an unlikely one as the two species involved are closely related morphologically and they can share the same chromosome number. (*C. africanum* can have a chromosome number of 2n=34 or 68, while *C. hederifolium* has a count of 2n=34, although tetraploids, 2n=68, have been recently discovered in the wild). Like the other hybrids so far discussed, these two species do not hybridize in the wild as they inhabit different geographical regions. Unfortunately, the hybrid origins of plants in cultivation often has to be doubted and some that I have been shown as putative hybrids fit comfortably into the range of variation of ordinary *C. hederifolium*. To confound matters, plants are often seen in collections (or dare one say even supplied by some nurseries) purporting to be *C. africanum* when they are in fact *C. hederifolium*. Having said this, however, I am quite sure that there are plants in cultivation that are genuinely hybrids and if they can be authenticated then the hybrid can be given a formal scientific name, if desired. The best way to do this would be to cross diploid plants of authenticated parentage and evaluate the results. Those who grow *C.* x *hildebrandii* report that it is hardier than *C. africanum* which is much as might reasonably be expected. For the differences between *C. africanum* and *C. hederifolium* see p.120.

DESCRIPTION (taken from a cultivated plant, not from the type specimen). *Leaves* borne on erect to ascending petioles, the lamina ovate with a heart-shaped base, lamina 6.3–8cm (2.5–3.1in) long, 5.8–7cm (2.3–2.8in) wide, often as wide as long or almost so, the margin toothed to lobed but not angled, the lobes (often 2–3 on each side) often pronounced and rather triangular, deep green above with a rather pale hastate pattern in grey or paler green, paler green beneath, sometimes slightly flushed with pink; petiole rather thick, 7.2–14cm (2.8–5.5in) long. *Pedicels* spreading to erect, slightly to markedly elbowed near to the base, 11.5–19.5cm (4.5–7.7in) long, coiling from the top downwards in fruit. *Flowers* borne with the semi-mature leaves (September to October), occasionally with the very young leaves, not scented; corolla pale to deep pink with a broad, V-shaped, deep magenta mark at the base of each petal; petal lobes elliptical, often rather narrow, twisted, 2.6–3.1cm (1–1.2in) long, erect.

Cyclamen x *hildebrandii* is a fully fertile hybrid. Back crossing with either parent is common in cultivation, especially when the parent species are grown in close proximity in a glasshouse. As a result all types of intermediates are possible and these greatly interfere with the accurate determination of the genuine species, particularly *C. africanum*. Hybrids tend to inherit the leaf toothing and lobing characteristics of *C. africanum*, as well as the long pedicels. On the other hand, the spreading leaf pedicels are more characteristic of *C. hederifolium*. The flower size is generally intermediate between the parent species, although the details of flower shape and patterning is very similar in all three.

The hardiness of this hybrid is not understood because of confusion between it and the parent species, *C. hederifolium* being fully hardy, whereas *C. africanum* is frost-tender.

Cyclamen x *meiklei* Grey-Wilson

C. creticum x *C. repandum*
My attention was first drawn to this interesting hybrid by Desmond Meikle when we worked together at the Royal Botanic Gardens, Kew. In his mild garden near Minehead, Somerset, besides other species, Desmond cultivates both *C. repandum* (var. *repandum*) and *C. creticum* in the open garden and he noticed over a number of years how the two populations had merged with many individuals intermediate between the parent species. It is perhaps not surprising that these two species should hybridize for they are not only very similar in appearance but share the same basic chromosome number, 2n=20, although some forms of *C. creticum* have two additional chromosomes. In the wild they are excluded from interbreeding by their geographical isolation from one another.

The leaves are more or less intermediate between the parent species, and the flowers show a gradation of colour from the white of *C. creticum*, through various pale and mid-pinks to the more vibrant carmine-magenta of *C. repandum* var. *repandum*.

The *Cyclamen repandum* group (*C. repandum*, *C. balearicum*, *C. creticum* and *C. peloponnesiacum*), as far as I know, all appear to interbreed freely when brought together. This is especially true with the various subspecies and forms of *C. repandum*, with the result that it is often difficult now to obtain the pure plant, unless seed is obtained from authenticated wild sources.

Most of the hybrid plants are attractive and gardenworthy, though they differ somewhat in their hardiness, like the parent species. On the whole *C. repandum* subsp. *repandum* is the hardiest and *C. balearicum* the least hardy, with *C. creticum* and *C. peloponnesiacum* falling somewhere in between, so that the hardiness of the hybrid offspring is likely to depend very much on the parent species or subspecies. The name *C.* x *meiklei* applies only to hybrids between *C. repandum* var. *repandum* and *C. creticum*.

I am very pleased to have the opportunity to name this interesting hybrid in honour of a fine colleague and friend who has done much to enable a better understanding of the genus *Cyclamen* and whose *magnum opus*, 'The Flora of Cyprus', is a major source of information on my bookshelf.

DESCRIPTION *Leaves* broadly cordate, 5.5–8.7cm (2.2–3.4in) long, 50–76mm (2–3in) wide, rather thin, the margin somewhat dentate (the teeth rather distant, giving the margin a scalloped appearance) to shallowly lobed, green or grey-green above, generally with a broad hastate pattern in grey or silvery-grey but often rather muted, often overlain with pale specks or dashes, these sometimes extending to the leaf margin, usually suffused with carmine-purple beneath. *Flowers* borne with the mature leaves (March to early May), very pale pink to deep pink or deep magenta, sweetly scented; corolla-lobes elliptical, twisted, 1.5–2.4cm (0.6–0.9in) long.

Many of the hybrids have pleasing flowers in shades of pale to mid-pink, though the colour is nearly always more intense than it is in the pale pink forms of *C. creticum* occasionally found among the ordinary whites on Crete. In mild areas where *C. creticum* can be grown successfully in the open garden it will be difficult to prevent hybridization with *C. repandum*, especially if the two are grown in close proximity.

191 *Cyclamen* x *saundersiae* (*C. balearicum* x *C. repandum*).

192 *Cyclamen* x *schwarzii* (*C. libanoticum* x *C. pseudibericum*); the white form often sold as *C. pseudibericum* 'Album'.

193 *Cyclamen* x *schwarzii*: a pale pink form often mistaken for *C. pseudibericum* forma *roseum*.

Cyclamen x saundersiae Grey-Wilson

C. balearicum x *C. peloponnesiacum*

The fact that members of the *C. repandum* persuasion hybridize readily with one another is not disputed. In fact they appear to hybridize more readily than any other cyclamen species. This is not surprising as the species are so closely related, both in morphological as well as cytological characteristics. As has been noted such hybrids are precluded in the wild by the geographical isolation of the constituent species (*C. balearicum*, *C. creticum*, *C. peloponnesiacum* and *C. repandum*).

This hybrid was first shown to me by Jill White and is quite one of the most splendid cyclamen hybrids that I have seen to date, with beautiful patterned leaves and large flowers held high above the foliage and powerfully

scented. The cross is almost certainly between *C. balearicum* and *C. peloponnesiacum* rather than with *C. repandum*, to account for both the leaf patterning and the flower colours (in fact both these plants grow in close proximity in Jill White's cyclamen house).

In the *Cyclamen Society Journal* 12, 2 (1988) there are several colour illustrations of this hybrid showing rather different crosses. Their characteristics very much depend on the parent plants but also on which of the subspecies of *C. repandum* was involved. The hybrid name *C.* x *saundersiae* encompasses all crosses between *C. peloponnesiacum* (any subspecies) and *C. balearicum*.

This hybrid is generally rather robust and floriferous in the first generation with the flowers tending on the small side, this no doubt inherited from *C. balearicum*. In the second and subsequent generations a wide variety of leaf patterning and flower colours appear, although the flowers tend always to be on the small side; flowers range in colour from pure white to deep pink, some of the loveliest being those that are white or pale pink with a deeper pink nose.

DESCRIPTION *Leaves* broadly heart-shaped, 3–6.5cm (1.2–2.6in) long, 2.5–6cm (1–2.3in) wide, with a poorly defined or rather well-defined toothed or scalloped , but not lobed, margin, deep green or grey-green above with a hastate pattern (sometimes ill-defined) in grey, overlain usually with numerous specks and blotches in cream or silver, pale green beneath; petiole 3.5–7cm (1.4–2.8in) long. *Flowers* borne with the mature foliage (late March to early May), held well above the foliage, pale pink with a broad, deep magenta-pink zone around the mouth; corolla-lobes narrow-elliptical, strongly twisted, 1.5–1.8(–2.2)cm/0.6–0.7 (–0.9)in long; style not protruding or protruding up to 1mm.

The leaves are generally more markedly and sharply toothed than those of normal *C. balearicum* but often retain the dull mottling characteristic of the species, often without a well-defined hastate pattern, although some forms have very attractively speckled leaves. The leaf characters and rather small flowers are clearly inherited from *C. balearicum*, the richer flower colour from *C. peloponnesiacum*.

Plants are reasonably hardy in warm, sheltered gardens. If grown in the proximity of one or both parents they will backcross readily to produce an even greater range of variability.

Cyclamen x *saundersiae* is fully fertile and sets seed readily.

Cyclamen x schwarzii Grey-Wilson

C. libanoticum x *C. pseudibericum*

This interesting hybrid first appeared by chance in the late 1980s in the collection of Phil Cornish in Gloucestershire. Some doubts were expressed initially as to its authenticity but I have examined a number of plants and have no doubts personally about the hybrid origin of this plant, or its parentage. It is not surprising that these two species should in fact hybridize for they are undoubtedly closely related and, furthermore, they share the same chromosome number (2n=30), not that these factors necessarily guarantee such a liaison, for cyclamen are, as we have seen, notoriously difficult to hybridize in the main.

It is interesting that *C. libanoticum* has been crossed artificially with another species, *C. cyprium*, the resultant hybrid having been given the name *C.* x *wellensiekii*; in fact this hybrid was the second in the genus *Cyclamen* to be given formal recognition and a Latin epithet. I have decided to name this new hybrid after the late Professor Otto Schwarz, for it seems fitting that he should have some recognition for all the researches he accomplished in *Cyclamen* over many years. *C.* x *schwarzii* is an extremely attractive plant and is a fine addition to any collection. It is perhaps surprising that this new hybrid did not appear before *C.* x *wellensiekii* for its parents are in flower at the same time, whereas *C. libanoticum* and *C. cyprium* flower at different times, the former in the late winter and early spring, the latter in the autumn and early winter. The cross *C.* x *wellensiekii* was only possible because late blooms of *C. cyprium* overlapped with early blooms of *C. libanoticum*, see p.194.

In overall characters *C.* x *schwarzii* is more or less intermediate between the parent species. The foliage is brighter than *C. libanoticum* but not as well marked as

194 *Cyclamen* x *wellensiekii* (*C. cyprium* x *C. libanoticum*).

C. pseudibericum. In shape it perhaps more closely resembles *C. pseudibericum* but with the slight angles and width of *C. libanoticum*. The flower colour ranges from white to mid-pink, with pure white or white flushed with very pale pink predominating. At the base of each petal the blotch is more substantial than that of *C. libanoticum*, but usually less so than for *C. pseudibericum*. The petals themselves are rather wider than *C. pseudibericum* but less so than those of *C. libanoticum*, yet they inherit the rather overlapping character of the latter species. The scent can best be described as a mild form of *C. libanoticum*; the hybrid certainly has not inherited the sweeter perfume of *C. pseudibericum*.

Cyclamen x *schwarzii* appears to be a fully fertile hybrid. Seedlings come into flower in the third or fourth season and second generation plants tend to have white rather than pink flowers; in some of these the petals flush with pale pink as they age, in much the same manner as in *C. libanoticum*.

Interestingly, similar hybrid plants have also appeared unintentionally in at least one other collection: most notably the very pale forms of *C. pseudibericum* forma *roseum* catalogued by Tilebarn Nursery are almost certainly of the same cross.

DESCRIPTION *Leaves* with a broad heart-shaped lamina, 3.4–5.2cm (1.3–2in) long, 3.5–5.4cm (1.4–2.1in) wide, as broad as long or somewhat broader, with a narrow basal sinus with the basal lobes slightly diverging from one another, the margin shallowly scalloped, deep green and somewhat shiny above with a broad greyish-green hastate pattern and greyish speckling towards the margin of the leaf, green flushed with reddish-purple beneath; petioles 3.5–6.2cm (1.4–2.4in) long, slightly elbowed close to the base. *Pedicels* ascending to erect, not elbowed, to 11cm (4.3in) long, green flushed with purplish-brown. *Flowers* borne with the mature leaves, mostly held just above the foliage, with a mild peppery scent; corolla white or very

Cyclamen x *schwarzii* (*C. libanoticum* x *C. pseudibericum*).

Cyclamen x *wellensiekii*

pale pink, with a magenta or pinkish-purple W-shaped or ace of spades blotch at or close to the base of each petal, without auricles but with the corolla-lobes slightly overlapping towards the base; corolla-lobes broad-elliptical, somewhat twisted, 2.1–2.6cm (0.8–1in) long; style slightly protruding.

Cyclamen x *wellensiekii* Iestwaart

C. libanoticum X *C. cyprium*

This hybrid was first described in 1974 and, for a genus in which hybridization between species is a rarity, it might seem improbable, especially as the parent species look so different at first glance in both leaf and flower characteristics. However, both species are restricted to the eastern Mediterranean (one restricted to Cyprus, the other to the Lebanon) and share a similar chromosome number; in addition there are close similarities between chromosome size and chromosome morphology.

Of course, any hybridization between these two species is precluded in the wild because they do not share the same geographical location. In cultivation hybridization is also rather unlikely because *C. cyprium* is basically autumn-flowering, whilst *C. libanoticum* flowers in the late winter and early spring. However, *C. cyprium* occasionally produces a few late flowers and this factor was noted by Professor Wellensiek at the Agricultural University of Wageningen. In 1969 a few late flowers of *C. cyprium* overlapped with early blooms of *C. libanoticum*, the cross was accomplished artificially and seed was produced. The resultant offspring proved to be very uniform, revealing almost intermediate characters between the parent species and, as if to prove the point, flowering from November through to February.

There is some doubt and confusion over the origin of this hybrid. It was named in honour of Professor S.J. Wellensiek, who until his retirement in 1969 was head of the department of horticulture at the Agricultural University of Wageningen. After his retirement the university gave up the collection of cyclamen, distributing them among several botanical gardens. He relates that "At this stage Iestwaart must have picked up the cross, studied it and named it. I was not over-enthusiastic about this procedure, because I was of the opinion that there were not enough facts. However, neither were there arguments to prevent it". However, in the Alpine Garden Society Bulletin (61:380, 1993) Dr. Ietswaart, writing from Heemstede in the Netherlands, states that "… I made the cross *Cyclamen* X *wellensiekii* by my own hands in 1966. The results of this cross-breeding have been published in *Acta Botanica Neerlandica* 23,4 (August 1974) with the full agreement of Professor Wellensiek in all respects. In 1985 I sent F2 seedlings to Peter Moore …".

In the Alpine Garden Society Bulletin (61: 380, 1993) Dr Ietswaart suggests (unknowingly) that all the material of *C.* X *wellensiekii* in Britain has stemmed from the original cross. This is incorrect as it has been reproduced by at least one person in Britain. Robin Metcalf has recreated the hybrid (using *C. cyprium* 'E. S.' as the pollen parent) which first flowered for him in 1992. He has also succeeded with the reverse cross using *C. libanoticum* as the male rather than the female parent.

The flowering period of this hybrid is greatly extended with flowers appearing from October to early March.

Robin Metcalf reports on his recreation of *C.* X *wellensiekii*: "The problem of the disparate flowering periods was overcome by using a technique read about in a book on the hybridization of lilies. This consisted of keeping the pollen of the male parent, in this case *C. cyprium*, in a dry cold situation, until required. This was achieved by tapping the pollen into a small plastic vial which had a tiny hole in the lid (0.5mm) and then placing the vial inside an airtight container containing a desiccant (silica gel); the whole lot was then placed in a deep freezer, taking care not to upset the small pollen container. It should be possible to use a folded piece of aluminium foil instead of the small vial, if the latter is not available. A word of warning! If you try this method of keeping pollen be sure to allow the whole container to warm to room temperature before opening it, otherwise everything will be coated in condensation, ruining both the pollen and the silica gel."

Incidentally the photograph that accompanies an article on *C.* X *wellensiekii* in the *Bulletin of the Alpine Garden Society* (61:129, 1993) is almost certainly that of another hybrid, *C.* X *schwarzii*, and not *C.* X *wellensiekii*.

DESCRIPTION *Leaves* broad heart-shaped, 2.8–6cm (1.1–2.3in) long, 3–6cm (1.2–2.3in) wide, about as long as wide, with a narrow basal sinus with the basal lobes converging to slightly overlapping, the margin somewhat angled and slightly scalloped, deep green above with an irregular grey hastate pattern which breaks up into blotches and spots towards the margin of the leaf; petiole 3.5–7cm (1.4–2.8in) long, somewhat elbowed in the lower half. *Pedicels* ascending to erect, 6–11.5cm (2.3–4.5in) long, green flushed with purplish-brown. *Flowers* borne with the young or mature leaves (late September to December) and held just above the foliage, sweetly scented; corolla pale pink or white with a pink flush, with a deep purple-magenta blotch, often W- or V-shaped, at the base of each petal; corolla-lobes narrow-oval, twisted, 16–22mm (0.62–0.86in) long, with a small but obvious auricle at the base of each; style not protruding.

Cyclamen x *wellensiekii* inherits the rather smaller flowers with narrower petals and petal auricles from *C. cyprium* but the pink in the corolla from *C. libanoticum*. The mark at the base of the corolla-lobes is more marked than in either parent. On the other hand the rather dull leaf characters with a rather poorly defined leaf margin is closer to *C. libanoticum* than to *C. cyprium* which tends to have a more obvious toothed and angled margin.

In both *C.* x *saundersiae* and *C.* x *wellensiekii*, *C. libanoticum* is one of the parents. It would be interesting to complete the trio of crosses possible in the group by attempting hybrids between *C. cyprium* and *C. pseudibericum*.

AWARDS
• P.C. 1992

Cyclamen x *whiteae* Grey-Wilson

C. graecum x *hederifolium*

This putative hybrid was drawn to my attention by Jill White who gardens in Brightlingsea, Essex. The plants in question were the result of a deliberate cross between *C. hederifolium* and a Turkish form of *C. graecum* (now subsp. *anatolicum*). A number of plants resulted, characterized by thick rather bright leaves with little lobing and rather unusually stubby flowers with a broad mouth and short corolla-lobes, but with the general markings of *C. hederifolium*.

DESCRIPTION *Tuber* rooting from the shoulders and base, without thick anchorage roots. *Leaves* thick and fleshy, lyre-shaped to sagittate, 3.8–5.2cm (1.5–2in) long, 2.2–2.6cm (0.9–1in) wide, somewhat folded lengthways (not flat as in the parent species), with an unlobed but finely denticulate, somewhat beaded margin, deep green

195 *Cyclamen* x *whiteae* (*C. graecum* x *C. hederifolium*).

above with a narrow pale green or whitish zone close to the margin, pale green beneath; petiole stiff, thick and ascending, 4.5–7cm (1.8–2.8in) long. *Pedicels* thick and stiffly erect, 9–15.2cm (3.5–6in) long; coiling unknown as no fruit has set. *Flowers* borne with the young and semi-mature leaves, not scented; corolla pale pink with a deeper pink or carmine-magenta, rather uneven, blotch at the base of each petal, the colour sometimes suffusing the whole of the basal half of the petal; corolla-lobes broadly ovate, strongly reflexed but scarcely twisted, 10–16mm (0.4–0.6in) long, often as wide as long, with well-pronounced but rather lax auricles at the base; corolla mouth very broad, 10–15mm (0.4–0.6in) diameter; style not protruding.

A hybrid between *C. graecum* and *C. hederifolium* is both unexpected and highly unlikely. The two species are not closely related, with *C. graecum* showing some unique characters in the genus such as the presence of thick anchor roots and the coiling of the pedicels from the centre. In addition, the general cytology of the two species is very different with *C. graecum* having (on average) 2n=84 chromosomes, while *C. hederifolium* has 2n=34 usually. In the world of genetics unlikely liaisons do very occasionally occur so they cannot be ruled out altogether. The cross has not been replicated by Jill White or indeed anyone else. Jill White's collection includes some half-dozen plants of this particular hybrid (all from the same initial cross). All have the same thick leaves and odd dumpy flowers. They have never set seed, indeed they all appear to be sterile for I can detect no pollen whatsoever.

Hybridizing cyclamen by hand is an operation that requires some care. Simply transferring pollen from one species to another may result in hybrid offspring but unless flowers are properly emasculated before the stigma is receptive then one cannot guarantee that the seed produced is genuinely hybrid; for instance the flower may have already been pollinated or it may have pollinated itself after the artificial cross was made. In this instance, however, I have no doubt that the plants represent a very unusual hybrid.

In the commercial production of hybrid *C. persicum* the flowers are emasculated in bud by the entire removal of the corolla with the attached stamens, an operation completed before the stigma is receptive; under controlled conditions, with sterilized brushes for transferring pollen, and in an insect-free environment, crosses can be guaranteed.

Fortunately the female parent plant (*C. graecum*) is still alive. This in itself is interesting as the plant in question is unusual in its small leaves and rather short flowers and I hope that both this and the hybrid will shortly be examined cytologically, for it would be most interesting to learn something of the chromosome profile of this improbable hybrid.

It is fair to say that this is not a particularly attractive hybrid, inheriting none of the grace or charm of either parent species.

Cyclamen x marxii Halda

A name applied by Josef Halda to hybrids between *C. purpurascens* and *C. fatrense*. However as the latter is not generally recognised the hybrid is of no standing.

UNNAMED HYBRIDS

These are plants whose origins are somewhat uncertain and whose supposed parentage has yet to be adequately confirmed.

C. balearicum x C. creticum

Such hybrids undoubtedly exist in cultivated collections, for the species of the *C. repandum* group are known to cross freely with one another. Unfortunately, I have not been able to authenticate any specimens sent to me as unquestionable hybrids of this cross, so I am unable at the present time to draw up a description and to give it a formal name.

C. cilicium x C. intaminatum

These two species are closely related, indeed *C. intaminatum* was at one time regarded as a variety of *C. cilicium*. Both share the same chromosome number of 2n=30. In addition both species are native to southern Turkey although they do not appear to overlap in distribution, and there is no evidence that the two grow in close proximity to one another so that natural hybrids are unlikely to occur.

In cultivation the two species are distinctive in both leaf and flower, although the flower shape is similar and the majority of plants are unlikely to be confused. The small white (occasionally pink-flushed), unmarked flowers, with grey veins to the petals, characterize *C. intaminatum*, while *C. cilicium* has larger, normally pink, flowers, without grey veins but with an obvious dark blotch at the base of each petal. In recent years a number of plants have appeared in collections with *C. intaminatum*-like flowers but rather larger and pinker; they may represent hybrids between the two species but this is far from certain and requires further investigation.

Hybrids between different plants, especially different subspecies or varieties within species can produce extremely attractive plants. The promiscuity of the members of the *C. repandum* group has already been noted (see *C.* x *meiklei* and *C.* x *saundersii*) but hybrids between the subspecies of *C. repandum* have not been substantiated. In any collection of the species such hybrids are certain to occur. In many ways they are a nuisance because they blur the boundaries between what are fairly distinct subspecies. In the finest hybrids the best features of the parents are combined. Of those that I have seen to date the most attractive are hybrids between subsp. *peloponnesiacum* and subsp. *rhodense* in which the leaves are handsomely marked with silvery or cream splashes or dots (sometimes over a faint hastate pattern) and the white or pale pink flowers have a broad, deep pink zone around the mouth that suffuses the lower quarter to third of the petals. Any crosses in this group are likely to produce very variable offspring and they require careful selection, retaining only the very finest forms.

LABORATORY HYBRIDS

Today the spectre of wholly artificial hybrids raises moral issues in the animal world and to a lesser extent among plants. It is now possible artificially to induce hybrids between species that can never normally cross, either because of some incompatability mechanisim in the pollination biology, or because of their very different cytology. The fact that this can be overcome by gene manipulation means that it is possible, in theory at least, to produce hybrids between any chosen species, or indeed a mixture of different species. Although there have been failures along the way, there have been some notable successes amongst Dutch, German and Japanese breeders. To date the most notable hybrids (neither has been given a name yet) both involve *C. persicum*, first with *C. purpurascens* and secondly with *C. hederifolium*.

The method used is basically as follows: the selected plants are crossed, transferring pollen from one flower to another by the traditional method. Normally where the species involved are so incompatible nothing happens and no hybrid results. However, before the embryos abort they are artificially removed (rescued in the cytologist's jargon) and then cultured *in vitro*. In this very artifical and sterile environment the embryos develop and will eventually, given the right conditions of light, temperature and nutrients, develop small plantlets that can be weaned out and grown on. However, such plants have only a single set of chromosomes from each parent and, because of the gross discrepancy, will be 'mules', infertile plants incapable of producing fertile pollen or seed. For instance, the cross between *C. persicum* (2n=48) and *C. hederifolium* (2n=34) results in a hybrid with 41 chromosomes. Such plants are useless commercially and of only passing interest. But if the chromosomes can be doubled so that there are in effect two full sets from each parent, then the result will invariably be a fertile hybrid. This is accomplished by introducing the *in vitro* culture to colchicine (remarkable for its powers of doubling chromosomes).

The hybrid *C. persicum* x *C. purpurascens* was produced by the Institute for Vegetable and Ornamental Crops, Grossbeeren/Erfurt in Germany, and several pictures of hybrid plants appeared in the *Cyclamen Society Journal* in December 2000. These show rather squat plants with, dare one say, rather ungainly flowers with the colour of *C. purpurascens* (and apparently the scent!) but leaves and flower sizes intermediate between the parent species. The flowers have a rather narrow mouth without any sign of auricles. Some of the leaves are attractively zoned with silver; others are decidedly dull.

In contrast, the *C. hederifolium* x *C. persicum* cross (made by Sahin in Holland) is visually, at least, more exciting. The plants are larger with some very attractive leaf forms, mostly the general shape of *C. persicum*. The flowers are quite large with some showing a trace of auricles, derived from *C. hederifolium*, as well as some markings at the base of the corolla. Some of the plants are fragrant. The following notes have been provided by John Grimshaw (from the firm of Sahin): "In both the selected clones the plants grow and flower continuously in warm greenhouse conditions (over two years now!) They rapidly fill a new pot ... Some clones produce pollen and one is apparently self-fertile, having

196 Experimental hybrid, *C. hederifolium* x *C. persicum*, from Sahin in Holland.

produced a pod that is being watched with great interest .... [clone 112.3.3] Flowers proportionate and well-shaped, although the petals have a tendency to flop; fragrant like *C. hederifolium*. Petals 49 x 20mm (bluish) pale pink, stained deep magenta at mouth with the darker colour fading more or less evenly up the petals, but darkest along the veins. Mouth regular, 10mm across, auricles rudimentary ... This is a good-looking plant with pewtered foliage and flowers not unlike a large *C. hederifolium*. A plant in my parents' garden at Maidenhead has done quite well through the winter (planted in full growth and flowering in October 2001) and has continued to flower throughout the winter, although the midwinter flowers were frost-damaged." John Grimshaw also reports that another clone [112.3.10] is "an ugly, ill-formed thing (the corolla lobes do not fit into a decent mouth) and the uniformly dark green leaves are uninteresting."

Well, I am sure the reader will want to know just what the point of all this is, apart from an interesting exercize in genetics. One thing breeders are keen to acquire is a hardy, long-flowering cyclamen that would be ideal for containers and summer bedding. By crossing two species with disparate flowering times and hardiness it is hoped such a hybrid can be produced. Early results, especially with the latter cross, are encouraging. Now there is the real prospect of producing a whole new race of hardy cyclamen, to enhance gardens over many months. Some of the hybrids have proved to be far hardier than *C. persicum* and flower over many months, besides giving some resistance to diseases such as fusarium wilt, a real bane in the commercial production of *C. persicum* as a house plant.

Chapter Ten

Aberrations

Cyclamen, like many plants grown in gardens, produce the occasional abnormalities or sports. These can affect various parts of the plant but are most obvious when they affect the flowers. Abnormalities are only occasionally genetic (mutations) and their cause is arguable; they may be the result of physical damage or temperature regimes, or perhaps they may be influenced by pests or diseases. Whereas genetic mutations affect the whole plant and the character or characters are inherited, other (non-genetical) aberrations that often only affect part of the plant are not inherited. It can be irritating on occasions to note an interesting aberration such as doubling of the corolla only to discover that it is not a heritable characteristic; occasionally, as in the upward-facing flowers of *C. hederifolium* 'Stargazer', the character is inherited or partly inherited in the offspring. A fairly common aberration is drooping corollas in which the petals point downwards and do not reflex, or do so only partly. All these aberrations are freaks and as such have generally little influnce on the species or its genetical

197 Sporting in cyclamen is quite rare but does happen in some old cultivars of *C. persicum*; here a chimera has produced a pink flower as well as a part-pink flower on an otherwise white-flowered plant.

evolution. In nature most have a much reduced competitive edge and soon disappear. Of course, variants and freaks are of great interest to gardeners and horticulturists and many can be maintained for long periods in cultivation. Indeed many of the bizarre forms of *Cyclamen persicum* noted in this book, such as striated or bearded petals, enlarged and petal-like sepals and so on, are of this kind.

TYPES OF GENETIC MUTATIONS – generally affect the whole plant

Such characteristics may not be inherited in the first generation but may reappear to some extent in succeeding generations. Genetic mutations are best known in *C. persicum* where a great deal of breeding and hybridization within the species has taken place in the past 150 years. Unattractive mutations are best destroyed unless they are kept for their curiousity value, but while they live there is always the possibility that they may 'infect' succeeding generations of otherwise normal plants with their undesirable genes.

Double flowers

This term is generally applied to the doubling of the corolla. Flowers with more than the normal 5 petals are rare. Cultivated forms of *C. persicum* with 10 petals are known in Holland and elsewhere. The extra 5 petals are in place of the stamens and such plants are usually sterile or at least they are male-sterile. In some instances not all the stamens are replaced by additional petals so that the flowers may be capable of producing a reduced quantity of pollen. Twinning also occurs in which two separate flowers are fused partly or wholly together. In extreme cases they form Siamese twins with the pedicels fused for all the length and the two flowers fused along one side by calyx and corolla.

Enlargement of the calyx

This again is rare but is known to occur in *C. persicum*. In Holland today there is an extraordinary series of plants (see Whirlygig Series, p.182) in which the calyx-lobes are expanded to half the length of the petals and are coloured and petal-like. The expanded calyx lobes can be the same colour as the petals or a contrasting colour,

198 Doubling of the corolla (hose in hose) can happen in *C. persicum* cultivars, but here it is seen in *C. coum* subsp. *coum*; the stamens are generally replaced by extra petals.

which can give a very bizarre effect. Occasional enlargement of one or more of the calyx-lobes is occasionally observed in other species but is rarely an inherited characteristic.

Chimeras

Where the tissue of two different plants becomes partly absorbed into one another chimeras may result giving rise to striping or variegation of the leaves or flowers, although not all variegations are caused in this way. In cyclamen the chimeras manifest themselves in striping of the petals (as seen in the cultivar 'Harlequin' or 'Striata', p.184). The stripes are often uneven and do not necessarily affect each petal, or even flowers on the same plant, in a similar way. For instance, in extreme forms one petal may be all pink and another all white, with the remainder with varying amounts of pink striping.

Sporting

Essentially rather similar to the preceding. Sporting is well known in certain widely-grown flowers such as roses and chrysanthemums where the ordinary colour form for a particular cultivar may 'throw' a shoot with flowers of a different colour. These can often be propagated to maintain the sport. In cyclamen-flower sporting is quite rare and unfortunately they cannot be propagated, although several *C. persicum* cultivars frequently 'throw' flower sports.

Petal orientation

This can be an attractive feature. In most cyclamen the corolla-lobes are strongly reflexed into a vertical position. Occasionally seedlings appear in which the petals spread out horizontally or indeed point downwards and do not reflex at all. This character can sometimes be inherited, if not in the first generation, then in subsequent ones.

Cut petals

Seldom seen except in some cultivars of *C. persicum*, the cut or fringed petals can be an attractive feature. The only plant that I know with cut (laciniate) petals is a single plant of *C. africanum* grown by Jill White at Brightlingsea in Essex. This plant also has somewhat cut leaves. Unfortunately, this lone plant has never set seed so I am unsure whether or not this characteristic will be inherited.

Uniting of the petals

This sometimes happens in a great range of different plants but is very rare in cyclamen, although it has on several occasions been reported in the *Journal of the Cyclamen Society*. The corolla is more or less tubular in such flowers, and the petals, because they are fused together, are unable to reflex.

Bearding of petals

In some cultivars of *C. persicum* the petals are bearded or crested on the middle of the inner surface (outer when the petals are reflexed in the fully open flower). The bearding is due to an outgrowth of cells from the wall of the petal, forming a series of uneven ridges. The beard can be the same colour as the rest of the petal but it is often paler or whitish, and thus quite conspicuous. Today bearded or crested flowers of this type have only a curiousity value but in late Victorian times they proved to be a popular novelty.

Feathering

Such a term applies to petals in which the deep colouring at the base feathers out in some or all the petals in a suffusion of deeper veins. This can be found in many species and cultivars. It is again quite common in *C. persicum* cultivars but also in some forms of *C. graecum* and *C. hederifolium* ('Ruby Glow', for instance). This can be inherited in some of the offspring. On the Continent plant breeders have produced pure lines of *C. persicum* with this attractive feature, the most notable being the Pastel Series, p.181.

Small blooms

Plants with unusually small blooms are sometimes found in batches of seedlings. They can occur in any species but I have noticed them to be particularly prevalent in the *C. repandum* group where plants with flowers half the normal size can be seen on occasions. This should not be confused with plants in which the flowers habitually open small but after a day or so assume their correct proportions. Exploitation of this characteristic has led to some of the mini-flowered forms of *C. persicum* available on the market today. *C. graecum* and *C. hederifolium* are also prone to produce the occasional seedling with exceptionally small flowers, although they are also capable of doing the reverse and producing extra-large blooms.

TYPES OF NON-GENETIC MUTATIONS –
often affect only part of the plant

Malformed leaves

These are not uncommon. Leaves may sometimes be puckered or distorted, or one half may grow larger than the other. Such malformations are generally caused by physical damage (such as treading on the tuber as growth commences) or by insects; aphids may cause puckering in young leaves which then become more pronounced malformations as the leaves mature.

Malformed flowers

Essentially the same as the previous category. Malformed leaves and flowers can be removed if desired by pulling them gently away from the tuber; ensure that the stalks come cleanly away from the base, otherwise they may invite fungus infection.

Twinning of flowers or leaves

Flowers may be partly or wholly fused together like Siamese twins. This happens in many plants and is generally a one-off (not affecting other flowers on the same plant). Sometimes more than two flowers on an otherwise normal-flowered plant may become wholly or partly united. The same can happen with the leaves.

Fusion of flowers and leaves

Flower and leaf stalks may be partly or wholly fused. Sometimes several leaves are fused by their petioles resulting in a thickened stem-like structure with a flower arising from the top.

Fasciation

A general term which encompasses many of the above categories. In extreme examples a number of leaves and flowers are borne on a flattened ribbon-like stem which can be extremely unsightly. Such fasciations can be removed with care and are unlikely to reappear on the same plant. It is unclear what causes such disorders but physical damage resulting from temperature imbalance or bruising, or even chemical damage, cannot be ruled out.

Extra petals

Blooms occasionally exhibit more than the usual number of 5 petals; 6 or 7 petals are sometimes seen in *C. persicum* and are not an uncommon sight in *C. libanoticum* in particular, often affecting the first blooms to open. Occasionally blooms may have only 4 petals. Extra petals are sometimes accompanied by extra sepals or extra stamens, but not invariably so.

Dumpy blooms

Plants with some flowers shorter and broader than normal are seen from time to time. Such blooms are not particularly attractive and generally lose the poise and elegance of normal blooms.

Virus infection

Viruses appear to be rare in cyclamen. Distortion of the foliage may be caused by a virus (or insects, see above) but more obvious signs are the uneven streaking of the foliage and/or the flowers. Plants suspected of virus infection should be destroyed, otherwise the infection may spread to other plants.

Chapter Eleven

A-Z
of scientific names of Cyclamen and new combinations

A complete A-Z list of *Cyclamen* names is presented below. On the left all accepted names are in **bold** non-italics, synonyms are in *italics*. All synonyms have an indication as to which accepted species they belong to, although a number remain in doubt as there is insufficient information to make a valid judgement. All authors and references are abbreviated according to internationally accepted formulae which allow for ready access to information as well as saving a good deal of space.

Cyclamen abchasicum (Medw. ex Kusn.) Kolak. in Fl. Abkhazya 3: 274 (1948) = *C. coum* subsp. *caucasicum*.

Cyclamen adzharicum Poped. in Bot. Mater. Gerb. Glavn. Bot. Sada SSR 13: 189 (1950) = *C. coum* subsp. *caucasicum*.

Cyclamen aedirhizum Jord. in Jord. & Fourr., Ic. Fl. Eur. 3: 21 (1903). Type: Ic. Fl. Eur. pl. CCCCXVIII = *C. hederifolium* var. *hederifolium*.

Cyclamen aegineticum Hildebr. in Gartenflora 57: 296 (1908). Type: Greece, Aegina, cultivated at Freiburg, Hildebrand = *C. graecum* subsp. *graecum*.

Cyclamen aestivum Rchb., Fl. Germ. Excurs. 1: 407 (1830) = *C. purpurascens*.

Cyclamen africanum Boiss. & Reut., Pugill. Pl. Afr. Bot. HispaÒ.: 75 (1852). Type: N Africa, Algeria.

Cyclamen albidum Jord. in Jord. & Fourr., Ic. Fl. Eur. 3: 23 (1903). Type: Ic. Fl Eur. pl. CCCCXXV = *C. persicum* var. *persicum* forma *albidum*.

Cyclamen albiflorum Jord. in Jord. & Fourr., Ic. Fl. Eur. 3: 20 (1903). Type: Ic. Fl Eur. pl. CCCCXVII = *C. hederifolium* var. *hederifolium*.

Cyclamen aleppicum Fish. ex Hoffmanns., Verz. Pfl.-Kult.: 54 (1824) = *C. persicum* var. *persicum*.

Cyclamen aleppicum Hoffmanns. subsp. *puniceum* Glasau in Planta 30: 545 (1939) = *C. persicum* var. *persiceum* forma *puniceum*.

Cyclamen algeriense Jord. in Jord. & Fourr., Ic. Fl. Eur. 3: 22 (1903). Type: Ic. Fl Eur. pl. CCCXXII = *C. africanum*.

Cyclamen alpinum hort. Dammann ex Sprenger in Gartenflora 41: 526 (1892). Described from cultivated material from Dammann & Co. in Germany in the 1890s and later, in 1898, fully described by Hildebrand from material supplied by the same company; all material subsequently lost. Lectoype: Hildebrand, *Die Gattung Cyclamen* (1898), Taf (Pl) 111, figs 45–63.

Cyclamen alpinum sensu Turrill in Curtis's Bot. Mag. 174: t. 437 (1963) = *C. intaminatum*.

Cyclamen alpinum var. *album* hort. Dammann ex Sprenger in Gartenflora 41: 546 (1892). Type: not known = *Cyclamen alpinum* forma *leucanthum*.

Cyclamen alpinum hort. Dammann ex Sprenger forma leucanthum (Grey-Wilson) Grey-Wilson, Cyclamen: 175 (1997). Type: from material cultivated by Rod Leeds, near Lavenham, Suffolk (holotype, K), see p.207.

Cyclamen ambiguum O. Schwarz in Feddes Repert. Spec. Nov. Regni Veg. 58: 275 (1955). Type: as for *C. numidicum* = *C. africanum*.

Cyclamen angulare Jord. in Jord. & Fourr., Ic. Fl. Eur. 3: 19 (1903). Type: Ic. Fl Eur. pl. CCCCXIII = *C. hederifolium*.

Cyclamen antilochium Decne in Rev. Hortic. ser. 4, 5: 23 (1855) = *C. persicum* var. *persicum*.

Cyclamen apiculatum Jord. in Jord. & Fourr., Ic. Fl. Eur. 3: 15, t. 402 (1903). Type: Ic. Fl Eur. pl. CCCCII = *C. coum* subsp. *coum*.

Cyclamen atkinsii Glasau in Planta 30: 516 (1939), non T. Moore = *C. coum* subsp. *coum*.

Cyclamen atkinsii hort. = *C. coum* subsp. *caucasicum*.

Cyclamen x atkinsii T. Moore in A Henfrey *et al.*, Gard. Compan. Florist's Guide 1:89 (1852).

Cyclamen autumnale Boos, Schönbrunnís Fl.: 45 (1816) = name of uncertain affinity.

Cyclamen barborense Batt. in Marie, Herbier de l'Afrique du Nord [in sched.], without date.

Cyclamen balearicum Willk. in Oesterr. Bot. Z. 25: 111 (1875). Type: Majorca, Cambessedes (MPU).

Cyclamen breviflorum Jord. in Jord. & Fourr., Ic. Fl. Eur. 3: 18 (1903). Type: Ic. Fl Eur. pl. = *C. purpurascens*.

Cyclamen brevifrons Jord. in Jord. & Fourr., Ic. Fl. Eur. 3: 15, t. 401 (1903). Type: Ic. Fl Eur. pl. CCCCII = *C. coum* subsp. *coum*.

Cyclamen calcareum Kolak. in Izv. Glavn. Bot. Sada SSSR 3: 83 (1949) = *C. coum* subsp. *caucasicum*.

Cyclamen caucasicum Willd. ex Boiss., Fl. Orient. 4: 11 (1875) = *C. coum* subsp. *caucasicum*.

Cyclamen caucasicum Willd. ex Steven, Bull. in Soc. Imp. Naturaliste Moscou 30: 327 (1857) = *C. coum* subsp. *caucasicum.*

Cyclamen cilicicum Boiss. & Heldr. in Boiss., Diagn. ser. 1, 11: 78 (1843). Type: Turkey, Cilicia, 'in fissuris rupium umbrosarum faucis Gulek Boghas (Pylae Ciliciae)', Heldreich (isotype K).

Cyclamen cilicicum Boiss. & Heldr. forma album E. Frank & Koenen in R. Frank & E. Frank in Bull. Alp. Gard. Soc. Gr. Brit. 51: 150 (1983). Type: Turkey, S Anatolia, Toros Daglari, Murtici-Akseki, 1200 m, Oct. 1982 (holotype K).

Cyclamen cilicicum Boiss. & Heldr. var. *intaminatum* Meikle in Notes Roy. Bot. Gard. Edinburgh 36: 2 (1978); Meikle in Davis, Fl. Turkey 6: 130 (1978). Type: Turkey, Eskisehir, 53km from Kutahya to Cukurhisar, 1000 m, Oct. 1975, T. Baytop ISTE 33888 (holotype K, isotype ISTE) = *C. intaminatum.*

Cyclamen cilicicum Boiss. & Heldr. var. [sic] Turill in Curtis's Bot. Mag. 171: t. 307 (1957) = *C. intaminatum.*

Cyclamen cilicicum Hildebr., Gattung Cyclamen: 36 (1898), name of uncertain affinity.

Cyclamen circassicum Poped. in Bot. Zhurn. (Moscow & Leningrad) 33: 226 (1948) = *C. coum* subsp. *caucasicum.*

Cyclamen clusii Lindl., Bot. Reg. 12: t. 1013 (1826). Type: Hort. Florence, as t. 1013 = *C. purpurascens.*

Cyclamen colchicum (Albov) Albov in Wien Ill. Gart.-Zeitung 23: 7 (1898).

Cyclamen commutatum O.Schwarz & Lepper in Feddes Repert. Spec. Nov. Regni Veg. 69: 91 (1964). Type: Hortus Botanicus Jenensis, Lepper = *C. africanum.*

Cyclamen cordifolium Stokes, Bot. Mat. Med. 1: 295 (1812), name of uncertain affinity.

Cyclamen coum Mill., Gard. Dict. ed. 8, n. 6 (1768). Type: described from material cultivated at the Chelsea Physic Garden (holotype BM).

Cyclamen coum sensu Rchb., Fl. Germ. Excurs. 1: 406 (1830), non Mill., name of uncertain affinity.

Cyclamen coum Mill. subsp. *alpinum* (Sprenger) O.Schwarz in Feddes Repert. Spec. Nov. Regni Veg. 58: 250 (1955) = *C. intaminatum.*

Cyclamen coum Mill. subsp. caucasicum (K. Koch) O. Schwarz in Feddes Repert. Spec. Nov. Regni Veg. 58: 250 (1955).

Cyclamen coum Mill. subsp. coum forma albissimum R. H. Bailey, Koenen, Lillywh. & P. J. M.Moore in Cyclamen Soc. Journ. 13(1): 27 (1989). Type: Turkey, Hatay, between Topbogazi and Belen, M. Koenen, 20.3. 1980, cult. P.J.M. Moore (holotype K).

Cyclamen coum Mill. subsp. coum forma pallidum Grey-Wilson, Cyclamen: 174 (1997). Type: from material cultivated near Sudbury, Suffolk, 1995, C. Grey-Wilson (hototypus, K).

Cyclamen coum Mill. subsp. *elegans* (Boiss. & Buhse) Grey-Wilson, Cyclamen: 174 = *C. elegans.*

Cyclamen coum Mill. subsp. *hiemale* (Hildebr.) O.Schwarz in Feddes Repert. Spec. Nov. Regni Veg. 58: 249 (1955) = *C. coum* subsp. *coum.*

Cyclamen coum Mill. var. abchasicum Medw. ex Kusn. in Fl. Cauc. Crit. [?Mat. Fl. Cauc.] 4(1): 167 (1902) [There is some uncertainty as to whether this should be Medw. in or ex Kusn., as Schwarz (1955) gives it as Medw in Kusn, and Popedimova (1952) takes up Medw. instead of Kusn. Reference not seen] = *C. coum* subsp. *caucasicum.*

Cyclamen coum Mill. var. *caucasicum* (K.Koch) Meikle in Davis, Fl. Turkey 6: 133 (1978) = *C. coum* subsp. *caucasicum.*

Cyclamen coum Mill. var. *ibericum* Boiss., Fl. Orient. 4: 11 (1879) = *C. coum* subsp. *caucasicum.*

Cyclamen crassifolium Hildebr. in Beih. Bot. Centralbl. 22(2): 195, t. 6 (1907) = *C. hederifolium* subsp. *confusum.*

Cyclamen creticum (Dörfl.) Hildebr. in Beih. Bot. Centralbl. 19(2): 367 (1906). Type: cult. Freiburg, Hildebrand.

Cyclamen creticum (Dörfl.) Hildebr. forma pallideroseum Grey-Wilson, Cyclamen; 174 (1997).

Cyclamen cyclaminus Bedevian, Illustr. Polyglot. Dict.: 218 (1936) = *C. hederifolium* var. *hederifolium.*

Cyclamen cyclophyllum Jord. in Jord. & Fourr., Ic. Fl. Eur. 3: 18 (1903). Type: Ic. Fl Eur. pl. CCCCX = *C. purpurascens.*

Cyclamen cyprium Glasau in Planta 30: 537 (1939), non Kotschy = ?*C. graecum* subsp. *anatolicum*

Cyclamen cyprium Kotschy in Unger & Kotschy, Die Insel Cypern: 295 (1865). Type: Cyprus, cult. in Vienna from tubers collected near Galata in 1862, Kotschy (holotype W).

Cyclamen cyprium Sibth. in Walpole, Travels: 25 (1820) = *C. persicum* subsp. *persicum.*

Cyclamen cypro-graecum E. Mutch & N. Mutch in Bull. Alpine Gard. Soc. Gr. Brit. 23: 164 (1954), nomen illegit = *C. graecum* subsp. *anatolicum.*

Cyclamen deltoideum Tausch in Flora 12(2): 667 (1829) = *C. purpurascens.*

Cyclamen X drydeniae Grey-Wilson, Cyclamen: 174 (1997), as "*drydenii*". Type: Cult. Suffolk, 1995, C. Grey-Wilson (holotypus, K).

Cyclamen durostoricum Pantu & Solacolu in Bull. Sect. Sci. Acad. Roumaine. 9: 23 (1924) = *C. coum* subsp. *coum.*

***Cyclamen elegans* Boiss. & Buhse** in Nouv. Mém. Soc. Imp. Naturalistes Moscou 12: 145 (1860).

Cyclamen eucardium Jord. in Jord. & Fourr., Ic. Fl. Eur.

3: 16 (1903). Type: Ic. Fl Eur. pl. CCCCV = *C. peloponnesiacum* subsp. *vividum*.

Cyclamen europaeum L., Sp. Pl. 1: 145 (1753), pro parte = *C. hederifolium*, *C. purpurascens* and *C. repandum* subsp. *repandum*.

Cyclamen europaeum L. subsp. *orbiculatum* O. Schwarz in Gartenflora n.s., 1: 16 (1938), non orbiculatum Mill. = *C. purpurasecns*.

Cyclamen europaeum L. subsp. *orbiculatum* (Mill.) O. Schwarz var. *immaculatum* Hrabetova in Ceskoslov. Bot. Listy 3: 35 (1950) = *C. purpurascens*.

Cyclamen europaeum L. var. *typicum* Albov in Bull. Herb. Boiss. 2: 254 (1894) = *C. purpurascens*.

Cyclamen europaeum L. var. *ponticum* Albov in Bull. Herb. Boiss. 2: 254 (1894) = *C. colchicum*.

Cyclamen europaeum L. subsp. *orbiculatum* (Mill.) O. Schwarz var. *immaculatum* Hrabetova in Ceskoslov. Bot. Listy 3: 35 (1950) = *C. purpurascens*.

Cyclamen europaeum L. subsp. *ponticum* (Albov) O. Schwarz in Gartenflora n.s., 1: 16 (1938) = *C. colchicum*.

Cyclamen europaeum L. var. *caucasicum* K.Koch in Linnaea 23: 619 (1849) = *C. coum* subsp. *caucasicum*.

Cyclamen europaeum L. var. *colchicum* Albov in Trudy Tbilissk. Bot. Sada. 1: 166 (1895) = *C. colchicum*.

Cyclamen europaeum L. var. *ponticum* Albov in Bull. Herb. Boiss. 2: 254 (1854). Type: CIS Abchasia, Okum, c. 300 m, N. Alboff s.n., 1892–3 (G) = *C. colchicum*.

Cyclamen europaeum Pall. in Nova Acta Acad. Sci. Imp. Petrop. Hist. Acad. 10: 306 (1796) = *C. coum* subsp. *coum*.

Cyclamen europaeum Savi, Fl. Pis. 1: 213 (1798). Type: Italy, Pisa = *C. purpurascens*.

Cyclamen europaeum sensu Aiton, Hort. Kew. ed. 1, 196 (1789) = *C. purpurascens*.

Cyclamen europaeum sensu Albov in Bull. Herb. Boissier 2: 254 (1894) = *C. colchicum*.

Cyclamen europaeum sensu Mill., Gard. Dict. no 1. (1768), *nomen confusum*.

Cyclamen europaeum Sm. in Engl., Bot. t. 548 [reference not found, as listed in Index Kewensis], name of uncertain affinity.

Cyclamen fatrense Halda & Soják in Cas. Nár. Muz. Odd. Prír. 140(1–2): 64 (1971). Type: Slovakia, Velkafatra, 550 m, July 1971, Halda & Sojak s.n. (holotype PR) = *C. purpurascens*.

Cyclamen ficariifolium Rchb., Fl. Germ. Excurs. 1: 407 (1830) = *C. repandum* subsp. *repandum*.

Cyclamen floridum Salisb., Prodr. stirp. Chap. Allerton: 119 (1796) = *C. purpurascens*.

Cyclamen gaidurowryssii Glasau in Planta 31: 539 (1939) = *C. graecum* subsp. *graecum*.

Cyclamen gaydurowryssii (authographic variant) Glasau

in Planta 31: 539 (1939) = *C. graecum* subsp. *graecum*.

Cyclamen graecum Link in Linnaea 9: 573 (1834). Type: Greece, Naplion, 'Ad rupes circa Naupliam frequens flore-bat Septembri', Berger (B, destroyed; M).

Cyclamen graecum Link subsp. anatolicum Ietsw. in Cyclamen Soc. Journ. 14(2): 51 (1990). Type: Turkey, Antalya Province, c. 3km W of Kemer, c. 100 m, Oct 1988, Ietswaart 1167 (holotype L).

Cyclamen graecum Link subsp. candicum Ietsw. in Cyclamen Soc. Journ. 14(2): 50 (1990). Type: Crete, between Pervolitza and Rhizokloko, c. 80 m alt., Nov 1987, Ietswaart 1031 (holotype L).

Cyclamen graecum Link subsp. graecum forma album R. Frank & E. Frank in Bull. Alp. Gard. Soc. Gr. Brit. 50(3): 251 (photo. on p. 250) (1982). Type: Greece, S Peloponnese, Gythio-Kastania, Oct 1980 (holotype K).

Cyclamen graecum Link subsp. *mindleri* (Heldr.) A.P. Davis & Govaerts = *C. graecum* subsp. *graecum*.

Cyclamen hastatum Tausch in Flora 12: 668 (1829) = *C. purpurascens*.

Cyclamen hederaceum Sieber ex Steud., Nomencl. Bot. ed. 2, 1: 458 (1821) = *C. persicum* var. *persicum*.

Cyclamen hederaefolium Sibth. & Sm., Fl. Graec. Prod. 1: 128 (1813) = *C. hederifolium* var. *hederifolium*.

Cyclamen hederaefolium Sims in Bot. Mag. 25: t. 1001 (1807) = *C. repandum* subsp. *repandum*.

Cyclamen hederaefolium Willd., Sp. Pl. 1(2): 810 (1798) = name of uncertain affinity.

Cyclamen hederifolium Aiton, Hort. Kew. ed. 1, 196 (1789). Type: described from cultivated material; probably best typified by the plate in Gerard's *Herball* 694, f. 2, '*Cyclamen folio hederae*' (1597).

Cyclamen hederifolium Kotschy in Unger & Kotschy, Ins. Cypern: 295 (1865) = *C. persicum* var. *persicum*.

Cyclamen hederifolium Aiton subsp. *balearicum* O. Schwarz in Gartenflora n.s., 1: 22 (1938) = *C. balearicum*.

Cyclamen hederifolium Aiton subsp. confusum (Grey-Wilson) Grey-Wilson, see p.207.

Cyclamen hederifolium Aiton subsp. *creticum* (Dörfl.) O. Schwarz in Gartenflora n.s., 1: 22 (1938) = *C. creticum*.

Cyclamen hederifolium Aiton subsp. *romanum* (Griseb.) O. Schwarz in Gartenflora n.s., 1: 22 (1938) = *C. hederifoilum* var. *hederifolium*.

Cyclamen hederifolium Aiton var. *confusum* Grey-Wilson, Cyclamen: 174 (1997) = *C. hederifolium* subsp. *confusum*. Type: W Crete, Platanos to Polyrinia (S of Kissamos), *Grey-Wilson* s.n. (holotypus, K).

Cyclamen hederifolium Aiton var. hederifolium forma albiflorum (Jord.) Grey-Wilson, Cyclamen: 174 (1997). Type: Ic. Fl. Eur., Pl. CCCCXVII.

Cyclamen hiemale Hildebr. in Gartenflora 53: 70 (1904) = *C. coum* subsp. *coum*.

Cyclamen ×hildebrandii O. Schwarz in Feddes Repert. Spec. Nov. Regni. Veg. 58: 280 (1955).

Cyclamen holochlorum Jord. in Jord. & Fourr., Ic. Fl. Eur. 3: 19 (1903) = *C. purpurascens*.

Cyclamen hyemale Salisb., Prodr. stirp. Chap. Allerton: 118 (1796) = *C. coum* subsp. *coum*.

Cyclamen ibericum Goldie ex G.Don in Sweet, Hort. Brit. ed. 3: 560 (1839) = *C. coum* subsp. *caucasicum*.

Cyclamen ibericum Lem., Jard. Fleur. 3: t. 297 (1853), excl. descr., non Goldie = *C. coum* subsp. *caucasicum*.

Cyclamen ibericum Steven ex Boiss., Fl. Orient. 4: 11 (1875) = *C. coum* subsp. *caucasicum*.

Cyclamen ibericum T. Moore in A. Henfrey *et al.*, Garden Companion Florists' Guide 1: 90, f. 2 (1852) = *C. coum* subsp. *caucasicum*.

Cyclamen ilicetorum Jord. in Jord. & Fourr., Ic. Fl. Eur. 3: 20 (1903). Type: Ic. Fl Eur. pl. CCCCVII = *C. repandum* subsp. *repandum*.

Cyclamen immaculatum Pieri in Ionios Anthol. 5: 192 (c.1835), name of uncertain affinity.

Cyclamen indicum L., Sp. Pl.: 145 (1753), *nomen confusum*.

Cyclamen insulare Jord. in Jord. & Fourr., Ic. Fl. Eur. 3: 20 (1903). Type: Ic. Fl Eur. pl. CCCCXVI = *C. hederifolium* var. *hederifolium*.

Cyclamen intaminatum (Meikle) Grey-Wilson, The Genus Cyclamen: 71 (1988).

Cyclamen intermedium Wender., Ind. Sem. Hort. Marb.: [page number not known] (1825) = name of uncertain affinity.

Cyclamen jovis Hildebr. in Gartenflora 57: 294 (1908), name of uncertain affinity.

Cyclamen kusnetzovii Kotov & Czernova in Fl. RSS Ucr. 8: 521 (1958) = *C. coum* subsp. *coum*.

Cyclamen latifolium Sm. in Sibth. & Sm., Fl. Graec. 2: 71, t. 185 (1813) = *C. persicum* var. *persicum*.

Cyclamen libanoticum Hildebr. in Engl. Bot. Jahrb. 25: 477 (1898). Type: Lebanon, 64km NE Beirut, 800–1400 m, Dec 1895, E. Hartman; described from cultivated material at Freiburg, Hildebrand.

Cyclamen libanoticum Hildebr. subsp. *pseudibericum* (Hildebr.) Glasau in Planta 30: 523 (1939) = *C. pseudibericum*.

Cyclamen lilacinum Jord. in Jord. & Fourr., Ic. Fl. Eur. 3: 19 (1903). Type: Ic. Fl Eur. pl. CCCCXII = *C. purpurascens*.

Cyclamen linaerifolium DC., Fl. Fr. 3: 433 (1805) = *C. hederifoium* var. *hederifolium*.

Cyclamen littorale Sadler ex Rchb., Fl. Germ. Excurs. 1: 406 (1830) = *C. purpurascens*.

Cyclamen lobospilum Jord. in Jord. & Fourr., Ic. Fl. Eur. 3: 17 (1903). Type: Ic. Fl Eur. pl. CCCCVI = *C. repandum* subsp. *repandum*.

Cyclamen macrophyllum Sieber in Isis: 259 (1823), name of uncertain affinity.

Cyclamen macropus Zucc., Del. Sem. Hort. Monac.: 4 (1846), name of uncertain affinity.

Cyclamen maritimum Hildebr. in Gartenflora 57: 293 (1908). Type: not traced but almost certainly described from material cultivated at Freiburg, Hildebrand = *C. graecum* subsp. *anatolicum*.

Cyclamen × marxii Halda in Skalničky 1973(10: 28 (1973).

Cyclamen × meiklei Grey-Wilson, Cyclamen: 174 (1997). Type: from material cultivated by R.D. Meikle near Minehead, Somerset (Holotype K).

Cyclamen miliarakesii Heldr. ex Halácsy, Consp. Fl. Graec. 3: 9 (1904). Type: Heldreich Herb. n. 1575 = *C. graecum* subsp. *graecum*.

Cyclamen miliarakesii Heldr. ex Hildebr. in Gartenflora 55: 634 (1906) = *C. graecum* subsp. *graecum*.

Cyclamen mindleri Heldr. in Bull. Herb. Boiss 6: 386 (1898). Type: from Aigina (island S of Athens), Mindler (P) = *C. graecum* subsp. *graecum*.

Cyclamen mirabile Hildebr. in Beih. Bot. Centralbl. 19(2): 370 (1906). Type: described from cultivated material thought to have come from the neighbourhood of Izmir, Turkey (B, destroyed).

Cyclamen mirabile Hildebr. forma niveum Grey-Wilson & J. White, Cyclamen: 174 (1997). Type: SW Turkey, photo taken between Yatagan and Çine, 330 m, 13 Oct 1993, Colin White (holotypus, K).

Cyclamen neapolitanum sensu Boiss., Fl. Orient. 4: 13 (1875) = *C. cyprium*.

Cyclamen neapolitanum sensu Duby in DC., Prodr. 8: 57 (1844) = *C. africanum*.

Cyclamen neapolitanum Ten., Prodr. Fl. Nap. suppl. 2: 66 (1813) = *C. hederifolium* var. *hederifolium*.

Cyclamen numidicum Glasau in Planta 30: 528 (1939) = *C. africanum*.

Cyclamen officinale Wender. ex Steud., Nomencl. Bot. ed. 2, 1: 458 (1841), name of uncertain affinity.

Cyclamen orbiculatum Mill., Gard. Dict. ed. 8, n. 5 (1768) = *C. coum* subsp. *coum*.

Cyclamen orbiculatum Mill. var. *alpinum* Saunders in Bull. Alpine Gard. Soc. Gr. Brit. 27: 49 (1959) = *C. alpinum* hort. Dammann ex Spremger.

Cyclamen orbiculatum Mill. var. *coum* (Mill.) Door. in Meded., Landbouwhogeschool 50: 25 (1950) = *C. coum* subsp. *coum*.

Cyclamen pachylobum Jord. in Jord. & Fourr., Ic. Fl. Eur. 3: 22 (1903). Type: Ic. Fl Eur. pl. CCCCXXI = *C. africanum*.

Cyclamen parviflorum Poped. in Bot. Mater. Gerb. Bot. Inst. Komarova Akad. Nauk SSSR 9: 250 (1946). Type: Turkey, Artvin (L).

Cyclamen parviflorum Poped. subsp. subalpinum (Grey-Wilson) Grey-Wilson, Cyclamen: 174 (1997). Type: from material cultivated at Brightlingsea, Essex, 1995 by Jill White (holotypus, K), see p. 207.

Cyclamen peloponnesiacum (Grey-Wilson) Kit Tan in Endemic Plants of Greece – the Peloponnese: 238 (2001).

Cyclamen peloponnesiacum (Grey-Wilson) Kit Tan subsp. peloponnesiacum in Endemic Plants of Greece – the Peloponnese: 238 (2001). Type: Greece, Peloponnese, Taigetos Mts, Langada gorge, W of Sparta, April 1987, *Grey-Wilson s.n.* (holotype, K).

Cyclamen peloponnesiacum (Grey-Wilson) Kit Tan subsp. vividum (Grey-Wilson) Kit Tan in Endemic Plants of Greece – the Peloponnese: 239 (2001). Type: Greece, Peloponnese, Mt Parnon, SW of Kosmas, c. 700 m, April 1987, *Grey-Wilson s.n.* (holotypus, K).

Cyclamen peloponnesiacum (Grey-Wilson) Kit Tan subsp. rhodense (Meikle) Kit Tan in Endemic Plants of Greece – the Peloponnese: 239 (2001).

Cyclamen peloponnesiacum (Grey-Wilson) Kit Tan subsp. peloponnesiacum forma albiflorum (B. Mathew) Grey-Wilson comb. nov. *C. repandum* Sm. subsp. *peloponnesiacum* Grey-Wilson var. *peloponnesiacum* forma *albiflorum* B. Mathew in *Journ. Cyclamen Soc.* 23: 51 (1999). Type: Greece, Peloponnese, Mani Peninsula, S of Gythio, 21 April 1002, *Cyclamen Society no.* 92/258 (holotype K), see p. 207.

Cyclamen pentelici Hildebr. in Bot. Jahrb. 18: n. 44 (1894) = *C. graecum* subsp. *graecum*.

Cyclamen persicum sensu Sibth. & Sm., Fl. Graec. Prod. 1: 128 (1813) = *C. graecum* subsp. *graecum*.

Cyclamen persicum Mill., Gard. Dict. ed. 8, n. 3 (1768). Type: Cultivated Chelsea Physic Garden (BM).

Cyclamen persicum Mill. subsp. *eupersicum* Knuth in Engl., Pflanzenr. 4, 237: 248 (1905) = *C. persicum* var. *persicum*.

Cyclamen persicum Mill. subsp. *mindleri* (Heldr.) Knuth, Pflanzenr. 4, 237: 248 (1905) = *C. graecum* subsp. *graecum*.

Cyclamen persicum Mill. var. autumnale Grey-Wilson, Cyclamen: 174 (1997).

Cyclamen persicum Mill. var. persicum forma albidum (Jord.) Grey-Wilson, Cyclamen: 174 (1997). Type: Ic. Pl. Eur., Pl. CCCCXXV.

Cyclamen persicum Mill. var. persicum forma puniceum (Glasau) Grey-Wilson, Cyclamen: 174 (1997): see *C. aleppicum* Hiffmanns subsp. *puniceum* Glasau.

Cyclamen persicum Mill. var. persicum forma roseum Grey-Wilson, nom. provis., Cyclamen: 112 (1997).

Cyclamen poli Chiaje, Opusc, Giorn. Med. Nap. 2, fasc 1: 11 (1824) = *C. hederifolium* var. *hederifolium*.

Cyclamen ponticum (Albov) Poped. in Bot. Zhurn (Moscow and Leningrad) 33: 223 (1948) = *C. colchicum*.

Cyclamen pseudibericum Hildebr. in Beih. Centralbl. Bot. 10: 522 (1901). Type: Turkey, described from material cultivated at Freiburg, Hildebrand.

Cyclamen pseudibericum Hildebr. forma roseum Grey-Wilson, Cyclamen: 174 (1997). Type: from material cultivated near Sudbury, Suffolk, 1995, by *C. Grey-Wilson* (holotypus, K).

Cyclamen pseudograecum Hildebr. in Gartenflora 60: 629 (1911). Type: not traced = *C. graecum* subsp. *candicum*.

Cyclamen pseudomaritimum Hildebr. in Gartenflora 57: 293 (1908). Type: cultivated at Freiburg from specimens sent from Mersina, Turkey, by Siehe, Hildebrand = *C. graecum* subsp. *anatolicum*.

Cyclamen punicum Pomel in Bull. Soc. Bot. France 36: 356 (1889) = *C. persicum* var. *persicum*.

Cyclamen purpurascens Mill., Gard. Dict. ed. 8, n. 2 (1768). Type: specimens in the Burser and Clifford herbaria (BM, not lectotypified).

Cyclamen purpurascens Mill. forma album Grey-Wilson, Cyclamen: 174 (1997). Type: Cult, 1995 (holotypus, K).

Cyclamen purpurascens Mill. forma carmineolineatum Hendrikx in Saussurea Type: Photo: Manfred Koenen 1983; Eastern France, Haute-Savoie, between Geneva and Albertville, 1000m (3250ft).

Cyclamen purpurascens Mill. subsp. *immaculatum* (Hrabetova) Halda & Soják in Folia Geobot. Phytotax. 3(6): 322 (1971) = *C. purpurascens*.

Cyclamen purpurascens Mill. subsp. *ponticum* (Albov) Grey-Wilson, The Genus Cyclamen: 106 (1988) = *C. colchicum*.

Cyclamen pyrolaefolium Salisb., Prodr. stirp. Chap. Allerton: 119 (1796) = *C. persicum* var. *persicum*.

Cyclamen rarinaevum Jord. in Jord. & Fourr., Ic. Fl. Eur. 3: 17 (1903). Type: Ic. Fl Eur. pl. CCCCVIII = *C. repandum* subsp. *repandum*.

Cyclamen repandum sensu R.Knuth in Engl., Pflanzenr. 4, 237: 251 (1905) = *C. balearicum*.

Cyclamen repandum sensu Texidor, Nuev. Apunt. Fl. EspaÒ.: 23 (1872) = *C. balearicum*.

Cyclamen repandum Sm. in Sibth. & Sm., Fl. Graeca Prodr. 1: 128 (1806). Type: best regarded as an illustration in Sibth. & Sm., Fl. Graeca, t. 186 (1806).

Cyclamen repandum Sm. subsp. *balearicum* (Willk.) Malag., Las Subesp. y Variac. Geogr.: 13 (1973). [without basionym date] = *C. balearicum*.

Cyclamen repandum Sm. subsp. *peloponnesiacum* Grey-Wilson, The Genus Cyclamen: 60 (1988). Type: Greece, Peloponnese, Taigetos Mtns, Langada Gorge, W of Sparta, April 1987, Grey-Wilson s.n. (holotypus K) = *C. peloponnesiacum.*

Cyclamen repandum Sm. subsp. *peloponnesiacum* Grey-Wilson forma *vividum* Grey-Wilson, The Genus Cyclamen: 60 (1988). Type: Greece, Peloponnese, Mt Parnon, SW slopes, April 1987, Grey-Wilson s.n. (holotypus K) = *C. repandum* subsp. *peloponnesiacum* var. *vividum.*

Cyclamen repandum Sm. subsp. *peloponnesiacum* Grey-Wilson forma *peloponnesiacum* Grey-Wilson, The Genus Cyclamen: 60 (1988) = *C. repandum* subsp. *peloponnesiacum* var. *peloponnesiacum.*

Cyclamen repandum Sm. subsp. *peloponnesiacum* var. *peloponnesiacum* (Grey-Wilson) Grey-Wilson, Cyclamen: 174 (1997) = *C. peloponnesiacum* subsp. *peloponnesiacum.*

Cyclamen repandum Sm. subsp. *peloponnesiacum* var. *peloponnesiacum* (Grey-Wilson) Grey-Wilson forma *albiflorum* B. Mathew = *C. peloponnesiacum* subsp. *peloponnesiacum* forma *albiflorum.*

Cyclamen repandum Sm. subsp. *peloponnesiacum* Grey-Wilson var. *vividum* (Grey-Wilson) Grey-Wilson, Cyclamen: 174 (1997) = *C. peloponnesiacum* subsp. *vividum.*

Cyclamen repandum Sm. subsp. repandum forma album Grey-Wilson, Cyclamen: 175 (1997). Type: Cult. (holotypus, K).

Cyclamen repandum Sm. subsp. *rhodense* (Meikle) Grey-Wilson, The Genus Cyclamen: 60 (1988) = *C. peloponnesiacum* subsp. *rhodense.*

Cyclamen repandum Sm. var. barborense Debussche & Quézel in *Acta bot. Gallica* 144, 1: 23–33 (1997). Type: Algeria, Petite Kabylie, El Ma Berd, 1890, Battandier (MPU).

Cyclamen repandum Sm. var. *creticum* Dörfl. in Ver. K.K. Zool.-Bot. Ges. Wien. 55: 20 (1905) = *C. creticum.*

Cyclamen repandum Sm. var. *rhodense* Meikle in J. Roy. Hort. Soc. 90: 29, pl. 121 (1965). Type: Greece, Rhodes, Mt Prophitis Elias, NW slope, c. 150 m, April 1964, L. Palmer 4 (holotype K) = *C. peloponnesiacum* subsp. *rhodense.*

Cyclamen repandum Sm. var. *stenopetalum* Loret. in Loret & Barrandon, Fl. Montpellier 1st ed., 2: 425 (1827) = *C. balearicum.*

Cyclamen retroflexum Moench, Suppl. Meth.: 177 (1802) = *C. purpurascens.*

Cyclamen rhodium R.Gorer ex O. Schwarz & Lepper in Feddes Repert. Spec. Nov. Regni Veg. 86: 491(1975). Type: as for *C. repandum* var. *rhodense* = *C. peloponnesiacum* subsp. *rhodense.*

Cyclamen rohlfsianum Aschers. in Bull. Herb. Boissier 5: 528 (1897). Type: Libya, Benghazi, Nov 1879, Rohlfs & Stecker.

Cyclamen romanum Griseb., Spic. Fl. Rumel. 1: 5 (1843) = *C. hederifolium* var. *hederifolium.*

Cyclamen rotundifolium St.-Lég. in Cariot., Etud. des fl. ed. 8, 2: 573 (1899), name of uncertain affinity.

Cyclamen sabaudum Jord. in Jord. & Fourr., Ic. Fl. Eur. 3: 20 (1903). Type: Ic. Fl Eur. pl. CCCCXV = *C. hederifolium* var. *hederifolium.*

Cyclamen saldense Pomel in Bull. Soc. Bot. France 36: 354 (1889) = *C. africanum.*

Cyclamen ✕ saundersiae Grey-Wilson, Cyclamen: 175 (1997), as "saundersii". Type: best regarded as the illustrations in the *Cyclamen Society Journal* 12, 2: Pl. 1–2 (1988).

Cyclamen ✕ schwarzii Grey-Wilson, Cyclamen: 175 (1997). Type: from material cultivated near Sudbury, Suffolk, 1994, by C. Grey-Wilson (holotype, K).

Cyclamen somalense Thulin & Warfa in Pl. Syst. Evol., 166(3–4): 249 (1989). Type: Somalia, Bari region, Al Miskat Mts, SW of Qandala, 26.11.1986, Thulin & Warfa 6084 (holotype, UPS).

Cyclamen spectabile Jord. in Jord. & Fourr., Ic. Fl. Eur. 3: 16 (1903). Type: Ic. Fl Eur. pl. CCCCIV = *C. repandum* subsp. *peloponnesiacum* var. *vividum.*

Cyclamen stenopetalum Jord. in Jord. & Fourr., Ic. Fl. Eur. 3: 16 (1903). Type: Ic. Fl Eur. pl. CCCCIII = *C. repandum* subsp. *peloponnesiacum* var. *vividum.*

Cyclamen subhastatum Rchb., Fl. Germ. Excurs. 1: 407 (1830) = *C. hederifolium* var. *hederifolium.*

Cyclamen subrotundum Jord. in Jord. & Fourr., Ic. Fl. Eur. 3: 21 (1903). Type: Ic. Fl Eur. pl. CCCCXX = *C. africanum.*

Cyclamen tauricum hort. Dammann ex Sprenger in Regel, Gartenflora 41: 525 (1892), name of uncertain affinity.

Cyclamen trochopteranthum O. Schwarz in Feddes Repert. Spec. Nov. Regni Veg. 86: 493 (1975). Type: Turkey, 'planta culta ex seminibus a Peter Davis sub. no. 25368, prope Denizli in regione inferiore Cadmi montis collectis orta (holotype JE) = *C. alpinum* Dammann ex Sprenger.

Cyclamen trochopteranthum O. Schwarz forma *leucanthum* Grey-Wilson = *C. alpinum* forma *leucanthum.*

Cyclamen tunetanum Jord. in Jord. & Fourr., Ic. Fl. Eur. 3: 23 (1903). Type: Ic. Fl Eur. pl. CCCCXXIV = *C. persicum* var. *persicum.*

Cyclamen umbratile Jord. in Jord. & Fourr., Ic. Fl. Eur. 3: 18 (1903). Type: Ic. Fl Eur. pl. CCCCXI = *C. purpurascens.*

Cyclamen utopicum Hoffmanns., Verz. Pfl.-Kult.: 54 (1824) = *C. persicum* var. *persicum.*

Cyclamen variegatum Pohl, Tent. Fl. Bohem. 1: 192 (1810) = *C. purpurascens.*

Cyclamen velutinum Jord. in Jord. & Fourr., Ic. Fl. Eur. 3: 22, t. 423 (1903). Type: Ic. Fl Eur. pl. CCCCXXIII = *C. graecum* subsp. *graecum*.

Cyclamen venustum Jord. in Jord. & Fourr., Ic. Fl. Eur. 3: 22 (1903). Type: Ic. Fl Eur. pl. CCCCXIX = *C. africanum*.

Cyclamen vernale hort. No indication of earliest usage = *C. coum* subsp. *coum*.

Cyclamen vernale sensu O. Schwarz in Feddes Repert. Spec. Nov. Regni Veg. 58: 243 (1955) = *C. repandum* subsp. *repandum*.

Cyclamen vernale Mill., Gard. Dict. ed. 8, n. 4 (1768) = *C. persicum* var. *persicum*.

Cyclamen vernum Lobel ex Cambess, Enum. Pl. Balear.: 127 (1827), non Sweet = *C. balearicum*.

Cyclamen vernum Lobel ex Rchb., Fl. Germ Excurs. 1: 407 (1830) = *C. repandum* subsp. *repandum*.

Cyclamen vernum Sweet, Brit. Flower Gard. 1: t. 9 (1823) = *C. coum* subsp. *caucasicum*.

Cyclamen vernum Sweet forma *alpinum* O. Schwarz in Gartenflora n.s., 1: 20 (1938) = *C. parviflorum*.

Cyclamen vernum Sweet var. *caucasicum* O. Schwarz in Gartenflora n.s., 1: 20 (1938) = *C. coum* subsp. *caucasicum*.

Cyclamen vernum Sweet var. *hiemale* (Hildebr.) O. Schwarz forma *alpinum* (Sprenger) O. Schwarz in Gartenflora n.s., 1: 20 (1938) = *C. parviflorum*.

Cyclamen vernum Sweet var. *hiemale* (Hildebr.) O. Schwarz forma *pseudocoum* O. Schwarz in Gartenflora n.s., 1: 20 (1938) = *C. coum* subsp. *coum*.

Cyclamen x wellensiekii Ietsw. In *Acta Bot. Neerl.* 23(4): 555 (1974).

Cyclamen x whiteae Grey-Wilson, Cyclamen: 175 (1997), as *"whitei"*. Type: from material cultivated at Brightlingsea, Essex, 1995, by Jill White (holotype, K).

Cyclamen zonale Jord. in Jord. & Fourr., Ic. Fl. Eur. 3: 15, t. 401 (1903). Type: Ic. Fl Eur. pl. CCCCI = *C. coum* subsp. *caucasicum*.

Cyclaminos miliarakesii Heldr., Herb. norm. graec. no 1575 (1900) = *C. graecum* subsp. *graecum*.

Cyclaminum vernum Bubani., Fl. Pyren. 1: 229 (1897), name of uncertain affinity.

NEW COMBINATIONS

Cyclamen alpinum forma *leucanthum* (Grey-Wilson) Grey-Wilson, comb. nov.

C. trochopteranthum forma *leucanthum* Grey-Wilson in Cyclamen: 175 (1997).

Cyclamen hederifolium subsp. *confusum* (Grey-Wilson) Grey-Wilson, comb. nov.

C. hederifolium var. *confusum* Grey-Wilson in Cyclamen: 174 (1997).

Cyclamen parviflorum subsp. *subalpinum* (Grey-Wilson) Grey-Wilson, comb. nov.

C. parviflorum var. *parviflorum* Grey-Wilson in Cyclamen: 174 (1997).

Cyclamen peloponnesiacum subsp. *peloponnesiacum* forma *albiflorum* (Grey-Wilson ex Mathew) Grey-Wilson, comb. nov.

C. repandum subsp. *peloponnesiacum* forma *albiflorum* B. Mathew in *Journ. Cyclamen Soc.* 23: 51 (1999)

Chapter Twelve

Cyclamen & Conservation

Habitats and species have become under increasing pressure from Man in recent years. This applies to nearly all regions of the world and to all nations. Species, both plants and animals, come under threat from various causes of which human population growth and land development and resultant pollution are perhaps the dominant forces. It is easy to criticize measures to curb the pressure on wild animals and plants; laws and regulations may not be perfect but they have certainly helped to curb some of the excesses. Today, there is far greater awareness of the need to conserve wild species by preserving their habitats. Conservation measures are designed to protect wild species from exploitation by Man.

In all this, the removal by individuals of a few plants from the wild may seem insignificant compared with habitat destruction (land development, road building, etc.), or the wholesale removal of species for commercial reasons. However, the fact is that even repeated small-scale removal from the wild, particularly of plants, can have a long-term and lasting effect. It is easy to be fooled into thinking that all is well when you come across a large and thriving colony of a particular species but it may be one of only a few such colonies, or indeed the only one. It is not difficult to see that repeated visits to such colonies can have a devastating effect in the long-term.

From the horticultural point of view it is desirable that new species and interesting forms of certain plants in the wild are brought into cultivation. There is also need for a certain amount of material to be introduced for scientific study and analysis. However, any removal of material must in all cases follow the strict rules of conservation (the species' needs must come first) and comply with both international and local laws.

How does this affect *Cyclamen*? Of all the horticulturally desirable groups, *Cyclamen* appears to have one of the most prolonged histories of conservation-related problems. In the 1970s and much of the 1980s the removal of cyclamen from the wild by commercial plant hunters, together with other 'bulbs', reached alarming proportions. The region most affected was Turkey but it was not alone by any means. Although the situation has greatly improved in more recent times the removal of cyclamen (by whatever means) is still a problem.

There is in fact no reason to buy them; young plants raised from seed and bought in active growth from nurseries and garden centres will have been reared in cultivation from seed. Furthermore, such plants adapt far more readily to cultivation and are generally easier to grow and come from reputable sources. In addition, you are far more likely to get the correct species and interesting forms by buying from a reliable and established source and you can have the luxury of choosing plants in flower or leaf, picking out the most desirable.

But how are wild cyclamen protected? In 1973 the first meeting of the Convention on International Trade in Endangered Species of Wild Fauna and Flora (CITES) was held in Washington, DC. By 1996 there were more than 130 countries party to the Convention. The parties meet regularly and discuss the effectiveness of the Convention; species proposals, new names to be added to the list, and those thought no longer at risk considered for deletion.

All species are listed in three appendices.
- Appendix I: Those species considered most at risk are placed here. All commercial trade in wild plants and animals on the Appendix is banned by all the member-states of the Convention. Trade in artificially propagated or captivebred specimens is allowed subject to licence.
- Appendix II: This includes all those species not currently in danger but which are potentially at risk, if current levels of exploitation continue. International trade in them is monitored by means of a licensing system to ensure that it stays below a level at which the species may become endangered. Trade in wild, captive-bred and artificially propagated specimens is allowed, subject to licence.
- Appendix III: This exists to help protect species only threatened in a limited part of their range. If a particular country already has legislation protecting certain species and there is a risk of these entering international trade, then placing them on Appendix III (making trade from that country only possible by licence), provides additional protection.

Since I wrote 'The Genus Cyclamen' in 1988 things have changed quite significantly. The strictly conservation approach has given way to a new philosophy on how we treat wildlife. At the Earth Summit in Rio de Janeiro in 1992 (United Nations Conference on the Environment and

Development) crucial points were discussed and agreed. Recognizing the huge significance of biological diversity and its importance to the future of Mankind, the summit came to the understanding that these resources could be exploited by individual countries for their own good provided that such exploitation could be sustained without detriment to wild populations of plants and animals. Here the word sustainable is absolutely crucial, for it is by no means easy to judge, for instance, how much plant material of a particular species can be removed from the wild without endangering the survival of that species. In effect each country decides what and how much can be exploited. In essence, the sustainable use of natural resources is seen working closely with conservation needs.

What does this all mean to the average citizen and cyclamen fanatic? In simple terms it means that it is illegal (i.e. you are breaking the law) to bring wild-collected cyclamen plants into any country that is party to the CITES Convention (this includes all European Community countries), without the relevant documentation. Whatever you collect, it is controlled. Most countries in which cyclamen grow wild (whether or not they belong to the Convention) have laws which forbid the digging up of wild specimens. To break any of these laws is an offence which at least will incur a fine and at worst a prison sentence. The Appendix I cyclamen (*C. balearicum*, *C. creticum* and *C. graecum*) are even more strictly controlled within the European Community. With these, trade is only possible in artificially propagated plants and is subject to licensing; all parts of the wild plants are controlled, including the seeds.

At the same time it is legal to bring in wild-collected seed (except those species on CITES Appendix I) providing the species is not protected in its country of origin.

New CITES regulations came into force on 1st January 1997, negotiated by the European Community. On that date all *Cyclamen* were cited on Appendix II. These regulations may eventually also include seed: on a national level wild seed as well as wild plants may already be protected.

In certain circumstances, where a suitable case can be made on scientific grounds, a licence may be granted by CITES regulators allowing the limited importation of wild-collected specimens into a particular Convention country. However, this in no way gives permission to collect wild plants in the first instance and permission also needs to be sought from the appropriate authorities in the country concerned. 'Plants in Danger' (Davis *et al*, 1986) gives key addresses of relevant government departments in all major countries in the world and it is easy to find out well in advance of a visit what the regulations and restrictions in a particular country are likely to be. Information about CITES licences and controls can be obtained from the appropriate management authorities (in Britain this is the Department of Environment, Farming and Rural Affairs (DEFRA), Wildlife Licensing, Tollgate House, Houlton Street, Bristol BS2 9J; outside Britain it is the CITES Secretariat, United Nations Environment Programme, 15 Chemin des Anemones, Case Postale 356, 1219 Chatelaine, Geneve, Switzerland).

In summary, to collect wild cyclamen you need:
1. A permit to collect.
2. A permit to export the plants from that country.
3. If you live within the European Community, a permit to import.

For the majority of cyclamen lovers there is absolutely no reason to collect plants from the wild and even those contemplating a scientific reason for collecting a limited number should do so with the utmost care and for truly bona fide reasons. Bringing plants into one's own private collection, even for 'study', will not satisfy the authorities. In recent years The Cyclamen Society has undertaken several expeditions specifically to study cyclamen in the wild. Under the appropriate licences they have been able to collect a limited number of live wild plants for scientific analysis. This approach has been carefully planned and thought out and it is a good example of how the needs for further research and conservation can come together happily to the benefit of everyone.

Many hope that interesting and new forms can be introduced into cultivation from these scientific studies. But herein lies the rub: whereas a particular country may allow the removal of a limited amount of live material or seed for scientific analysis it may not allow for commercial exploitation of that material, at least not without some form of royalty going to the country concerned; the need for scientific research and commercial development are quite independent of one another. At a national level individual countries may see potential income from their own wild genetic resources and they may not want any individual collecting plants that may perhaps become important agriculturally or horticulturally.

In all cases seeds (from cultivated plants) and tissue cultures are exempt from these controls. In recent years there has been an increasing awareness of these problems, with various seed merchants offering seed for sale in the larger retail outlets such as the national garden centres and even major chain stores. In Turkey there has been a strong move towards rearing seed-grown plants in special nurseries for future export, although there is still a large legal trade in wild collected plants. By making the species more widely available the need to import stocks from the wild is greatly reduced. It is very encouraging that some growers (particularly in Britain, Germany and Holland) are raising plants from their own seed stocks in sufficient numbers that they even have a surplus and that this is being exported. Once plants are obtained then with most cyclamen (especially the hardier types) it is all too easy to increase your own stock from seed.

As a final note the CITES Conference in Zimbabwe in June 1997 adopted a proposal modifying the treatment of one species, *C. persicum*, which is widely grown commercially for the pot plant trade. In future artificially propagated cultivars (which covers the vast majority of plants sold) are exempt except when traded as dormant tubers (this in effect is scarcely ever done!) This measure effectively prevents wild-dug tubers of other species of *Cyclamen* evading CITES controls by masquerading as *C. persicum* cultivars.

Little has happened since the last edition of this work in 1997. However, in one country at least, Turkey, important strides have been made towards conserving more carefully the wild populations of *Cyclamen*. This has been brought sharply into focus by the recent publication of 'The Cyclamen of Turkey' by Brian Mathew and Neriman Özhatay (2001), published by the Cyclamen Society.

Appendix I

Generic subdivisions & Latin diagnoses of new subgenera & new series

Cyclamen Miller

Subgenus *Psilanthum* Schwarz [2n=20, 22]: tubers relatively small, smooth and velvety, rooting from the centre below; leaves thin and without cartilaginous teeth; pedicels coiling in fruit; calyx-lobes 1-veined; corolla exauriculate, plain or with a deeper zone of colour around the mouth, eglandular; corolla-lobes not toothed; anthers not aristate. Spring flowering. *C. balearicum, C. creticum, C. peloponnesiacum, C. repandum.*

Subgenus *Gyrophoebe* Schwarz [2n=30; pollen (3-)4(-5)-colporate]: tubers generally rather small, velvety to corky, rooting from the lower surface; leaves without cartilaginous teeth; pedicels coiling in fruit; sepals 3-5-veined; corolla exauriculate usually, generally with a dark blotch at the base of each petal, generally glandular; anthers usually aristate:

> **Series One (Series *Pubipedia* Schwarz)**: tubers velvety, rooting from the middle of the base; leaves not angled, rarely slightly lobed; corolla glandular or eglandular; corolla-lobes generally toothed, often weakly so, generally about as long as wide; anthers aristate. Winter and early spring flowering. (the equivalent of Series *Pubipedia* Schwarz with the omission of *C. cilicium* and the addition of *C. elegans*). *C. alpinum, C. coum, C. elegans, C. parviflorum.*

> **Series Two (Series *Pseudibericum* Grey-Wilson, ser. nov.)**: tubers corky, rooting from the lower surface; corolla exauriculate, with a narrow mouth; anthers not aristate. Spring flowering. Type of series: *C. pseudibericum.* Species in new series: *C. pseudibericum* [Series 2 (*Pseudibericum* Grey-Wilson, ser. nov): **tubera suberosa, a pagina inferiore radicantia; corolla exauriculata, ore angusto; antherae non aristatae. Vere florens. Seriei typus: *C. pseudibericum.* Species in serie nova: *C. pseudibericum*]**

> **Series Three (Series *Cilicium* Grey-Wilson, ser. nov.)**: tubers velvety or corky, rooting from the middle of the base usually; leaves not lobed; corolla

glandular; corolla-lobes toothed, often weakly so, considerably longer than wide; anthers aristate. Autumn flowering. Type of series: *C. cilicium.* Species in new series: *C. cilicium, C. intaminatum, C. mirabile.*

[Series 3 (Series *Cilicium* Grey-Wilson, ser. nov.): tubera velutina vel suberosa, e medio basis vulgo radicantia; folia non lobata; corolla glandulosa, lobis dentatis, saepe ita infirme, aliquantum longioribus quam latioribus; antherae aristatae. Autumno florens. Seriei typus: *C. cilicium.* Species in serie nova: *C. cilicium, C. intaminatum, C. mirabile*]

Subgenus *Corticata* (Schwarz) Grey-Wilson (*Cyclamen* subgenus *Gyrophoebe* Schwarz series *Corticata* Schwarz) [2n=30; pollen 3-colporate]: tubers corky, rooting over the base, sometimes on one side; leaves weakly angled or coarsely toothed; corolla glandular, weakly to strongly auriculate, with a wide mouth; corolla-lobes untoothed; sepals 3-5-veined; anthers not aristate. Autumn to early Spring flowering. (This equals Series *Corticata* Schwarz except for the absence of *C. mirabile* and *C. pseudibericum*). Autumn to early Spring flowering. *C. cyprium, C. libanoticum.*

Subgenus *Persicum* Grey-Wilson, subgen. nov. [2n=48, 72; pollen 3-colporate]: tubers generally rather large and corky, rooting from the lower surface; leaves with somewhat cartilaginous teeth; pedicels curving but not coiling in fruit; calyx 1-veined; corolla exauriculate, plain or with a deeper zone of colour around the mouth, eglandular; corolla-lobes untoothed; anthers not aristate. Winter and Spring flowering. A new subgenus derived by removing *C. persicum* from subgenus *Eucosme* and adding *C. somalense.* Type of subgenus: *C. persicum.* Species in new subgenus: *C. persicum, C. somalense.*

[Subgenus *Persicum* Grey-Wilson, subgen. nov. [2n=48, 72; pollen tricolporatum]: tubera aliquantum magna atque suberosa, a pagina inferiore radicantia; folia dentibus aliquantum cartilagineis; pedicelli fructu flectentes sed non circinantes; calyx univenatus; corolla exauriculata, unicolor vel circum orem zona percolorata instructa, eglandulosa, lobis non dentatis; antherae non aristatae. Hieme atque Vere florens. Subgenus novum detractione *C. persici* e subgenere Eucosmi atque adiectione *C. somalensi* oriundum. Typus subgeneris: *C. persicum.* Species in subgenere novo: *C. persicum, C. somalense*]

Subgenus *Cyclamen* (including subgenus *Eucosme* Schwarz): tubers generally rather large and corky, sometimes uneven; leaves often with cartilaginous teeth; pedicels coiling in fruit; calyx-lobes 1-veined; corolla auriculate, occasionally weakly so, marked with a deeper zone or lines around the mouth, eglandular (except for petal margins); corolla-lobes untoothed; anthers not aristate:

Series One (Series *Cyclamen*) [2n=34, 68; pollen 3-colporate]: tubers regular rooting mainly over the sides and the top, the roots always fibrous; leaves lobed or angled or unlobed; pedicels coiling from the top downwards. Autumn flowering. *C. africanum, C. hederifolium.*

Series Two (Series *Purpurascens* Grey-Wilson, ser. nov.) [2n=34]: tubers becoming irregular, often nobbly, rooting unevenly over sides and base; leaves not angled or lobed; pedicels coiling from the top downwards. Summer and autumn flowering. Type of series: *C. purpurascens.* Species in new series: *C. colchicum, C. purpurascens.*

[Series 2 (Series *Purpurascens* Grey-Wilson, ser. nov.) [2n=34]: tubera irregularia fiunt, saepe nodosa, super lateres atque basin inaequaliter radicantia; folia non angulata neque lobata; pedicelli a vertice deorsum circinantes. Aestate et Autumno florens. Seriei typus: *C. purpurascens.* Species in serie nova: *C. colchicum, C. purpurascens*]

Series Three (Series *Graecum* Grey-Wilson, ser. nov.) [2n=84, rarely 85-87]: tubers rooting only from the base, with thick anchorage roots; leaves unlobed or only slightly so; stamens not protruding; pedicels coiling from the base or from the middle in both directions. Autumn flowering. Type of series: *C. graecum.* Species in new series: *C. graecum.*

[Series 3 (Series *Graecum* Grey-Wilson, ser. nov.) [2n=84, raro 85-87]: tubera solum e base radicantia, radicibus crassis stationi instructa; folia non lobata vel ita leviter tantum; stamina non exserta; pedicelli e basi vel e medio in cursibus ambobus circinantes. Autumno florens. Seriei typus: *C. graecum.* Species in new serie nova: *C. graecum*]

Series Four (Series *Rohlfsianum* Grey-Wilson, ser. nov.) [2n=96; pollen 3-colporate]: tubers rooting mainly from the lower sides, the roots all fibrous; leaves prominently and evenly lobed; stamens protruding; pedicels coiling from the base. Autumn flowering. Type of series: *C. rohlfsianum.* Species in new series: *C. rohlfsianum.*

[Series 4 (Series *Rohlfsianum* Grey-Wilson, ser. nov.) [2n=96; pollen tricolporatum]: tubera e lateribus inferis plerumque radicantia, radicibus omnibus fibrosis; folia manifeste ac aequaliter lobata; stamina exserta; pedicelli e basi circinantes. Autumno florens. Seriei typus: *C. rohlfsianum.* Species in serie nova: *C. rohlfsianum*]

Appendix II

Identification keys for Gardeners

These keys have been devized using simple terminology to enable the gardener to identify cyclamen species in cultivation based primarily on the characters of the leaves and flowers. They will work for most plants but not the more unusual cultivars nor for hybrids, nor indeed for any cultivars of *C. persicum*. They have been split into four blocks based on flowering time. Where a species flowers over two blocks (say summer and autumn) then it is keyed out in both separately. The keys will also work for plants in the wild, where geographical location should also be taken into consideration. I do not pretend that they will work for every plant, no key ever will, but they should work for the majority. In certain cases there is some overlap in measurements; if a plant being keyed 'fits' then the other characters used in the key take prime importance.

For a more strictly botanical key to the species in the wild see p.51.

For subspecies, varieties and most formas see under the appropriate species in the main text.

    * = rare in cultivation

Summer-flowering Species (June–August)

1. Flowers with prominent auricles   – to 2
or Flowers without auricles   – to 3

2. Leaves generally angled or lobed and mostly longer than wide; petals (in non-albino forms) with a distinctive basal V-shaped mark: *C. hederifolium*
or Leaves not angled and mostly as wide as long; petals without a basal mark   – to 3

3. Flowers white or very pale pink with grey veins, only 3–4mm (0.12–0.16in) across at the mouth:
                                              C. intaminatum
or Flowers carmine-pink or purple, rarely pure white, 6–9mm (0.23–0.35in) across at the mouth   – to 4

4. Leaves very thick and fleshy with a distinct but finely toothed margin and diverging basal lobes; flowers 11–15mm (0.4–0.6in) long: *C. colchicum**
or Leaves thin with an indistinctly toothed or untoothed margin and converging or overlapping basal lobes; flowers mostly 17–25mm (0.7–1in) long:
                                              C. purpurascens

Autumn-flowering Species (September–November)

1. Leaves kidney-shaped with 5–7 broad lobes; flowers with a protruding cone of stamens: *C. rohlfsianum*
or Leaves not as above, generally heart-shaped or rounded, if kidney-shaped then not lobed; stamens included within the corolla-tube   – to 2

2. Flowers without auricles, the corolla mouth not more than 5mm (0.2in) across   – to 3
or Flowers with auricles, generally well defined, the corolla mouth at least 7mm (0.3in) across   – to 10

3. Flowers plain and unmarked   – to 4
or Flowers marked with a distinctive zone or blotch, in a different colour, at the base of each petal   – to 6

4. Flowers white with greyish veins, or very pale pink, 10–16mm (0.4–0.6in) long: *C. intaminatum*
or Flowers pink, purple or carmine, 11–25mm (0.4–1in) long   – to 5

5. Leaves very thick and fleshy with a distinct but finely toothed margin and diverging basal lobes; flowers 11–15mm (0.4–0.6in) long: *C. colchicum*
or Leaves thin with an indistinctly toothed or untoothed margin and converging or overlapping basal lobes; flowers mostly 17–25mm (0.7–1in) long:
                                              C. purpurascens

6. Leaves often more than 6cm (2.2in) long; flower-stalks (pedicels) not coiling in fruit   – to 6
or Leaves less than 6cm (2.2in) long, the leaf-margin never angled; flower-stalks coiling in fruit   – to 8

7. Flowers 12–15mm (0.4–0.6in) long; leaves distinctly angled: *C. somalense**
or Flowers 18–37mm (0.7–1.4in) long (excluding large-flowered cultivars); leaves not angled:
                                      C. persicum var. *autumnalis*

8. Flowers 18–23mm (0.7–1in) long, the petals with 'eyes' at the base of the dark blotch; leaves pointed, often slightly lobed: *C. elegans**
or Flowers 10–19mm (0.4–0.8in) long, the petals with a solid basal dark blotch, occasionally pure white; leaves rounded, not lobed   – to 9

9. Petals toothed at the tip; leaves as broad as long, often flushed or marbled with pink or red when young: *C. mirabile*
or Petals not toothed; leaves longer than broad, never flushed or marbled with pink or red: *C. cilicium*

10. Flowers white with an M-shaped magenta mark at the base of each petal: *C. cyprium*
or Flowers pink, carmine or reddish-purple, marked with lines or blotches at the base of each petal; if plain white then unmarked **– to 11**

11. Flowers pure white without any markings **– to 12**
or Flowers pink to reddish-carmine, often with a darker mark or zone close to the 'mouth' **– to 14**

12. Leaves distinctly angled (angles 2–6 usually): *C. hederifolium* forma *album*
or Leaves rounded to oval, not angled **– to 13**

13. Leaves with an untoothed or shallowly toothed margin, shiny green, sometimes pewtered or silvered, often persisting throughout the year: *C. purpurascens* forma *album*
or Leaves velvety green, sometimes pewtered, with a finely beaded margin, seasonal: *C. graecum* forma *album*

14. Leaves with a finely beaded margin, not angled; flower-stalks (pedicels) coiling from the middle in two directions in fruit: *C. graecum*
or Leaves without a beaded margin, generally angled; flower-stalks coiling from the top downwards in fruit **– 15**

15. Flowers and leaves rising directly up from the tubers, their stalks not elbowed; flowers 18–35mm (0.7–1.4in) long: *C. africanum*
or Flowers and leaves apparently arising to the side of the tuber on elbowed stalks; flowers 14–22mm (0.5–1in) long: *C. hederifolium*

Winter-flowering Species (December–February)

1. Flowers with well-defined auricles: *C. cyprium*
or Flowers without auricles **– to 2**

2. Flowers large, the petals 18–37mm (0.7–1.4in) long, the mouth of the corolla plain or with a zone of darker colour; flower-stalks not coiling in fruit: *C. persicum*
or Flowers smaller, the petals 8–25mm (0.3–1in) long, the mouth with a distinct dark marking; flower-stalks coiling in fruit **– to 3**

3. Flowers with a musty acetylene smell, the petals 16–25mm (0.6–1in) long; mouth of corolla at least 10mm (0.4in) wide: *C. libanoticum*
or Flowers unscented or with a sweet honey scent, the petals not more than 16mm (0.6in) long, generally

only 8–13mm (0.3–0.5in) long; mouth of corolla not more than 6mm (0.23in) across **– to 4**

4. Corolla not propeller-like, with the petals more or less upright, the dark basal mark with a pair of pale 'eyes'; flowers usually unscented or only very faintly so **– to 5**
or Corolla often propeller-like, with the petals spreading outwards at right angles (if erect then flowers only 4–8mm/0.16–0.3in long), the dark basal blotch appearing solid; flowers sweetly scented **– to 6**

5. Flowers 18–23mm (0.7–1in) long; leaves heart-shaped, pointed, with a scalloped margin: *C. elegans*
or Flowers smaller, 8–20mm (0.3–0.8in) long; leaves rounded to kidney-shaped or heart-shaped but without a scalloped margin: *C. coum*

6. Leaves oval, usually blotched or zoned with a paler or darker colour; petals 9–13mm (0.35–0.5in) long, with spreading, almost horizontal, petals; blotch solid: *C. alpinum*
or Leaves rounded to kidney-shaped, plain; flowers only 4–11mm (0.16–0.4in) long, with erect or spreading petals; blotch composed of a number of close lines: *C. parviflorum*

Spring-flowering Species (March–May)

1. Leaves and flowers arising erect from the tuber; flower-stalks (pedicels) not coiling in fruit; petals often more than 30mm (1.2in) long: *C. persicum*
or Leaves and flowers arising to one side of the tuber on bent stalks; flower-stalks coiling in fruit; petals mostly less than 30mm (1.2in) long **– to 2**

2. Petals plain or with a darker zone around the base (mouth of the corolla) **– to 3**
or Petals with a distinct marking towards the base, often M- or ace of spades-shaped, or solid **– to 6**

3. Flowers mid- to deep pink, or white, with a deep pink zone around the mouth, or entirely deep magenta-pink or magenta-purple; leaves with a deep or bright green base colour **– to 4**
or Flowers plain, white or very pale pink; leaves with a grey-green base colour **– to 5**

4. Flowers magenta-pink; leaves longer than wide, with a clear hastate pattern: *C. repandum*
or Flowers pale pink or white with a deep pink zone around the mouth, or intense magenta-purple; leaves as long as wide, or wider than long, generally speckled above, with or without a hastate pattern: *C. peloponnesiacum*

5. Flowers 15–26mm (0.6–1in) long, white or very pale pink; leaves flat, with a pointed apex: *C. creticum*
or Flowers 9–16mm (0.35–0.6in) long, off-white, often with greyish or pinkish veins; leaves usually somewhat curved (concave) with a blunt apex:

C. balearicum

6. Flowers with a musty acetylene smell, the mouth of the corolla 10mm (0.4in) across or more; leaves often angled: *C. libanoticum*
or Flowers unscented or with a sweet honey or primrose fragrance, the mouth of the corolla not more than 6mm (0.23in) across; leaves with an entire or distinctly toothed margin   **– to 7**

7. Dark blotch at base of petals not solid   **– to 8**
or Dark blotch at base of petals appearing solid, basically M- or ace of spades-shaped   **– to 9**

8. Flowers 18–25mm (0.7–1in) long, the petals with an ace of spades-shaped mark towards the base; leaves with coarsely toothed margins: *C. pseudibericum*
or Flowers usually 8–18mm (0.3–0.7in) long (very rarely to 20mm/0.8in), the petals with a more or less M-shaped marking at the base; leaves with untoothed or only finely toothed margins: *C. coum*

9. Leaves oval, usually blotched or zoned with a paler or darker colour; petals 9–13mm (0.35–0.5in) long, with spreading, almost horizontal, petals; blotch solid: *C. alpinum*
or Leaves rounded to kidney-shaped, plain; flowers only 4–11mm (0.16–0.4in) long, with erect or spreading petals; blotch composed of a number of close lines: *C. parviflorum*

Appendix III
Awards

The Royal Horticultural Society makes various awards to plants as follows:

First Class Certificate (F.C.C.) This, the highest award, goes to plants of outstanding excellence for exhibition and is reserved for plants that are incontestably first rate.

Award of Merit (A.M.) This is given to plants of great merit for exhibition but those that have proven their gardenworthiness; in other words they have proven themselves in cultivation.

Certificate of Preliminary Commendation (P.C.) This award is given to those plants deemed to show promise for exhibition. This is generally given to plants that are not widespread in cultivation or those submitted for the first time.

Plants can move up the scale of awards as their behaviour in cultivation is reassessed; they have to be resubmitted to the appropriate committee at the RHS; in the case of most cyclamen (excluding cultivars of *C. persicum*) the appropriate committee is the Joint Rock Garden Plant Committee.

In addition, plants can be awarded a **Cultural Commendation (C.C.)** by the Alpine Garden Society if the plant submitted is assessed to have been cultivated to a high degree of excellence.

In 1992 the Royal Horticultural Society re-instituted the **Award of Garden Merit (A.G.M.** or **AGM)** which recognizes plants of outstanding excellence for garden decoration, whether grown in the open or under glass. This award is the highest accolade that can be bestowed on a plant by the RHS for its ornamental use in the garden. As such, the award is of great use to ordinary gardeners, helping them to make a choice from the great range of plants available in the horticultural trade in Britain. The award applies both to plants for the open garden as well as those grown under glass. Awards are indicated in the text by their abbreviations.

Appendix IV
Nurseries selling Cyclamen in Britain
(excluding *C. persicum* cvs)

A & A Thorp, Bungalow No 5, Main Street, Theddingworth, Leicestershire LE17 6QZ.

~~Aberconwy Nursery~~, Graig, Glan Conwy, Colwyn Bay, Clwyd LL28 5TL.

Ashwood Nurseries*, Greensforge, Kingswinford, West Midlands DY6 0AE.

Avon Bulbs, Burnt House Farm, Mid-Lambrook, South Petherton, Somerset TA13 5HE.

Blackthorn Nursery, Kilmeston, Alresford, Hampshire SO24 0NL.

Bressingham Plant Centres, Bressingham, Diss, Norfolk IP22 4HJ.

Bridgemere Nurseries, Bridgemere, Nr Nantwich, Cheshire CW5 7QB.

Broadleigh Gardens, Bishops Hull, Taunton, Somerset TA4 1AE.

Cambridge Bulbs, 40 Whittlesford Road, Newton, Cambridge CB2 5PH.

Compton Lane Nurseries, Little Compton, Moreton-in-Marsh, Gloucestershire GL65 0SJ.

Cotswold Garden Flowers, Sands Lane, Badsey, Evesham, Worcestershire WR11 5EZ.

CTDA, 174 Cambridge Stree, London SW1V 4QE.

De Jager & Sons, The Nurseries, Marden, Kent TN12 9BP.

Elm Tree Nursery, Court Farm, Sidbury, Sidmouth, Devon EX10 0QG.

Greenslacks Nurseries, Ocot Lane, Scammonden, Huddersfield, Yorkshire HD3 4DH.

Hartside Nursery Garden, Nr Alston, Cumbria CA9 3BL.

Highgates Nursery, 166a Crich Lane, Belper, Derbyshire DE56 1EP.

Holden Clough Nursery, Holden, Bolton-by-Bowland, Clitheroe, Lancashire BB7 4PF.

Hoo House Nursery, Hoo House, Gloucester Road, Tewkesbury, Gloucestershire GL20 7DA.

Hythe Alpines, Methwold Hythe, Thetford, Norfolk IP26 4QH.

Jacques Amand Ltd, The Nurseries 145 Clamp Hill, Stanmore, Middlesex HA7 3JS.

Jill White, 'St Davids', Recreation Way, Brightlingsea, Essex CO7 0NJ.

Kim W. Davis, Lingen Alpine Nursery, Lingen, Nr Bucknell, Shropshire SY7 0DY.

Little Creek Nursery, 39 Moor Road, Banwell, Weston-super-Mare, Avon BS24 6EF.

Marley Bank Nursery, Bottom Lane, Whitbourne, Worcestershire WR6 5RU.

Mill Cottage Plants, The Mill, Henley Lane, Wookey, Somerset BA5 1AP.

Monocot Nursery, Jacklands, Jacklands Bridge, Tickenham, Clevedon, Avon BS21 6SG.

Manavlins, Mrs K. N. Dryden, 30 Sheering Lower Road, Sawbridgeworth, Hertfordshire CM21 9LF.

Paradise Centre, Twinstead Road, Lamarsh, Bures, Suffolk CO8 5EX.

Paul Christian (Rare Plants), PO Box 468, Wrexham, Clwyd LL13 9XR.

Potterton and Martin, The Cottage Nursery, Moortown Road, Nettleton, Caistor, Lincolnshire LN7 6HX.

R D Plants, Homelea Farm, Tytherleigh, Axminster, East Devon EX13 7BG.

R V Roger Ltd, The Nurseries, Pickering, North Yorkshire YO18 7HG.

Richard Stockwell, 64 Weardale Road, off Hucknall Road, Sherwood, Nottingham NG5 1DD.

Rookhope Nurseries, Rookhope, Upper Weardale, Co. Durham DL13 2DD.

S & S Perennials, 24 Main Street, Nomanton Le Heath, Leicestershire LE67 2T.

Slack Top Alpines, Hebden Bridge, West Yorkshire HX7 7HA.

Sonia Wright Plants, (Office) Westfield Farmhouse, West Street, Aldbourne, Wiltshire SN8 2BS.

The Firs Nursery, Chelford Road, Henbury, Macclesfield, Cheshire SK10 3LH.

Thuja Alpine Nursery, Glebelands, Hartpury, Gloucestershire GL17 9QS.

Tilebarn Nursery*, Standen Street, Iden Green, Benenden, Kent TN17 4LB.

Van Tubergen UK Ltd, Bressingham, Diss, Norfolk IP22 2AB.

W E Th. Ingwersen Ltd, Birch Farm Nursery, Gravetye, East Grinstead, West Sussex RH19 4LE.

In addition, many large garden centres sell hardy cyclamen in flower or leaf, especially *C. coum* and *C. hederifolium*: in particular the Wisley Plant Centre at the RHS Gardens, Wisley, near Woking and the various Blooms of Bressingham garden centres at Diss, Bicester, Dorney near Windsor, Elton near Peterborough and at Rugby, Warwickshire.

Check the latest edition of the *RHS Plant Finder* for availability of species and cultivars, as well as latest additions.

Appendix V

Societies to Join

The Alpine Garden Society The largest and most important society in the world for alpine and rock garden plants, including cyclamen. The Society offers a quarterly journal with numerous articles and colour pictures, local groups, lectures, foreign tours, flower shows, plant sales and a very large annual seed-distribution scheme. The Director and Secretary, Alpine Garden Society, AGS Centre, Avon Bank, Pershore, Worcestershire WR10 7JP, U.K.
www.alpinegardensociety.org

The Cyclamen Society The premier society in the world concerned with cyclamen, offering a twice-yearly journal full of information on the species in the wild and in cultivation, an annual seed-distribution, expert advice, weekend conferences, talks, shows and plant sales. If you want to know more about cyclamen then it is well worth becoming a member of this Society. The Publicity Officer, Vic Aspland, 27 Osmaston Road, Norton, Stourbridge, West Midlands, DY8 2AL, U.K.
www.cyclamen.org

The Scottish Rock Garden Club The Scottish equivalent of the Alpine Garden Society, also with members in many countries around the world. Offers a twice-yearly journal, lectures, shows, weekend conferences and a seed-distribution scheme as well as plant sales. The SRGC, P.O. Box 14063, Edinburgh EH10 4YE.
www.srgc.org.uk

The North American Rock Garden Society The North American society dealing with alpine plants. produces a journal, seed distribution, with regional groups (chapters), lectures and special weekends. Executive Secretary, Jacques Mommens, P.O. box 67, Millwood, NY10456, USA.
www.nargs.org

Appendix VI

National collections of Cyclamen

The National Council for the Conservation of Plants and Gardens (NCCPG) includes in its Directory national collections of many different plants including *Cyclamen*. For *Cyclamen* there are two main holders of species and their cultivars (excluding the florist's cyclamen):

Mr R. W. Evans, 12 Albert Road, Bunny, Nottingham NG11 6QE.
Mr Graham Simpson, 13 Hurst Farm Road, East Grinstead, West Sussex RH19 4DQ (he co-ordinates six other collection holders besides his own collection!)
In addition, Mr Roger Poulett, Nurse's Cottage, North Mundham, Chichester, Sussex PO20 6JY, keeps an extensive collection of *C. coum* and its forms and cultivars.

Florist's cyclamen (*C. persicum* cultivars) collections exist mainly in continental Europe, especially on some of the larger cyclamen nurseries. The firm of Sahin at Alphen aan den Rijn in Holland keeps seeds of many different types, including some of the old tetraploid cultivars which are no longer available, or at least no longer grown commercially.

Glossary

acentric away from the middle

actinomorphic regular; in reference to flowers that are symmetrical, irrespective of the numbers of petals

acuminate drawn out gradually into pointed tip; refers usually to leaves or petals

acute sharply pointed, the point forming an angle of less than 90°

anchor roots stout roots that anchor the plant to the soil or rocks

angled with abrupt angles, being neither rounded nor lobed

anther the male organ of the flower which contains the pollen

apex the top or tip

apiculate terminating abruptly in a little point

aristate provided with a bristle-like appendage or point

ascending in a more or less upright position but not erect

auricle small ear-like appendage

axil the angle between leaf and stem, where flowers often arise

back-crossing crossing a hybrid with one or both of its parents

basal leaf leaf (or leaves) arising from the base of the plant; in cyclamen all leaves are basal

beaded bead-like; in cyclamen refers to the leaf of certain species which have a row of tiny even bumps along the margin

bearded provided with a beard; in plants hair-like outgrowths usually from the surface of petals or sepals

calyx the outer whorl of the flower, often small and green; in the cyclamen flower there are five equal small pointed sepals located on the outside of the corolla tube

carpel the compartment or compartments of the ovary that contain the ovules (seeds after fertilization); carpels may be free from one another or united; in cyclamen five carpels are fused into a single open compartment without separating walls

cartilaginous flexible but tough, strengthened with cartilage or similar strengthening material

cline a gradation in form over the range of a single species, or a specified part of the range the natural distribution of a species or other taxa

converging coming together

cordate heart-shaped

corolla the collective name for all the petals in a flower

cotyledon the seed leaves; in cyclamen there are two seed leaves but only one appears above ground, the other remaining within the seed coat

crested provided with a crest or crests, like the comb of a cockerel

cuspidate tapering gradually to a rigid point; usually applies to leaves, sepals or petals

cytology the study of the details within plant cells, especially the chromosomes

decumbent spreading outwards (often along the ground) then upwards

depressed-globose like a globe that has been pressed from the top; solid doughnut-shaped

diploid the normal full chromosome number (two sets) for a particular species; half the number (the basic number) is haploid, twice the number (i.e. two sets) tetraploid, or with many sets polyploid

diverging going apart

double hastate pattern with one similarly shaped pattern inside the other; refers to leaf patterning; see also **hastate**

ecotype a 'form' of the species adapted or evolved to a distinctive habitat within the main species range; ecotypes are often developed at high altitudes and although they may keep their particular characteristics in cultivation they are not generally considered to be distinct species

eglandular without any glands

elliptical oval, with rounded ends

emasculate to remove the male organs

endemic restricted to a certain area, often a country, island or mountain range

endosperm the seed food, located between the seed coat and the embryo

entire when applied to leaves means without any teeth along the margin

erect upright

exauriculate without auricles

exserted protruding

eye in the context of cyclamen refers to the eye-like markings present in some species at the base of each corolla-lobe, e.g. *C. coum*

floral trunk stem-like trunks developed from the tuber. The leaves and flowers ariserom the tips of the floral trunk.

garrigue a secondary vegetation type developed in Mediterranean

glabrous without hairs

glandular with glands; these are often minute and glistening and need to be viewed through a x10 lens of microscope

globose like a globe or an orb

hastate literally halberd-shaped but in the context of cyclamen leaf-pattern, the shape can vary from heart- to arrow- or halberd-shaped

holotype a designated specimen upon which the original description of a species or other taxon was based. Where duplicate specimens exist only one is the holotype, the others being isotypes

included within, not protruding; see **exserted**

incompatibility mechanism a physical or chemical barrier that prevents plant species (or animals) hybridizing.

karyotype the general characteristics of the chromosomes, their morphology

lamina the leaf blade

lanceolate lance-shaped; elliptical but broadest in the lower third

lax loose, slack

lectotype when several different collections (or syntypes) have been designated as the type of a species or other taxon (i.e. no holotype is designated!) then a future researcher can select one as meeting most closely the original description of the species and this becomes the lectotype

lobes refers to leaf blade when the margin is drawn out into obvious lobes or segments; can also refer to the individual petals of the corolla, i.e. corolla-lobes

maquis the original natural vegetation of the Mediterranean region consisting of drought-resistant, mostly evergreen, trees and shrubs with numerous aromatic herbs; secondary maquis when the woodland has been depleted by man or repeated fires is garrigue

morphology the study of the outer form of living things, their overall shape and appearance

narrow-elliptical a slender ellipse, narrow oval with acute ends; refers primarily to leaf shapes

nose the area adjacent to the mouth of the corolla; in the cyclamen flower the zone where the petals are reflexed which bears the auricles (when present) and any colour markings

oblong oval with obtuse (broadly rounded) ends; refers primarily to leaf-shape

oblong-elliptical midway between elliptical and oblong

obtuse rounded or blunt, forming an angle of more than 90°; refers primarily to leaf and petal tips

orbicular fully and symmetrically rounded, perfectly circular

outbreeding in reference to plants, those that cross with other individuals of the same species rather than themselves; in cultivation, outbreeding can refer to any crosses (natural or artificial) between different individuals of the same or different species; selfing, on the other hand, is inbreeding

ovary the female part of the flower that contains the ovules which, once fertilized, become the seeds

ovate flat but egg-shaped, i.e. oval but broadest in the lower third

ovule the unfertilized seed found in the ovary of the flower

pallisade cells the layer of long, closely parallel cells immediately below the skin (epidermis) of the leaf

pedicel the flower stalk

petiole the leaf stalk

picotee flowers in which the petals are narrowly edged in a contrasting colour

placenta the part of the ovary to which the ovules (later the seeds) are attached

polyploid with more than the normal basic number of chromosomes; those with three times the basic number are triploids, with four they are tetraploids, with six they are hexaploids, and so on

primitive species the species in the genus which, it is believed, most closely resembles the ancestral type

protandry flowers in which the pollen is shed before the stigma is receptive

reflexed bent or turned back on itself; generally refers to petals

relict referring to plant populations, refers to isolated populations surviving in a rather limited area and isolated from other populations of the same or different species

remote distant; remotely scalloped, with a few distant scallops; usually refers to leaf or petal margins

reniform kidney-shaped

revolute folded back downwards along or towards the central axis; refers to leaves

scalloped with shallow rounded indentations; refers to leaf-margins which are not obviously toothed or entire

self-incompatibility species which are unable to breed with themselves, a situation very common among flowering plants; self-incompatibility promotes free exchange of genes and prevents inbreeding

sepal an individual segment of the calyx, often small and green

sinus the gap between two lobes such as at the base of the cyclamen leaf where the stalk meets the blade

stamen the male organ of a flower, consisting of a stalk or filaments and an anther which contains the pollen

style part of the female organs of the flower that link the stigma to the ovary in cyclamen there is a single style but in other flowers there is often more than one

subacute not quite acute

subglobose not quite globose like a moon that is not quite full

suborbicular not quite rounded

taxon a biological unit (can be a species or variety, etc.); plural is taxa

terra fusca rich dark brown friable soils, developed often on non-calcareous rocks in hot, dry regions, especially in the Mediterranean

terra rossa red clay-like soils rich in ferruginous compounds, developed in limestone regions with a hot, dry climate such as in the Mediterranean

tetraploid with twice the normal chromosome number

toothed with tooth-like projections, like the edge of a saw; generally applies to leaves or petals

type specimen the specimen or specimens upon which the name of a species or other taxon is based and from which the description was prepared; to be certain of the identity of a particular name it is necessary to refer to the type specimen, which is usually a dried specimen in a herbarium

undulate wavy

Bibliography

(Only major references are cited; others will be found in the main text.)

Affre, L. (1996). Variation du systeme de reproduction et structuration genetique des populations chez quatre especes du genre Cyclamen (Primulaceae): à thesis Universite de Sciences Francois Rabelais (Academie d'Orleans-Tours).

Anderberg, A.A. (1993). Phylogeny and subgeneric classification of *Cyclamen* L. (Primulaceae) in *Kew Bulletin* 49, 3:455–467.

Anderberg, A.A., Trift, I. & Källersjo, M. (2000). Phylogeny of Cyclamen L. (Primulaceae): Evidence from morphological and sequence data from the internal transcribed spacers of nuclear ribosomal DNA in *Plant Syst. Evol.* 220:147–160.

Bennett, S.T. & Grimshaw, J. M. (1991). Cytological studies in Cyclamen subgenus Cyclamen (Primulaceae) in *Plant Systematics and Evolution* 176:135–143.

Blasdale, W.C. (1952). Cyclamen persicum – its natural and cultivated forms. Stanford, USA.

Brickell, C.D. (1979). Notes on the taxonomy of *Cyclamen cilicium, C. coum* and their close relatives. *Cyclamen* 3, 2: 49–54.

Chapman, G.P. (1981). The relevance of chromosome studies to improving Cyclamen. In Bailey, R.H. (ed.), *Cyclamen* 1980: Proceedings of the Conference Cyclamen Society 1980: 12–16. Cyclamen Society, Chigwell, U.K.

Clennett, J.C. (1997). A taxonomic review of Cyclamen L. subgenus Gyrophoebe O. Schwarz. University of Reading M.Sc. dissertation, unpublished.

Clennett, J.C. (1999a). Pollen studies in *Cyclamen*. *Cyclamen* 23, 1: 20–24.

Clennett, J.C. (1999b). *Cyclamen libanoticum* in Turkey – the plot thickens. Cyclamen 23, 2: 49–50.

Clennett, J.C. An analysis and revision of *Cyclamen* L. with emphasis on subgenus *Gyrophoebe* O. Schwarz: to be published in March 2002 in the *Botanical Journal of the Linnean Society*, London.

Cyclamen Society Journal (1977–). Many articles on cultivation and species in the wild. The Cyclamen Society, U.K.

Debussche, M and Thompson, J.D. (2002). Morphological differentiation among closely related species with disjunct distributions: a case study of Mediterranean *Cyclamen* L. subgen. *Psilanthum* Schwarz (Primulaceae) in the *Botanical Journal of the Linnean Society*, 139, 2: 133–144.

Debussche, M. & Quézel, P. (1997). *Cyclamen repandum* Sibth. & Sm. en Petite Kabylie (Algérie): un témoin biogéographique méconnu au statut taxonomique incertain, in *Acta bot. Gallica* 144, 1: 23–33.

Doorenbos, J. (1950). Taxonomy and nomenclature of *Cyclamen. Meded. Landbouwhogeschool* 50,2:1–29.

Edwards, F.C. (1894). *Cyclamen* and how to grow them (Levenshulme, Manchester).

Glasau, F. (1939). Monographie der Gattung *Cyclamen* auf morphologisch-cytologischer grundlage. *Planta* 30:507–50.

Greilhuber, J. (1989). Karyotype structure and evolution in *Cyclamen* L. subg. *Psilanthum* Schwarz (Primulaceae) in *Flora* 183:103–113.

Grey-Wilson, C. (1988). The Genus *Cyclamen*. A Kew Magazine Monograph. Christopher Helm/Timber press; later B.T. Batsford Ltd, London.

Grey-Wilson, C. (1990). Not another forma. *Cyclamen* 14, 1:18.

Grey-Wilson, C. (1991). *Cyclamen* – a reappraisal in *The Plantsman* 13,1:1–20.

Grey-Wilson, C. (1997). Cyclamen – a guide for gardeners, horticulturists and botanists. B.T. Batsford Ltd/Timber Press.

Grey-Wilson, C. (1999). *Cyclamen* in CITES Bulb Checklist (Ed. Aaron P. Davis), Royal Botanic Gardens, Kew.

Grimshaw, J. M. (1992). Red pigmentation in *Cyclamen* leaves. *Cyclamen* 16, 1:23–26.

Haan, I. de & Doorenbos, J. (1951). The cytology of the genus *Cyclamen. Meded. Landbouwhogeschool* 51,7:151–66.

Halda, J. (1975). *Cyclamen* in Skalnicky: 102–136. Klub Skalnickáru, Czech Republic.

Hildebrand, F.G.H. (1898). Die Gattung *Cyclamen, eine Systematische und Bioloische Monographie*. Jena. Gustav Fischer Verlag.

Hildebrand, F.G.H. (1907). Die *Cyclamen*-Arten als ein Beispiel fur das Vorkommen nutzlser Verschiedenheiten im *Pflanzenreich. Beih. Bot. Centralbl.* 22:143–196.

Hildebrand, F.G.H. (translated by Frank, E. 1999). The Genus *Cyclamen*, a systematic and biological monograph. The Cyclamen Society, London.

Ietswaart, J.H. (1974). *Cyclamen* x *wellensiekii* (*C. libanoticum* x *C. cyprium*) hybr. nov. in *Acta Bot. Neerl.* 23:555–559.

Lagarde, F. (1991). *Cyclamen balearicum* Willk. (Primulaceae) en France in *Bull. Soc. Mems. Linn. Lyon* 60, 5:150151.

Legro, R.A.H. (1959). The cytological background of *Cyclamen* breeding. *Meded. Arbor. Landbouwhoogeschool* 59,8:1–51.

Lepper, L. (1975). Nachtrag zur Cytologie von *Cyclamen* L. Wiss. Z. Friedrich Schiller-Univ. Jena., *Math.-Naturwiss. Reihe.* 24:429–436.

Lyons, R.E. & Widmer, R.E. (1980). Origin and historical aspects of *C. persicum* Miller. *Hort. Science* 15,2:132–5.

Maatsch, R. (1971). *Cyclamen.* Verlag Paul Parey.

Mathew, B. & Özhatay, N. (2001). The Cyclamen of Turkey. The Cyclamen Society, London.

Meikle, R.D. (1978). *Cyclamen* in Davis, P.H. (ed.), Flora of Turkey 6:128–134. University Press, Edinburgh.

– (1979). Some notes on *Cyclamen* in Bailey, R.H. (ed.). Proceedings of the Conference Cyclamen Society 1978: 3–12.

– (1985). *Cyclamen* in Flora of Cyprus 2: 1077–1082. Bentham-Moxon Trust, Royal Botanic Gardens, Kew.

Meikle, R.D. and Sinnott, N.H. (1972). *Cyclamen* in T.G. Tutin, *et al.* (eds.), Flora Europaea 3:25–26. Cambridge University Press.

Meikle, R.D. (1984). Some critical groups in the genus *Cyclamen.* *Cyclamen* 8,2:37–41.

Meikle, R.D. (1989). Variation in natural populations of *Cyclamen coum* sensu lato. *Cyclamen* 13, 2:63–64.

Meikle, R.D. (1978). Some notes on *Cyclamen.* Proceedings of the Conference of the Cyclamen Society 1: 3–12.

Melchior, H. (1964). Primulales in Melchior, H. (ed.). Syllabus der Pflanzenfamilien 2: 389–394. Bornträger, Berlin.

Neuray, G. (1973). Bud formation in *Cyclamen persicum. Acta Horticulturae* 31:77–9.

Nightingale, G. (1982). Growing *Cyclamen.* London.

Palmer, L. & Synge P.M. (1965). The winter-flowering *Cyclamen. Journ. Roy. Hort. Soc.* 40, 7:293–296.

Pax, F. (1889). Primulaceae. In Engler, A. & Prantl, K. (eds). Die Naturlichen Pflanzenfamilien 4 (1): 98–116. Engelmann, Leipzig.

Philip, C. (compiler) (1996). The Plant Finder 1996–97 edition. Moorland Publishing Co Ltd, Ashbourne, Derbyshire.

Pobedimova, E.G. (1952). Primulaceae in Shishkin, B.K. & Bobrov, E.G. (eds). Flora SSSR 18:279–290. Leningrad and Moscow: Izdatelstvo Akademii Nauk SSSR. Akademii Nauk SSSR, Botanicheskii Institut V.L. Komarova (Leningrad).

Punt, W. van Weenen, J. S. & van Oostrum, W.A.P. (1976). Primulaceae in The North-west European Pollen Flora. First Ed. 1: 31–70. Elsevier Scientific Publishing, Amsterdam.

Rampinini, G. (1991). La Coltivazione del Ciclamino. Pentagono Editrice, Milan.

Saunders, D.E. (1959). *Cyclamen*, a gardener's guide to the genus. *Bulletin Alpine Garden Society* 27:18–76.

Saunders, D.E., revised by Meikle, R.D. & Grey-Wilson, C. (1973, 1975). *Cyclamen*, the genus in the wild and in cultivation. Alpine Garden Society, Pershore, Worcestershire

Saunders, D.E., revised by Grey-Wilson, C. (1992). *Cyclamen* – a Gardener's Guide to the Genus. Alpine Garden Society, Pershore, Worcestershire

Schwarz, O. (1938). *Cyclamen* Studien. *Gartenflora n.s.*, 1938:11–38.

Schwarz, O. (1955). Systematische Monographie der Gattung *Cyclamen* L. *Feddes Repertiorum Specierum novarum Regni vegetabilis* 58:234–283.

Schwarz, O. (1964). Systematische Monographie der Gattung *Cyclamen* L. *Feddes Repertiorum Specierum novarum Regni vegetabilis* 69:73–103.

Schwarz, O. & Lepper, L. (1964). Kritische Revision der Gattung. In Schwarz, O., Systematische Monographie der gattung *Cyclamen* L. 2. *Feddes Repertiorum Specierum novarum Regni vegetabilis* 69: 79–92.

Schwarz, O. & Lepper, L. (1975). Zwei neue *Cyclamen* aus dem öslichen Mittelmeer gebeit in *Feddes Repertiorum Specierum novarum Regni vegetabilis* 86, 9: 491–497.

Tan, K. & Iatrou, G. (2001). Endemic Plants of Greece – The Peloponnese: 238–240. Gads Forlag, Copenhagen.

Thulin, M. & Warfa, A.M. (1989). *Cyclamen* (Primulaceae) in tropical Africa. *Plant Systematics and Evolution* 166: 249–252.

Ward, S. (1980). The cytology of the genus *Cyclamen.* In Bailey, R.H. (ed.), Cyclamen 1980: Proceedings of the Conference Cyclamen Society 1980: 17–25. Cyclamen Society, Chigwell, Essex, UK.

Wendelbo. P. (1961). Studies in Primulaceae III. On the genera related to *Primula* with special reference to their pollen morphology. Årbok Univ. Bergen, Mat.-Naturv. Ser. 19: 1–31.

Widmer, R.E. & Lyons, R.E. (1985). *Cyclamen persicum*; Handbook of Flowering Plants. CRC Press.

Index

Page numbers:
* indicates a photograph;
! indicates a map
Names of recognized taxa
are in bold